Rebirthing

BREATH · VITALITY · STRENGTH

Kundalini Yoga

As taught by Yogi Bhajan®

© 2011 Kundalini Research Institute
Published by the Kundalini Research Institute
Training • Publishing • Research • Resources
PO Box 1819, Santa Cruz, New Mexico 87532
www.kundaliniresearchinstitute.org

ISBN 978-1-934532-68-3

EDITOR Sat Purkh Kaur Khalsa

CONSULTING EDITOR Nirvair Singh Khalsa

KRI REVIEW Siri Neel Kaur Khalsa

COPY EDITOR Tara Joffe

PHOTOGRAPHY Ravitej Singh Khalsa

PHOTO EDITOR Guru Raj Kaur Khalsa

INTERIOR BOOK DESIGN & LAYOUT Guru Raj Kaur Khalsa

COVER DESIGN Ravitej Singh Khalsa—Khalsa Marketing Group

COVER PHOTO CREDIT Ram Dass Bir Singh

BIO PHOTO CREDIT Gurumustuk Singh Khalsa

MODELS
Nirinjan Kaur Khalsa, Bir Kaur Khalsa-O'Flaherty, Nirmal Kaur Khalsa, Mandeep Singh Sendher,
Ram Rung Kaur, Simranjit Kaur, Ashar Singh Neufeld, Guru Nam Kaur

About Yogi Bhajan

Yogi Bhajan was declared a Master of Kundalini Yoga at the age of 16. He came to the United States in 1969 and openly taught this transformative technology for the next 35 years.

In the turbulent, drug culture of the 60s & 70s, Yogi Bhajan first reached out to the youth. He recognized that their experimentation with drugs and "altered states of consciousness" expressed a desire to experience themselves and a longing for community, for family, for a connection to their own soul and to their community. In response to this innate longing, he created a family known as 3HO (Healthy, Happy, Holy Organization) and soon 3HO ashrams began springing up across the United States and throughout the world.

He sparked a movement whose tendrils have woven their way into numerous aspects of our culture. Yoga and meditation have gained widespread acceptance in the West, as well as the holistic health movement he introduced through diet, herbs and lifestyle technologies.

Born Harbhajan Singh in what is now Pakistan to a family of healers and community leaders, Yogi Bhajan studied comparative religion and Vedic philosophy in his undergraduate years. He went on to receive his Masters in Economics with honors from Punjab University. Years later, he earned his Ph.D. in communication and psychology from the University of Humanistic Studies in San Francisco.

He emerged as a religious, community and business leader with a distinguished reputation as a man of peace, world vision, wisdom, and compassion. He founded several foods companies that manufacture and distribute natural products based on these teachings. He fostered economic development in communities around the world and authored several books on yoga philosophy as well as business and communication during his lifetime.

The Kundalini Research Institute continues his legacy through The Yogi Bhajan Library of Teachings, International Teacher Training in Kundalini Yoga as taught by Yogi Bhajan®, and continuing to publish collections of lectures and kriyas to serve the community of teachers, students and practitioners around the world.

See www.yogibhajan.org and www.kundaliniresearchinstitute.org to learn how you can help keep the legacy alive!

Foreword

The Rebirthing series has been a favorite of mine since 1988 when I had the blessing of attending many of these courses with Yogi Bhajan in person. My experience was so profound, personal and intimate. I remember the original Rebirthing Series, and the Angelic Ghosting course, after each class I experienced a depth of meditation and a renewed sense of self, without the baggage of the past. The experience was so real that I wanted to share this technology with everyone.

I would purchase the raw videos from each of the new Rebirthing Courses when they were made available and then study them. In Tucson, where I lived at the time, I would offer the series of classes for the ashram members and yoga students, we would go through them one at a time, doing the diets and meditations he recommended, and really immersing ourselves in the experience of Rebirthing.

I encourage you to use the videos that are available in this series with your students. It is a rare gift that we now have the lectures, the kriyas and the videos available together to share with each other and our students. Back in the day, it took me hours of watching the videos to take notes and present the kriyas.

When I moved to Española I began to work with Kundalini Yoga teachers and yoga studios around the world, supporting them in initiating the Rebirthing Series at their centers. As deeply self-confronting as these classes were, they were often the most frequently attended. I wrote to Yogi Bhajan about this project and this is how he responded:

> *"I send you my love and prayers to excel in your excellence under God's protection and in His beauty. Shine from the beauty of your renewed chakras in your daily sadhana and these classes which yield the Guru's infinite love and glory as He radiates in your psyche, bringing strength and comfort on your journey up the snowy mountain through the crisp air of Khalsa Consciousness."*

The technology of Rebirthing as taught by Yogi Bhajan is such a gem; it is his gift to future generations. I hope that you enjoy this practice as much as I do.

Humbly,
HARI CHARN KAUR KHALSA
Director of Reach Out—Teach Out
Kundalini Research Institute

Table of Contents

A Note From the Editor

This collection of 31 lectures and kriyas was organized chronologically so that you, the reader, have an opportunity to see the complete arc of the rebirthing teachings by Yogi Bhajan, from the fall of 1988 through the winter of 1989. We strongly recommend you obtain the DVD where possible and take these courses with the Master, Yogi Bhajan, himself. Please see the resources page for more information about the Rebirthing DVD Series.

THE LECTURES

The lectures in this manual were edited for ease in reading and should not be considered transcripts. Within the lecture we have used three asterisks (◆ ◆ ◆) to indicate the point in the lecture where Yogi Bhajan began the kriya. Most comments within the kriyas have been moved to the accompanying kriya write-up, but some comments have been retained within the lecture where appropriate. The lecture and kriya are meant to be used together and have been organized to reflect that intention. For clarification, the end of each kriya write-up is indicated with a single (◆).

USING THE GONG

The sound of the gong is integral to the experience of Rebirthing and many of these kriyas require it. If you don't have access to a gong, KRI recommends the original recording of Yogi Bhajan teaching the class on DVD where available. Or, you can use *Nucleus of Sound*, a recording of Yogi Bhajan playing the gong, as the background when teaching the class. If you would like to learn to play the gong, KRI recommends the DVD, Learn the Gong with Yogi Bhajan, available on our website.

Through the practice of these profound kriyas, may you drop the pain of the past and experience a deep sense of renewal. May you be reborn to your truest and highest self.

Sat Nam.

SAT PURKH KAUR KHALSA
Editor & Creative Director
Kundalini Research Institute

Preface

Even after 40 years as a Kundalini Yogi, the depth, breadth, and power of the Teachings of Yogi Bhajan continues to inspire and amaze me. I have been blessed to be part of codifying these great Teachings over the years, and I never cease to be humbled by them, and immensely grateful for their existence.

As we close 2011 and enter into 2012, the years Yogi Bhajan told us about and prepared us for, it is fitting that this prolific compilation of Teachings presented to you as the Rebirthing Series is offered to serve humanity. Something was happening in the years 1988-89 when he revealed these kriyas. It had to do with the ancestral flow through the generations which transmits either pain or wholeness. He knew he had to help revitalize this primal movement of life. My daughter Nirinjan (pictured here and one of the models throughout the book) was born in that year, 1988.

Now she is a Kundalini Yogi in her own right, and has a son—Gobind Singh—one of Yogi Bhajan's students "of the future" for whom he left these priceless and timeless teachings. He often said his Teachings were for those who will live in generations to come, who will understand them better than even those who sat at his feet.

There are several Teachers around the world who have kept these kriyas alive, and understand their power, such as Hari Charn Kaur. This year I encountered two more in my own home! Sevak Singh of Phoenix and Ravi Kaur of Mexico, guest teachers for our Khalsa Men's Camp and Khalsa Ladies Camp this summer. I myself had never taught any of these kriyas and was excited about teaching one at Ladies Camp. I had already prepared one. I casually asked Sevak, who was also teaching a workshop at our Center, what he was planning to teach. To my utter amazement, he was teaching the same kriya I had chosen! What were the odds? He then shared how much he loved these kriyas. I knew then that truly the time for these great kriyas to be shared was upon us. Now!

Over the years, I had been aware of Ravi Kaur's quiet dedication to these kriyas, and we were going to teach two of them at Camp. Their simple but unusually powerful impact surprised me. It cleared so much, and brought an ease and joy to the 70+ women for the remainder of the Camp experience. The power of these kriyas, which was evident at Khalsa Ladies Camp, also heightened my reverence for them.

Yogi Bhajan always taught that we must carry the powerful Teachings of Kundalini Yoga with humility. It is a duty to do so. As powerful as we become through our practice of Kundalini Yoga, so, too, must it be matched with sweet humility, deep gratitude, reverence and grace. With hands in prayer pose, and a little bow of the head, honoring Guru Ram Das and the Golden Chain, may we practice these great and powerful kriyas in that spirit.

Humbly, with much gratitude,
GURU RAJ KAUR KHALSA
Vancouver, BC, Canada, November 2011

Crashing the photoshoot!
Gobind Singh, future yogi!

Before You Begin

BEGINNING YOUR PRACTICE—TUNING-IN

The practice of Kundalini Yoga as taught by Yogi Bhajan® always begins by tuning-in. This simple practice of chanting the Adi Mantra 3-5 times, aligns your mind, your spirit and your body to become alert and assert your will so that your practice will fulfill its intention. It's a simple bowing to your Higher Self and an alignment with the teacher within. The mantra is simple but it links you to a Golden Chain of teachers, an entire body of consciousness that guides and protects your practice: *Ong Namo Guroo Dayv Namo*, which means, I bow to the Infinite, I bow to the Teacher within.

Ong   Na-mo   Gu- roo   Dayv   Na- mo

HOW TO END

Another tradition within Kundalini Yoga as taught by Yogi Bhajan® is a simple blessing known as The Long Time Sun Shine song. Sung or simply recited at the end of your practice, it allows you to dedicate your practice to all those who've pre-served and delivered these teachings so that you might have the experience of your Self. It is a simple prayer to bless your-self and others. It completes the practice and allows your entire discipline to become a prayer, in service to the good of all.

> *May the long time sun shine upon you*
> *All love surround you*
> *And the pure light within you*
> *Guide your way on.*
> *Sat Nam.*

OTHER TIPS FOR A SUCCESSFUL EXPERIENCE

Prepare for your practice by lining up all the elements that will elevate your experience: natural fiber clothing and head covering (cotton or linen), preferably white to increase your auric body; natural fiber mat, either cotton or wool; tradi-tionally a sheep skin or other animal skin is used. If you have to use a rubber or petroleum-based mat, cover the surface with a cotton or wool blanket to protect and support your electromagnetic field. Clean air and fresh water also helps support your practice.

PRACTICE IN COMMUNITY

Rebirthing Kriyas are very powerful. We recommend you practice them with others when possible. Kundalini Yoga cul-tivates group consciousness, because group consciousness is the first step toward universal consciousness, which is the goal: transcend the ego and merge with Infinity. Find a teacher in your area at http://www.3HO.org/ikyta/. Studying the science of Kundalini Yoga with a KRI certified teacher will enhance your experience and deepen your understanding of kriya, mantra, breath and posture. If there isn't a teacher in your area, consider becoming a teacher yourself. There are Aquarian Teacher Trainings all over the world. Go to www.kundaliniresearchinstitute.org for more information.

BREATH & BANDHAS[1]

The Rebirthing Series is essentially a sequence of profound pranayam practices. Understanding and mastering the breath is an important part of successfully practicing these kriyas. We have provided the descriptions of three of the most basic pranayams in the practice of Kundalini Yoga but as you work through the Rebirthing Kriyas, read the instructions for the breath carefully. We've done our best to describe the breath pattern as closely to the original practice as possible. Consult the DVD where available for the best possible results.

Long Deep Breath

To take a full yogic breath, inhale by first relaxing the abdomen and allow it to expand. Next expand the chest and finally the collarbones. As you exhale, let the collar bones and chest relax first, then pull the abdomen in completely.

The diaphragm drops down to expand the lungs on the inhale and contracts up to expel the air on the exhale.

As you inhale feel the back area of the lower ribs relax and expand. On the exhale be sure to keep the spine erect and steady.

Breath of Fire

This breath is used consistently throughout Kundalini Yoga kriyas. It is very important that Breath of Fire be practiced and mastered. In Breath of Fire, the focus of the energy is at the navel point. The breath is fairly rapid (approximately 2 breaths per second), continuous and powerful with no pause between the inhale and exhale. This is a very balanced breath with no emphasis on either the exhale or the inhale, but rather equal power given to both.

Breath of Fire is a cleansing breath, renewing the blood and releasing old toxins from the lungs, mucous lining, blood vessels, and cells. It is a powerful way to adjust your autonomic nervous system and get rid of stress. Regular practice expands the lungs quickly.

Cannon Breath

Cannon Breath is a powerful inhalation and exhalation through the mouth, with a slight pause between the inhalation and exhalation. Very cleansing, this breath is invigorating, energizing and rejuvenating.

To consolidate the energy at the end of a kriya, many will call for a Cannon Fire exhale, which means we suspend the breath on the inhale and then use a single strong exhale through the mouth like a Cannon.

BANDHAS

Bandhas or locks are used frequently in Kundalini Yoga. Combinations of muscle contractions, each lock has the function of changing blood circulation, nerve pressure, and the flow of cerebral spinal fluid. They also direct the flow of psychic energy, prana, into the main energy channels that relate to raising the Kundalini energy. They concentrate the body's energy for use in consciousness and self-healing. There are three important locks: jalandhar bandh, uddiyana bandh, and mulbandh. When all three locks are applied simultaneously, it is called mahabandh, the Great Lock.

[1] Adapted from Kundalini Yoga Sadhana Guidelines, 2nd Edition.

Jalandhar Bandh or Neck Lock

The most basic lock used in Kundalini Yoga is jalandhar bandh, the neck lock. This lock is practiced by gently stretching the back of the neck straight and pulling the chin toward the back of the neck. Lift the chest and sternum and keep the muscles of the neck and throat and face relaxed.

Uddiyana Bandh or Diaphragm Lock

Applied by lifting the diaphragm up high into the thorax and pulling the upper abdominal muscles back toward the spine, *uddiyana bandh* gently massages the intestines and the heart muscle. The spine should be straight and it is most often applied on the exhale. Applied forcefully on the inhale, it can create pressure in the eyes and the heart.

Mulbandh or Root Lock

The Root Lock is the most commonly applied lock but also the most complex. It coordinates and combines the energy of the rectum, sex organs, and navel point.

Mul is the root, base, or source. The first part of the *mulbandh* is to contract the anal sphincter and draw it in and up as if trying to hold back a bowel movement. Then draw up the sex organ so the urethral tract is contracted. Finally, pull in the navel point by drawing back the lower abdomen towards the spine so the rectum and sex organs are drawn up toward the navel point.

PRONUNCIATION GUIDE

This simple guide to the vowel sounds in transliteration is for your convenience. More commonly used words are often spelled traditionally, for example, *Nanak, Sat Nam, Wahe Guru,* or *pranayam,* even though you'll often see them written *Naanak, Sat Naam, Whaa-hay Guroo,* and *praanayaam,* in order to clarify the pronunciation, especially in mantras.

Gurbani is a very sophisticated sound system, and there are many other guidelines regarding consonant sounds and other rules of the language that are best conveyed through a direct student-teacher relationship. Further guidelines regarding pronunciation are available at www.kundaliniresearchinstitute.org.

a	hut
aa	mom
u	put, soot
oo	pool
i	fin
ee	feet
ai	let
ay	hay, rain
r	flick tongue on upper palate

A NOTE TO THE PRACTITIONER

All comments found within the kriyas and meditations are from Yogi Bhajan unless otherwise indicated.

" The idea of rebirthing is to release the subconscious, the storehouse of misery. "

– Yogi Bhajan

"You lack the commitment to penetrate with the psyche, to break through the crisis confronting you. It's the law of cause and effect. It's not the law of religion, it's not the law of God; it's the law of human happiness. How can we be happy? Is there happiness without commitment? The answer is no. "

– Yogi Bhajan

HOUSE CLEANING I

November 10, 1988

THE IDEA IS NOT TO SELL MEDITATION TO YOU, or religion, or anything; the idea is that it is the Guru's birthday, and we believe in the word "Guru." People don't want problems. A problem doesn't come to you because you want to be miserable or because you try to make mistakes or anything. In life, the problem comes when you do not have the courage to face the problem. Just remember, there is no problem in a human's life that cannot be solved by a human herself. Every cause has an effect—that's a law of science. I can't make new laws for you. The law is. Cause has an effect, and effect must have a cause. That's the law; it can never change. That's how God is; that's how life is. But in this game of cause and effect, sometimes our fuse is off, sometimes we are off, sometimes our attitude is off. Blame it on anything. But in simple English, we lack commitment at that moment.

People say you should have religious commitment, that you should have physical commitment. I am not worried about all that, and I am not going to sell you that. People say, "Well, how did that happen? What happened to you? Where were you? What is going on?" Nothing happens, folks. At that moment, you lack the commitment to penetrate with the psyche, to break through the crisis confronting you. It's the law of cause and effect. It's not the law of religion, it's not the law of God; it's the law of human happiness. How can we be happy? Is there happiness without commitment? The answer is no.

There are seven steps to happiness: You commit, you get character, and from that you gain dignity; when you have self-dignity, you're radiant; you will become rich with opportunities; and after that you go another step. From that dignity, you get divinity. What is divinity, by the way? When you don't have duality, you have divinity. Normally you say, "Maybe this, maybe that"; but when you don't have this duality, you have divinity. Then from that divinity, you have grace. Grace brings you happiness, sources, opportunities, and understanding.

Nobody loves anybody. People lie to each other. You know what people are? People are hunters. They hunt each other's grace, share each other, suck each other, get to each other. It is an absolute lie, this "I love you, you love me." I am not wasting my time on that. Love has been abused more than any word in the whole planet. But that's the way we hook each other, by saying, "I love you." Put a little bait on it and get a few flowers and feel the gratitude. If that's what you call

There are seven steps to happiness: You commit, you get character, and from that you gain dignity; when you have self-dignity, you're radiant; you will become rich with opportunities; and after that you go another step. From that dignity, you get divinity.

"love," God bless you. I don't understand that kind of love, ever. You know what love is to me? Love is an experience of oneself within oneself. When you don't give in and there is no let down, that's the power of love. Love is the one testimony I can give you. If somebody has let you down, then he never understood what love is. Love doesn't let you down. I don't know—knock on wood, because I may go wrong tomorrow—but I am 58 years old, and I don't let anybody down, doesn't matter what. Somehow God comes through. I think these are miracles or whatever you call them. But anyway, it all comes to grace; grace gives you something. Grace gives you a power—the power to sacrifice, the power to give. Grace gives you that power. Guru Nanak said it is: *veksey veparva*.

> *Deinda dey leindey thak paah, juga jugantar kayi ka*
> *Hukumi hukum chalaye raah, nanak veksey veparva.*
> - Guru Nanak, Siri Guru Granth Sahib, page 2 (from *Japji*)
> God gives and gives and gives, for centuries and infinity.
> It is we who take and grow tired of it.
> God has put everything in order, and that order is absolute.
> Just remember, everything is in order, the order is absolute, carefree, and untroubled.

That carefree God, the infinite God, the unlimited God is with all of us. I'll make a bet with you: I am head of the Sikh religion for the Western Hemisphere, but I would never have become a Sikh if I had not found that one line—*Ang Sang Wahe Guru*—meditatively, by self-hypnosis, you feel God in every limb of yours. See how beautiful that is? I never saw a more beautiful thing in my life than when I had that angioplasty and died. I was gone; they were calling my name. Finally, I said, "Oh, I am all right. I am listening." And you know what I was listening to? I was listening to *Jaap Sahib*. You see how the subconscious works?

We have a lot of garbage. We do not believe. We think that if we take a bath and put on good clothes and a scent, then we're okay. But the subconscious needs a bath, too. So I thought, this is my family, these people who love me, let's give them a gift. It's a long meditation, and you'll go through a lot of pain. I know that it is going to hurt you. But it's that moment when you say, "Let me get through it." That's what it is; that's what we are going to do. You'll learn four sections in a very simple, honorable way. The idea is not to squeeze anything out of you; the idea is to clean, to give you a chance to clean yourself out. Simple as that. This is not a Zen meditation, nor is this a very high, anticholesterol meditation, nor is it an antifever meditation. I promise nothing. I only promise that if you go through this with me and be free with me, you'll not be who you were when you came. All right? But I am not promising you anything, because I know what it is. I have done it myself, and it is really a hell of a job. I know!

That's why I am not a very popular teacher, and I don't want to be! I don't want to be a stupid liar. Let me tell you something: I know we are all sick, and we suffer, and we are handicapped and poor, and sometimes our mind freaks out, but that is not what I believe in. I believe that every man and every woman is beautiful, and we have the right to be that way. But cleaning a house is a very difficult job, you know what I mean? Do you understand what I am saying to you? Are you with me on that? You go to restaurants, you talk; you go to the movies and sit there for hours; and at night you watch the Playboy channel. You see what's going on there? It's a crazy world. Let us see how we clean it out. Let us go inside and see what is inside of us, okay?

We want to cleanse this system. We are not here to become great yogis and make all kinds of claims. But we do want to clean the system, and we want to shape up our nerves. Find those handicaps right now.

◆ ◆ ◆

Normally you breathe automatically, but when automatic breathing is stopped, it is very painful for the body to understand. As yogis, we must create order in the body and the mind, and the body has its own mind. So it is to the mental order of the body that we are saying, "We have taken over. You're conquered; you're lost."

Brahmins never explained this to us, but they understood the importance of the breath and which nostril the breath comes in. The breath means, "What is my strength? What is my courage? What is my power to confront?" When you don't have the power to confront, you don't have the power to elevate. Now, this is the most boring moment—it is called anger, inverted depression. Some of you are showing the signs of anger, and some are not. I want all of you to show it; this is the moment to become stupidly angry, mad people. Get angry, get mad, think of something very stupid in your life that you just want to beat the hell out of. Get it out for God's sake. All the anger you have preserved, reserved, or saved—that real anger—has to get out now, and you have to feel the heat of it. It's a religion. Let me take the hell out of you.

Get angry and hit hard *(see Exercise 1)*; confront yourself. You know the American slang, "I am going to blow your mind"? Well, come on, blow it. The agreement was that those who really wanted to work on themselves should come to this meditation—that's what I came for. You know we want to cleanse this system. We are not here to become great yogis and make all kinds of claims. But we do want to clean the system, and we want to shape up our nerves. Find those handicaps right now, where the body has become stiff and the movements have become uncongenial, unfriendly. I want you to consciously overcome that. I want you to pull it all out of you; just consciously do it. If you are not sturdy, you cannot be steady.

This next exercise looks crazy, but it gets rid of the grief *(See Exercise 3)*. Grief is when you're sad because of some injustice in your life. We'll now begin to move chakra to chakra *(see Exercise 4)*.

Move the Heart Center and the navel *(see Exercise 9)*. Try this potency project—it's called potency projection. People have weird sexual habits. But if you do this, you'll totally take care of your creative energy, your ovaries, your gonads, that whole area. This will heal you of your degradation in regeneration. I am using very polite words because I am a holy man, but I think you know what I'm saying. When you were in the womb of your mother, you didn't breathe. You grew out of her, out of this energy. *Har Hare Hari, Wahe Guru*. Like Buddhist monks, like *Bhikshus*, like priests, like saints—dwell in the sound, dwell in the sound, go deeper into it, relax, relax, and get going. *(See Exercise 10.)*

Silently meditate at the *sahasrara*, beneath your skull. *(See Exercise 11.)* Switch to the *ajna*, the Third Eye. Switch to the Throat Chakra. Switch to the Heart Center. Relax and go deeper in, and in, and in, and in, and keep going. Keep repeating the mantra at the Heart Center. Keep on repeating the mantra; the mantra belongs to the Heart Center anyway. Just relax until you forget all the senses. Let all of the tension go; go deeper and deeper into your heart, like an onion, peel to the very center of it. Let the tension go, relax, deeper, please. Let the sound current continue. Word wins the world. Word wins the world.

This was just the first step, just to cleanse your being. Tomorrow we'll meet again, and we'll complete the second part of it. After that, we'll meet Saturday and Sunday of the next week to complete the four sides of it.

It's true I have to go many places, but I have to do what I was born to do.

◆ ◆ ◆

May the long time sun shine upon you,
all love surround you, and the pure light within you, guide your way on.

Blessed are those
who believe in peace. Blessed are those who work for it.
Blessed are those whose mind is at peace. Blessed are those who share with others.
Blessed are those who bring others to peaceful self-meditation and bliss.

Sat Nam

HOUSECLEANING I— THE KRIYA

November 10, 1988

There are no breaks between the exercises. Move immediately from one exercise to the next.

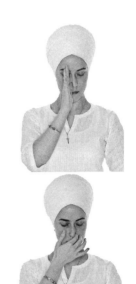

1. Using the right thumb, close off the right nostril and inhale through the left. Then, using the right forefinger close off the left nostril and exhale through the right. Go at a quick pace, with one cycle of inhalation and exhalation per second. Continue for **2-3 minutes**.

You are voluntarily making the pineal gland command the pituitary in order to adjust the glandular system.

2. Fully extend the tongue and begin inhaling and exhaling through the mouth. Go at the same quick pace as in Exercise 1.
Continue for **30 seconds**.

This will clean out the central nervous system.

3. Put the hands in Prayer Pose and begin pumping the navel. Breath is not indicated, but it is **not** a Breath of Fire. Just pump the navel consciously for **90 seconds**.

This stimulates the lower glandular system's circulation. Use the pelvic floor to move!

4. Interlace the fingers with the palms open and the thumbs extended up and hands in front of the face. Flex the first joint of the thumbs, moving only the distal joint of the thumb up and down. Simultaneously move the big toes of the feet. Just dance the thumbs and the big toes. Move quickly for **4 minutes**.

We are pulling the sciatica right from the base. We are doing nothing special; just a simple movement. It doesn't make any sense why we are doing it. Maybe we have gone crazy, who cares? We want to do it; we are doing it. Touch nothing, just pull the energy. The most healing power is in your own hands. They don't sell this in any store, you have to order it; these things you won't read in books, you have to do it! You must experience it for yourself. You have a lot of garbage, and you have a lot of pain in your life, but you can move it! There is a rhythm, there is a force, there is no tiredness, there is absolute harmony—it is beautiful. You'll enjoy it; you won't regret it. This exercise is why yogis used to go in caves; they didn't want people to see them doing these weird things.

5. 8-stroke inhale and 8-stroke exhale quickly through the nose for 2 minutes.

The 8-stroke breath puts the three nervous systems in tune and in harmony, which you need in order to start something in life.

6. Place the thumbs at the base of the pinkie fingers and make a fist over the thumbs. Extend the arms straight out in front with eyes closed. Focus at the Brow Point. Move the right arm back, as though pulling a bow. The chest moves with the arm. Then release the right arm forward and pull the left arm back in the same manner. Continue moving the arms alternately. Start slowly. Keep the arms tense through-out the movement. After the **first minute**, begin speeding up. After another **30 seconds**, continue speeding up until you reach a pace of one to two cycles (both left and right) per second. Mentally chant **Saa Taa Naa Maa** to keep up. Move as fast as possible for **12 minutes**.

After 5 minutes, you'll become very uncomfortable. "Now it's time to go faster! Satanama-satanama-satanama—like that! Get the anger out! From the chest area, move fast! Get angry, get mad, think of something very stupid in your life, something that you just want to beat up—get it out now! Get angry and hit hard! Every part of the body should start sweating. Don't you get angry? Don't you have an enemy? Just place that enemy in front of you and, Charge!"

7. Immediately stretch the arms into a V over the head, palms facing each other. Moving from the shoulders, be-gin touching the hands together over the head, but with-out clapping. Move the arms apart and together; touch the hands together. The hands must touch but not clap. Keep the arms straight with no bend at the elbows. Keep the palms flat with fingers together. Move fast; the pace is ap-proximately 22 repetitions every 15 seconds. Continue for **3 minutes**.

8. Bring the hands about 4–6 inches apart, palms facing each other, thumbs open, fingers pointing forward; hands are at the level of the throat. Move them quickly toward the upper chest, palms facing the chest, and then back to the starting position. Keep the hands equidistant throughout the movement. Don't touch your chest or your hands together. Move fast for **90 seconds**.
This exercise takes away grief.

9. Move through this next sequence with the eyes closed. Each hand moves about 12 inches out and back from the starting position. Touch nothing.

a. Right hand is over the crown of the head, left hand is in front of the brow. The right hand moves up about 12 inches, while the left hand moves forward the same distance. Move fast for **90 seconds**.

b. Right hand in front of the brow, left hand in front of the throat. Again, move the hands about 12 inches out and back. Move the hands together for **90 seconds**.

Exercise 9 continues on next page

9c. Right hand in front of the throat, left hand at the heart. Move forward and back two times per second or more. Move fast for **3 minutes**.

d. Relax and stretch the hands and body. Move in all directions for **30-60 seconds.**

e. Right hand in front of the heart, left hand in front of the navel. Move fast. The hands will want to run into each other; don't let it happen. Keep the same quick pace. Continue for **7½ minutes**.

People who have weird sexual habits should do this exercise. It will take care of creative energy and the sex organs. It all gets balanced out. This movement must be very fast so that you can create the magnetic field. Move with all your force. Your whole body will shake if you're doing it right. You're moving the First, Second, Third, and Fourth Chakras.

Comments

This was just cleansing your being; this was the first step. I hope you can go home and relax and go to sleep and figure it out. I don't promise anything to you today. But tomorrow, when you get up, you'll realize you have done something for yourself. Now you'll have enough energy to go and reach your homes. If you want to eat, just eat very polite and light and get to bed. That's all you can do.

10. Bring the hands into Gyan Mudra, about 12 inches away from each ear, elbows relaxed away from the sides of the body, palms facing forward. Close the eyes and chant **Har Hare Hari Wahe Guru** in a monotone while moving the fingers (as in Kirtan Kriya). Touch each finger to the thumb as you chant the mantra so the mudra moves in a complete circle.

First Repetition: **Har**—Jupiter finger; **Haray**—Saturn finger; **Haree**—Sun finger; **Wha**—Mercury finger; **Hay**—Jupiter finger; **Guroo**—Saturn finger.

Second Repetition: **Har**—Sun finger; **Haray**—Mercury finger; **Haree**—Jupiter finger; **Wha**—Saturn finger; **Hay**—Sun finger; **Guroo**—Mercury finger; and so on. With each repetition of the mantra, **Har** alternately begins with the Jupiter or Sun fingers.

After **9 minutes** begin whispering for **1 minute**. Continue moving the fingers and meditating in silence on the mantra throughout the sequence that follows:

a. Meditate in silence on the Sahasrara for **45 seconds**.
b. Meditate at the Third Eye for **45 seconds**.
c. Meditate at the Throat Chakra for **1 minute**.
d. Meditate at the Heart Center for **2½ minutes**.

Continue for approximately **15 minutes** total.

11. Relax the hands in the lap. Relax deeper and deeper into a sleepless sleep, the state of yoga nidra. Continue silently meditating on the mantra at the Heart Center. This is a Heart Center mantra. "Let the body go, let the word prevail. If the word can prevail, this world is all yours. If the word is yours, the world is just a gift." Let the tension go. Relax deeply, and keep the sound current going. "Word wins the world." Circulate deeper and relax deeper and deeper and deeper for **6½ minutes**.

12. Sleep in Baby Pose. Play beautiful, serene music. "It's essential for the human body to sleep in Baby Pose in order to regenerate itself." Singh Kaur's *Wahe Guru Wahe Jio* was played in the original class. After **11 minutes**, begin playing the gong, if available, for **13 minutes**.

13. Come sitting up in Easy Pose and continue meditating. Continue the gong for 2 minutes. Then sing along with Singh Kaur's *Wahe Guru Wahe Jio*. Concentrate and copy the sounds. Become one with the sound. Continue for **12 minutes**.

JUPITER   SATURN   SUN   MERCURY

"As long as you act out of fear, you have to compromise. Fear makes your range become short term. Your thinking becomes short term, your concept becomes narrow, you become a bootstrapper. You just want to survive, and that means survival now, which makes every human stupid. "

– Yogi Bhajan

HOUSE CLEANING II

November 12, 1988

AM TEACHING THESE FOUR MEDITATION CLASSES not to make you yogis or anything. No, my concept is very well settled. I don't care what anybody says or how they say it: In this life, the human operates from fear. As you grow up, you start dating; yet, you think you will never get married. As you grow up, you want to collect things and money and become rich; yet, when your old age comes, you still may not be taken care of. We are mostly guided by misery and fear—and misery needs company. Let me say one thing: In your life, as you are, it doesn't matter who you belong to, what philosophy you have, what you want to say, or what you want to feel—you are always afraid that you'll be lonely, you'll be rejected, you'll be unloved, you'll be poor, you won't have meals tomorrow.

Nobody acts out of love. Look, I regret to say this, but we are five billion people, and we don't have even an iota of understanding of God and what God is all about. We don't even have consequences to face or a story to tell. God does it all, but we feel like we do it all. Life is based on insecurity and fear. When you are insecure and you are fearful, that's reasonable, that's okay, that's animal. Animal is always insecure and very fearful. When he is hungry, he goes for a meal—even the lion, the king of the beasts, likes to make a kill and eat it for two, three, or four days. So it is with us.

Now, I can be misunderstood as only being a religious man and a yogi. But I am also a businessman, and I make my money and pay my taxes. I live my life much more normally than you live yours. But what I have found in my life, in the twenty years since I came here, is that I built up all this, and then I gave and gave and gave and tried to find out if anyone realized how much fear they lived in? The answer was no. There is no horizon, there is no infinity, there is no vastness in you, which all humans should have.

And then there are the meditators: the happy group, the group of light, and the group of Satan. Just walk out the door, and you will find two hundred yogis and three hundred groups and six hundred teachings and eight hundred religions, with all their branches and the priests, padres, swamis, and that whole thing. But not one single person can take away the fear in man. Isn't that a shame? When the concept of life is based on fear, where can happiness be?

I don't want to dig into your books, your bank accounts, your political power, or your religious conviction. I have nothing to do with all that. I just want to deal

We are mostly guided by misery and fear. Let me say one thing: In your life, as you are, it doesn't matter who you belong to, what philosophy you have, what you want to say, or what you want to feel—you are always afraid that you'll be lonely, you'll be rejected, you'll be unloved, you'll be poor, you won't have meals tomorrow. Nobody acts out of love.

with a fundamental elementary situation, which is, everybody is afraid and acts out of fear. As long as you act out of fear, you have to compromise. Fear makes your range become short term. Your thinking becomes short term, your concept becomes narrow, you become a bootstrapper. You just want to survive, and that means survival now, which makes every human stupid, period. You don't have to ask for a certificate, because when a vast range contracts to a small range—do you understand the impact? Do you understand this room as it is? If it is brought down to the size of this bench on which I am sitting, what will happen to you all? Do you have any idea what happens when a vast range contracts to a small range? Our goal with our children is short term, our goal in our mates is short term, our goal in our relationships is short term, and our goal in our love is short term. Everything is short, small; but we talk big.

On the eighth of November, we had an election. Let's put it simply and talk about our national strategy, all right? We are Americans. "Read my lips: no new taxes." Right? That's all it was. Nobody wants to pay taxes. So they say, "Who's this guy[1]?" If it is true that our national debt is whatever it is, it comes to $28,000 per person. If a baby is born this minute, she carries that debt at a rate of ten percent, which is, $2,800. So, forget about taxes; each year you pay the national debt's interest per individual—$2,800—whether you earned it or not. And not a single American wants to recognize that.

Are we educated? No. Are we real? No. Are we a nation? No. Are we Americans? No. So what do we do? We make short-term arrangements, write hot checks on the treasury, print more notes, steal it from here, steal it from there, and make ourselves feel good. Don't we do the same thing in our own homes? What Reagan did or what Bush is going to do, or what Dukakis wants to do are all the same thing. At the national and international level, we help everybody in the world and then we get kicked out. Meanwhile, our children are dying without medical care, our people are hungry, there is a homeless problem, and we are sending help to control rebels in another part of the world. You may not be interested in these political figures or in this news, but they show our behavior. It's not politics; it's our national thinking—short-term patchwork. Somebody gets scared, and he works it. We do the same at home. We work out of fear. There is no fearlessness, and still we talk of God.

I go to every church, I meet a lot of holy men. Before I got ill, I started this meeting of peace among all the elders. I started calling all the religious denominations—Christian, Hindu, whatever was in town—and they all came.

[1] Referring to the election of George Herbert Walker Bush.

But they all said, "We are willing to meet, we are willing to unite, we are willing to discuss, but what about our turf?" I never understood what they were talking about. There was an interdenominational priest, and I asked him, "Everywhere I go, I invite them, I spend money, I give them a good cup of tea. We just want to talk and communicate, and they talk about turf."

He said, "There is a problem."

I said, "What is the problem?"

He said, "You are a very clever man. You'll take Christians, Hindus, and Muslims, anybody in this country—you'll convert them."

I said, "That's fair. I convert them, they convert me. It's okay."

He said, "No, you don't understand. You go and teach and you charge. You earn money, you pay taxes, you have a different system. Here, if there is nobody in the congregation and that bucket comes back empty, the church doesn't get painted for two years. It's the dependency."

So the church has become dependent on the congregation. It's all upside down. Actually, the congregation should depend upon the church. The student should depend on the teacher; the teacher shouldn't depend on the student. Stupid is that teacher who depends on the student; what can a student do? Wood should depend on the artist or the carpenter; the carpenter shouldn't depend on the wood.

In our life, we have counselors; we pay them, and they counsel us. But do you know what counseling is? Lie down on a sofa and start telling your story, and the person says, "Uh-huh, uh-huh, uh-huh . . . " It's a mantra. He says, "Huh, huh, yeah, OK, more, yeah." After forty-five minutes, you get exhausted and feel you have let it all out; then you come back next week. That's what we have become. Give me one counselor who says, "You stupid idiot, why did you do this? How dare you do it! Look at this—this is your subconscious, this is your conscious, this is your top, your bottom, this is you, and you are naked. Drop dead." Is there anybody who can do that? Give me one.

My student says, "You!" But I say, "Oh, no way."

You know, I did my Ph.D., but not so that I could charge money or run the clock. My theory is very simple, and my life is very simple. Even my visit to America is very simple. I didn't come to this country to become rich and famous; that was not my idea. I believe in the creation of God. I believe man should be as God created him. I am not a Sikh because religion is great. I interpreted the religion, and I don't care that Sikhs don't like me. I am the head of the religion. Can you believe they have a head of the religion who they don't

Our goal with our children is short term, our goal in our mates is short term, our goal in our relationships is short term, and our goal in our love is short term. Everything is short term, small; but we talk big.

We hesitate to meditate, so we don't have the nerve. When we are struck by calamity or challenge, we don't know how to deal with it. We have become reactive. Reactive human is just a two-legged animal. Forget about his makeup and his titles and his degrees and his profession; forget about his religion, his grace, and his status. Animal reacts, period.

like? They don't like me because my conception and my concept and my experience are personal.

You can read anything in a book, and you can know anything you want. But, you know, people with knowledge are more stupid than people who don't know anything because they know and they think that's it. They are not willing to act; people don't act.

Do you know that every evening you have to have a drink, you have go to a movie, you have to do something, because you have not trained your butts to sit? You can't not move; you don't have the nerve. Everybody promises that there will be no drugs; I do not agree. There shall be drugs, and a flood of it. There shall be divorces, and a flood of it. There shall be lots of law-and-order problems that nobody can stop because Americans have lost their nerve. The itch doesn't make any sense except for the pain associated with it; and a pained person can act any way he wants. We act out of fear and pain. Tragedy was not that great until we started accepting it. The tragedy started when we started accepting it.

I won't name the state official, but he was a very high state official, close to the governor. I met him, and he said, "It's my special day. I am very honored you came. I would like to introduce you to my family. This is my first wife, and this is her husband; this my second wife, and this is her husband; this is my third wife and her husband; and this is my wife, and I am her husband."

I cracked up. That's his family? He has divorced three times, and all three are remarried, and all six of them were at his house, with his children and with their children. What can you do? And do you know why? We don't meditate. We hesitate to meditate, and therefore, we don't have the nerve. When we are eventually struck by calamity or challenge or anything, we don't know how to deal with it. We have become reactive. Reactive human is just a two-legged animal. Forget about his makeup and his titles and his degrees and his profession; forget about his religion, his grace, and his status. Animal reacts, period.

Human is rational—consolidated and rational. The angel in us is great. We are three: angel, beast, and man. Higher self, lower self, and middle self. Is there any treatment for it? Is there any way out? Yes, there is a way out, but you have to have the nerve. You have to have the guts, and you have to have the strength. First of all, you have to be noble. Then you have to have the honor to protect your own nobility. You don't have to do anything for me, and I don't have to do anything for you—not at all. You don't have to do anything for the world, neither does the world have to do anything for you. Look how simple this world is:

You simply have to do everything for yourself and then maintain it, protect it.

I will tell you the story of a rich man. He came to this country and became rich, rich, rich, very rich. One day we were sitting together, and he said, "You seem to be well-to-do, but you seem to be happy."

I said, "You seem to be very rich, but you seem to be very happy, too."

He said, "No, I pretend to be happy. I am miserable."

I said, "What can you be miserable about? What's wrong with you? Your wife has not divorced you, that's one credit. Your children are not disobedient. You are a reasonably spiritual person. You go to church, your children go to church. That's a phenomenon I had never seen—in fact, that's why I came to your house. You are one family that goes to church, and your children go to church because they want to go. And your parents go to church, too. "

He said, "That's right."

"And you have money—you have so many corporate holdings, so much investment, you are so rich. How can you be in difficulty?"

"Can we go into the study?"

I thought, here we go. "All right." So we sat in the study, and I said, "Cut it short and come out with it. I know it already, but if you just tell me straight, it'll ease my time, your time, and our time, you know?"

"I am scared."

"What for?"

"I am scared to be rich."

I have never heard of that phenomenon before. Somebody scared to be rich?

I said, "What can I do?"

He said, "I don't know. I am scared to be successful."

"Why do you feel so?"

"I think I have stolen from people. There are so many poor people, and I am rich. I think I am a thief."

"Do you do anything wrong?"

"No."

"Have you ever cheated?"

"No."

"Have you ever lied?"

"No."

"Have you done something under the table, over the table, beside the table?"

The angel in us is great. We are three: angel, beast and man. Higher self, lower self, and middle self. Is there any treatment for it? Is there any way out? Yes, there is a way out, but you have to have the nerve. You have to have the guts, and you have to have the strength.

"No."

"Then what is it?"

"I am just afraid. I am scared to be rich. I am scared . . ."

And listen to this, he said, "I am scared to be happy."

I said, "You are scared to be in one piece."

He said, "You're right. That's why I wanted to sit with you privately. What can I do?"

I won't tell you what I told him, but within three minutes, he believed he would never be unhappy, ever again. It's an Indian formula that doesn't work in America. But he volunteered himself.

He said, "I'll do anything. I honestly trust you. You're a man of God, and I really have reverence for you. I even went to your class once." He then asked me, "Get me out of the fear."

I said, "It's a very simple thing; it will take five minutes."

I told him to do something; you have never seen anyone more afraid.

I said, "Which one is better?"

He said, "I am okay."

I said, "Keep up."

Life is a comparative study. The further we go, the more afraid we become. Actually, to be very honest, we are not grateful for what we have; and what we don't have, we worry about. Why? Because we are basically lonely. We don't talk to our girlfriend, our soul. We have no relationship with it. There is a word called soul; and there are three words—sum, sun, sole. Sole or soul, spell it anyway you like; sum, the totality; sun, the light. I have seen groups that teach enlightenment. You think by burning a candle, there is light? Sure, the room gets lit, but do we get lit? The candle in us we have never lit. We don't even have a matchstick to trigger it. When we have that phony, shallow living, we don't have any relationship with our own soul. What can other relationships mean to us?

We live because of the soul, we die because of the soul, but we have no relationship with the soul. We want to win, we want to be victorious, we want to be great; yet we have no nerve, no grit, no courage. You think anybody wants to be foolish? Not at all. You think anybody wants to be wrong? No. Does anybody want to be rude? No. Is there any woman in the world who wants to be a prostitute? No. I will say daringly no. It is not having the nerve that puts us where we don't want to be. We don't have the power to challenge—and challenge to the death.

So I thought, let's have four sets to clean you out. I don't want to teach these days; it's not my prerogative anymore. But still, I thought, it's very ridiculous that I am still alive, and there are people who love me; people who have come with me so far; people who believe they have the right to be happy. But they have to have guts. I love imperial guts.

I love two things. You might think I love God. But no, I am very selfish. I don't love God. I don't love anything. I love only the identity of integrity and dignity—two things. If you don't love these two things, then you don't know who you are, and you don't love anything.

Scale out your life on two parallel lines. Let your loose caboose run and find out where your integrity is and where your dignity is. Don't go to anybody; analyze yourself. Do you have it? You can't be social because you are scared that you will be scandalized. You can't be rich because you are afraid that somebody will steal from you. You cannot be honorable because you don't know what it is. You need a mind, a vast computer, an intuitive mind. An intuitive mind will give you integrity; an undivided mind will give you divinity.

Religion, Marx said it is no good that I am religious. I don't know what they think religion is. Religion is nothing but a pure realism of self-acknowledgement and self-experience, which is God. Listen to me, tell me I am totally wrong, and I will tell you I am absolute. What I am telling you, according to your standard, is totally wrong. But I say there is no God out there, period; it's all within you. There never was a God, nor will there be, nor can there be. God is in you. God is in your integrity, in your identification of your divinity with dignity. What is divinity? When you have absolutely no duality.

I have said don't love anybody but God, and don't be two-faced: "Maybe, I don't know, no . . ." When you do those kinds of things, it means you are not intelligent, and you can't compute enough to even answer what needs to be answered. I understand that teachers need money, and they believe they have to please their students. Everybody asks, "How many students do you have? How many centers do you have? How rich are you? How poor are you?" It is totally ridiculous. You don't know rich. I have never seen richness in America. I was born rich. I was born not with a silver spoon but with a big gold spoon in my mouth. I never knew what poverty was. I don't know how to say no. The biggest thing for me is to say no. It doesn't exist for me.

Sometimes people think that I am just confused because I will never say no. But I don't believe in no. If I cannot do it, I will try to do it; if not, I'll twist

We live because of the soul, we die because of the soul, but we have no relationship with the soul. We want to win, we want to be victorious, we want to be great; yet we have no nerve, no grit, no courage.

What is divinity? When you have absolutely no duality.

the arm of God to make it happen. Why not? It takes a little time, but big deal. I don't know how to say no. I do not know how to put down another person. You make yourself look bad when, in my presence, you come and say, "So and so is bad." That makes me feel so horrible inside. I ask, "What is this? This is human?" When you say, "I don't like so and so, that person is stupid, that person is no good, that person is black, that person is yellow, on and on . . ." It looks like a cockroach trying to run like a horse, that's how I feel! And I'm just a man of God; imagine how God feels. Put down being jealous, set down being angry—it's unbelievable the way people yell and scream.

Senses are tools, not ends. Great sensitivity should be used as a tool so that you can move forward. So I thought, let me track down my own roots. Somebody did me good, somebody taught me to meditate. But I don't think any of you could have stayed more than a day and a quarter under my teacher; there is no way. With all my richness, with all my authority, can you believe he took me, put me in a tree, and said, "Stay there until I come back"? He showed up three days later; I was still in the tree. Try it sometime. I thought he was going to come back in an hour or two or three or something like that. Three days later he said, "How are you feeling?"

You know what I said? "Great."

"You must be miserable."

"No. I have learned how to sit in a tree for three days; that's more divine than any heavens God could give me."

"How did you manage?"

"Well, the greatest difficulty was to clean myself; that was the worst. I figured out that the tree had splits, and in each split, water gathered in the night, and it was drinkable; and then I found that the tree had small leaves. If you chewed on them you didn't feel hungry. The worst thing was that I couldn't bathe, and it was a hot summer. I stunk, you know? So, I thought, there must be something: I went to the top and found some leaves that were a yellowish color. I made a big bundle of them and rubbed my body with them. It was very cool! Somehow, survival of the fittest; I found everything I needed in the tree. It was okay, cozy, but hidden; I simply had to track it down. Then night came, how to sleep?"

Now, a guy like me, whose servants make the bed and sprinkle flower petals and that kind of stuff? I lived like a prince, and now I was in a tree. If I fell, it was eighteen feet down, and there were rocks. I mean, I had a good idea what would happen to me if I fell. But I figured out how to sleep: I found that if I curled on my side like a baby, I could tangle my legs into one twine and, if worst came to worse, I would hang by my feet, but I wouldn't fall. And it worked. Yes, it was very painful. But why did I do it? Because my teacher said get in this tree, and I'll come back and we'll go together—three days later—that is how the oriental teach. Very difficult.

You can't have a teacher. For you, teacher is a man; for us, teacher was a way to God—that's the difference. That's the difference! For me, my teacher was my way to God. I didn't care whether my teacher was educated or not, whether he was rich or not, whether he would cheat me or not, con me or not. I thought I had every intelligent right to decide who my teacher was; and once I made that decision, I was going to make it—doesn't matter what. To me it was a way to God. And look, I came to America, and I still say "trunk pie" (turnpike); I still pronounce it wrong. You're sitting there thinking, what is he going to say? I still say so many wrong words, but now I do it intentionally because that's the way my humor is.

But I never feared about not having students. I never feared that I wouldn't be successful. I never worried about who would do my public relations. No, I never feared those things. In Canada, when I arrived, everything fell apart. So I used to sing a song: "One day the day shall come when all the glory shall be Thine, people say it is yours, I shall deny not mine." Twenty years ago, a man came who couldn't by any virtue of sight, action, or otherwise even be allowed to imagine he was a Yogi—that man was me. When I came through immigration, they said, "Certify you are a Yogi if we are to give you a green card."

I said, "The Canadian government got me as a Yogi, and I am still a very valid Yogi. Don't bother me."

"No, that's Canada. This is America."

"What do you want?"

"I want a certificate that proves you are a Yogi. Then we'll give you a green card."

"Who can tell you that I am a Yogi or not?"

"I don't care who tells me. All I need is for somebody to tell me, which I cannot refuse."

So, I went down to Bank of America, paid one dollar, and told the girl to type: "I, Harbhajan Singh, so and so, hereby certify that I am a perfectly good Yogi." I got it signed and sworn and certified—the whole thing. I brought three copies, and I gave him one.

He said, "Well, this is your own declaration."

I said, "Who else can tell me that I am good?"

Fear can be good. You know what fear means to me? In my terms, in my dictionary, when I totally betray God Almighty, it is a treachery. It's my treachery against God—that's fear to me. Yes, I am afraid. I am afraid to say no. I am afraid to not help people; I am afraid to not uplift anybody; I have hundreds of fears. But that fear is a force that brings out my love.

Fear can be good. When we are afraid to be bad, we just live in fear, deal in fear, think in fear, imagine in fear. It's a terrible slap to the face of God. You know what fear means to me? In my terms, in my dictionary, when I totally betray God Almighty, it is a treachery. It's my treachery against God—that's fear to me. Yes, I am afraid. I am afraid to say no. I am afraid to not help people; I am afraid to not uplift anybody; I have hundreds of fears. But that fear is a force that brings out my love. I am afraid to deny anybody what good I can do. But to just make life nothing but a bunch of fear and to make of yourself a fool all of the time, what use is fear to you? It just makes you narrow, narrow, narrow. It shrinks you. Fear is a shrinking process. You want to expand. You want to be great, and you can. You can be wonderful. You want to be happy, but it won't come from smallness. Small is not all, and all is not small. Do you understand English? Do you understand all? It's an expression.

How do you spell small? S-M-A-L-L. How do you spell all? A-L-L. You are American, you are great; so why the hell don't you cut down that S-M and just believe in one word—all? Tell me! Yet, nobody can tell you anything. You don't have one person in your life who can just tell you, "Hey, get up! Don't act small." If your father tells you, you walk out of the house. If your mother tells you, you stop eating your food. If your wife tells you, you start flirting with other women. If your children tell you, you spit at them, because you don't want to listen.

I was just telling some kid, "You are very mischievous. Do you know what mischief is? When you miss becoming the chief."

He said, "No, I want to be a chief."

"You are going to miss it. There is nothing wrong in it. You can miss it if you want to miss it. You want to miss the meal, you want to miss being great, you want to miss having a good car, you want to miss all that?"

"No."

"All that belongs to a chief."

"You ride in a good car."

"I am Chief Religious Administrative Authority, so I have to, even though I may not like it."

"I want that car, too."

"Then don't miss being a chief and don't do mischief."

That child will never forget it to his last day.

◆ ◆ ◆

I have found that you clog your mind with subconscious, incomplete dreams and fears. If that overloaded subconscious lives in you, everything else falls under its weight. You don't have to do anything good or bad. You'll be miserable anyway. It's a simple thing. Sometimes you take a break, you go on holiday, you try to relax, and then you get diarrhea or you get into another miserable situation, you know? So nothing works out. The problem is the subconscious. You are not innocent, you are not clear, you are not pure—and you can't be, because you think you have to survive. You don't believe that God, who can rotate the Earth, can take care of your routine. You don't. That's not your religion, that's not your belief, that's not your philosophy. I don't like weakness. I believe that man is born to show the "I" of the God. And that "I" of the God—his attitude, his aptitude, and his projection—should be imperial.

My teacher taught such that I learned that way. I don't know anything more than that. I can't do that—sit down for twenty-three years. I don't believe that that's the way. I don't believe that there is anything that we cannot experience, nor is there any truth that we cannot express. I believe in "get it," otherwise don't get it.

Remember, if you are ever in the shit pit, move the armpit. Remember this. I am giving you a million dollar release, you understand? The armpit is not a small thing. Three nerve centers meet there. I believe in experience. I don't believe in this garbage of talking, talking. I have talked enough. What I can teach you in an hour or two can make you great. If I do that, I have to do something great; small won't work. By crossing the Heart Center's magnetic field and moving the armpit *(see Exercise 1)*, it is simple science—the brain has to re-pattern its neurons to reach the faculty so that it has the velocity to meet the challenge. Know it in English.

This is meditation. Meditation is not closing the eyes and sitting and looking good. This is it—if you cross right, and your angle is perfect, then you're doing it, you are getting to the perfection. If you keep on doing what I am telling you, you will start getting a sense of courage; it will give you grit. Because you will get a sense of challenge; this meditation contains a very powerful challenge.

You came here to become something. The job of the teacher is to build somebody, not build himself. Teacher is a teacher; he is already built in. Move. Cross left, cross right. It's a fight between the shushmana and the ida and pingala. If these things had been so easy, everybody would have become a yogi

Let's have four sets to clean you out. It's very ridiculous that I am still alive, and there are people who love me; people who have come with me so far; people who believe they have the right to be happy. But they have to have guts. I love imperial guts. I love two things. I love only the identity of integrity and dignity.

and wise and perfect and happy and nirvana. Rise, rise *(see Exercise 2)*. When milk is heated it rises, you know? Wine fragments rise, bread rises, cake rises? What is wrong with you? Get going, up, don't stop. Pull up. This is not a rehearsal. Give your system a chance. What we have done so far is to give your impulse a chance to respond to a challenge, and automatically, your brain will understand what the answer is. You don't have time to think, to compute it.

No freedom here is free. There is no liberty without labor. Your system must understand how to react under a shock, so create that shock. We are just creating a pattern in the brain to respond to. Is that a sin? This is a psychosomatic treatment for ENT—eyes, nose, and throat—that's it. *(See Exercise 4)*.

◆ ◆ ◆

May the long time sun shine upon you,
all love surround you, and the pure light within you, guide your way on.

Blessed is the peace,
peace of mind, peace to the nations, peace of the world. Blessed are those that put their pieces together and become one piece (peace) forever in the light and the guidance of God's grip. Blessed are those who seek to serve others and try to crown other's glory. Blessed are those who see God in all and in everything, and remain tranquil, in peace, and prepare their life to flow into the heavenly abode.

Sat Nam

HOUSECLEANING II— THE KRIYA

November 12, 1988

There are no breaks between the exercises. Move immediately from one exercise to the next.

1. Sit in Easy Pose. Place the hands in Shuni Mudra (thumbtip touching Saturn—middle—fingertip) with the elbows bent, crossing the arms in front of the chest so that the upper hand reaches beyond the shoulder to ear level. Alternate the arms, right arm on top and then left arm on top, and move quickly. Begin at approximately 1 cycle every second and increase to 108 cycles per minute. Continue for **15 minutes**.

Three nerve centers meet in the armpit. If you are ever in the pit, move the armpit. All you're doing is crossing the Heart Center's magnetic field and moving the armpit—simple science. The brain has to re-pattern its neurons so that it has the faculty and the velocity to meet the challenge, that's all it is. It's a fight between the shushmana, the center of you, and the ida and pingala—that's what it is.

2. Interlace the hands above the head with the Jupiter fingers (index) extended. Keep the arms straight as you jump with the whole body, using the arms to lift you. The buttocks jump off the floor along with the entire body. Get into a rhythm and continue for **4 minutes**.

You want a raise? This is the time. Rise, rise. You want to experience resurrection? Get going. If these things had been easy, everybody would have become a yogi, wise, perfect, happy—nirvana.

3. Spinal Twist: place the hands on the shoulders, fingers in front and thumbs in back. Twist quickly inhaling left and exhaling right for **30–60 seconds**.

4. Bring the hands directly in front of you, arms extended parallel to the ground, with the palms facing each other, fingers open. Place the thumb on the Mercury mound and make a fist. Draw the arms and elbows back—quick! The movement is very fast and harsh. Create a shock in your body with the motion of the arms. Continue for **6 minutes**.

Come on! Give a shock treatment to your own system. Your system must understand how to react under a shock, so create that shock. You are just creating a pattern in the brain to respond. First we shielded our self, then we resurrected our self, now we are shocking our self. Aren't these three responses essential for any human being who wants to live honorably?

5. Bring the hands in front of the face. With eyes open, look through the hands. Crisscross the forearms quickly, making an X with each movement of the arms. Move fast, so that the hands move in front of the eyes like the blades of a fan. Continue for **2½ minutes**.

6a. With the arms crossed, place the hands in the armpits. Close the eyes and concentrate at the tip of the nose. Press the hands beneath the armpits. Continue for **3 minutes**.

Look deeper and deeper at the tip of the nose. You will see the white lining underneath the eyes dancing for you or a dark horizon. The forehead and frontal brain will feel the pressure, the pattern will be sealed; it will give you a good start in life. Come with me to my heart and visit my heavens.

b. Begin listening to *Flowers in the Rain* by Guru Dass Singh for **5 minutes**. *(See Appendix for Lyrics.)*

c. Begin singing with *Flowers in the Rain* for **11 minutes**.

d. Begin singing with *Walking Up the Mountain* recording by Guru Dass Singh and Krishna Kaur for **8 minutes**. *(See Appendix for Lyrics.)*

TO END: Inhale deeply; hold for **30 seconds**, as you tighten the grip; synchronize. Tighter, tighter, tighter. Then let it go. Inhale deeply; hold for **30 seconds** as you start stretching the spine upward. Press inward tighter. Resurrect your spine and bring the ribs to an absolute solidity. Let it go. Inhale deeply and exhale deeply 3 times. Once more: Inhale! Deep! And stretch up! Tighter! After **30 seconds**, relax.

Exercise 6 should take **31 minutes total**.

7. Lie down in Corpse Pose and have a nap. Just sink in and get lost. Sat Peter's *Himalaya* was played in class along with other elevating music for **11–15 minutes**.

A quick sleep, a nap, can do your health a better service than anything else. Take it as a medicine.

" If the subconscious is clogged up, you start squeezing yourself, and you become limited, smaller and smaller and smaller. All to small—that's the game. When you are small, you cannot handle all. When you can handle all, you cannot act small. When you cannot act small, you are happy, you are gracious, you are giving, you are loving, you are righteous, you are religious. "

– Yogi Bhajan

HOUSE CLEANING III

November 19, 1988

You do something, you get it out, and then it comes back to you. After six months the same thing—I mean to say, how much can you cry?

W E ARE GOING TO LAY A TRIP ON YOU TODAY. In a very simple way, we are trying to put you through something and then put a support system behind it[1], because I don't believe that you have the mental consistency to sustain. Otherwise, why do we do it? I understand. I have been a Master for all these years. You do something, you get it out, and then it comes back to you. After six months the same thing—I mean to say, how much can you cry? The problem is not with you as people—that I agree; the problem is you are not human beings—that I also agree. I understand; I am not foolish.

Twenty years ago, I came. I was poorer than you, I was more alone than you, I was absolutely more illiterate than you, and I never knew anything about what you call the United States of America. Not a bit. I walked into Canada to set up a Chair at the University of Toronto. It all went flop. But I started working, and within the two months I was there, I was pretty successful. *Globe & Mail* picked me up and put me on the front page, a big huge article about me. I used to teach at the YMCA. I came here to Los Angeles for just three days—Friday, Saturday, Sunday—Monday I was supposed to go back, but I never did.

I was in the mood for an experiment. If in twenty years I can build an empire and withstand all the torture, the abuse, the lawsuits, you name it, and still I am keeping up, then I have found something in me that is much better—and it's in everybody. The two years when I was in bed and I was not teaching, I was thinking and analyzing, investigating myself. What is in me that is not in everybody else? I found out that I am different from other people.

I don't dream, but I do have visions of danger and other things. I am very quick, and I analyze even the ordinary things you say. I turn it around one hundred and eighty degrees. I don't react; instead I put my activity toward a certain ground level of understanding of where you come from, where everything in your life comes from, what your bottom line is. You might have read in the past few days that with yoga you can change anything. Yoga, vegetarian diet and so on; it's no big deal, but there are certain things you have to understand. If, in your body, whatever you eat you make certain that it comes out in twenty-four hours, then you will be healthy, you will be normal, and you can change anything you want. No big deal. This is not a miracle.

It is simple. The *Hatha Yoga Pradipika* stands as a guarantee to this fact, from page eight to last. No big deal. If you know how to lock the three bandhas—Root

1 Referring to an herbal formula he created for the class.

Lock, Abdominal Lock, and Neck Lock—you can balance your energy and penetrate any point you want to heal. You can heal anything, doesn't matter what the disease is. But five hundred years from now, Americans will be practicing the same thing that people practiced during the age of the *Pradipika*—no big deal. It's the game.

You know that if the subconscious is clogged up, you start squeezing yourself, and you become limited, smaller and smaller and smaller. All to small—that's the game. When you are small, you cannot handle all. When you can handle all, you cannot act small. When you cannot act small, you are happy, you are gracious, you are giving, you are loving, you are righteous, you are religious. Brand you with anything, who cares? You have the strength. Not that you have the knowledge, not that you have the degree, not that you have the beauty, not that you have the richness. That won't work; that you don't understand. If you do not have the courage and strength of commitment within you to deliver, you will not deliver; you will have to have a caesarian and it will be painful—that's the pain.

It is a mental game in which you are all victims. In twenty years, I have met rich people, poor people, nothing, everything, politician, nonpolitician, people who lie as a habit, people who lie because they want to, people who do not want to lie, people who act righteous, people who are crazy—all sorts of lies, beautiful, ugly, you name it. I have come to conclude that if there is courage, there is life. If courage has no priority, life has no meaning. That's my conclusion; that is the essence of what I have found.

I don't believe anybody can be poor. I don't believe everybody has to divorce. I don't believe everybody has to negate. If you are limited, you make yourself small. You cannot contain the universe, but you belong to universe. You live in this universe; this is your universe. A tribe cannot be a nation; and a nation cannot be a world. These are simple laws.

I am trying to do an experiment. It's a very simple theory. Your metabolism is proportionate to your breath and proceeds according to your age. So you lose the power to burn over time; on top of that, your skin does not breathe. The skin is your third lung. It's a very important thing! But thanks to your powder and your "extra extra" dry, you might as well take tar and a brush and do it twice so that you will never have any sweat, ever. One treatment, two cents, and you will never find anything smelly there other than that tar smell, you know? Like the highway. So you block your pores, and you call it extra dry. I mean, you are wonderful. I love you. You have a national license to kill yourself.

Your armpits are the central trigger points of the three nervous systems by which you live. If your meat and bones are taken away, your body is just a network of nerves; it is a fantastic nervous system. It is sharp, acute, and admirably fast, and yet you irritate it. You block it and reduce its electromagnetic field by doing lots of things that you should not be doing because they are unnatural. However it is not my job to put you before a firing squad. You want to live temporary, beautiful, comfortable, and permanently sick and tired? If that's your goal, what can I do? I am a spiritual teacher not a dictator. So I am trying to find some herbs and some exercises. I'm digging deeper into my notes to do something because all of you are entering your middle age—you know, when down the hill starts. I don't want to see you run down. I don't want to see that. That's not my thinking.

God knows that we are divine and we are ridiculous. But I have seen my grandfather, my grandmother, my granduncles, and they died just sitting and saying, "Goodbye, thank you, *Sat Nam*"—out. I saw my father-in-law dying, and I have never seen, in my whole life, anybody dying like that. He came and he said, "I am not feeling well. I am going to lie down." Then, "All right, now is the time to put the blanket on the ground and put me north and south on the ground. I am dying." He was dying. Everybody was called and told that he was dying. Then, "All right, now you read the *Sukhmani*." In the middle of *Sukhmani* are certain Hindu rituals or rites, dharmic things they do to give money for the poor and all that. So after we started, he said, "All right, this is halftime. Come let us do that." In the end he said, "Before that wall, nail a nail and put that picture of Guru Nanak that I always meditate with. I want to see it once more, and I want to close my eyes and goodbye." They did what he asked, and he closed his eyes and goodbye—and that was a permanent goodbye.

Nobody was troubled, nobody could be bothered. But there was a note left that said as his son-in-law, I was supposed to come and execute his will. So I came, and one thing was most shocking—there was a full account. Who was to do music, who was to do charity, how much langar was to be served, how many poor had to be fed, how many poor people and children he had educated and what was due them, the whole detail, even how much wood there should be for the pyre was written, and what quality of dryness the wood should be, that detail. Then he wrote one line: "I trust you to do it because I trust you. You are an honest officer." That was all. So I took the paper, and I understood the whole detail. That's called dying, conscious dying. Absolutely, calculative knowledge, I have never seen in my life that detail—and fully typed, too.

What I saw of that death has made me understand that death is a system. Getting old and not being mature, getting old and aging and not extending yourself in tolerance, in wisdom, in maturity is a tragedy. Because you must understand, after every eighteen-year life cycle, your intelligence ages eleven years, and your consciousness ages seven years. So as you mature in age, you should be proportionately more in intelligence and consciousness if you want to know what happiness is about.

Getting old and not being mature, getting old and aging and not extending yourself in tolerance, in wisdom, in maturity is a tragedy.

*Everybody wants
their kundalini to rise
but nobody wants
to work for it.*

Tonight we are concerned with your five tattvas and your two hemispheres, left and right. You are a product of ether, air, fire, water, and earth. You have five tattvas, and you have seven chakras; the eighth chakra is the shield, and in that shield the most important is the Arcline. A female and male have no difference in Arcline as far as the earlobe to earlobe is concerned, the halo; but the female also has an Arcline at the breast that the male doesn't have. That's the only difference that I can see between a girl and a boy, until I change the focus of my eyes; otherwise, you all look alike. And although people can lie, the aura will never lie. But this also has a responsibility with it: use it to help—not to bug, but to hug. Understand the depth.

◆ ◆ ◆

This exercise we are dedicating to the central nervous system, the central channel called the shushmana. It is imaginary for certain people, but it is real for other people. The central nervous system runs between the tip of the tongue to the tip of the tailbone, that first little vertebra, which if you ever sit on it wrong and that little thing gets moved inward, your whole life will be nothing but full of irritation. That little thing can do so much damage; in fact, that little thing is not little. The base of the spine and the central nervous system are attached to only that vertebra. That is the tragedy of the whole system. So we are going to work today on that.

The ida and the pingala will change the frequency, and then immediately the sympathetic nervous system will respond. That's why when somebody attacks us, we react to save our self, to protect our self. It is called automatic response. I hope it won't happen. I mean, if you have the determination to do it once and for all and get rid of all this nonsense we are suffering from, right? That kind of attitude we need.

There is a saying: "One who does not know what is in one's armpit is always in the pit of so and so." I am not naming. But that's okay. *(See Exercise 1.)* Life runs in a circular motion, like a little boat upon the sea.

Everybody wants their kundalini to rise but nobody wants to work for it.

I said to a student of mine, "Why don't you come to my classes?"

"Sir, they are very hard."

"Well, go to those other classes."

"Sir, they are very soft."

Some are hard, some are soft; purpose is not to go. Shoulders go up or shoulders go down—keep going.

You people all want to be healthy, so what are you stopping for? Come on! I am very busy. It's not going to end like this. You have to change your aura, and I know when it will be. Should I do it with you? Will that give you satisfaction? All right, come on, let's do it. If you do it right, you will hit all the lower three vertebrae automatically; you can't help it, you can't do it without that. There will be pain in the pelvic area, and there will be a terrible pain in the shoulders. The elbows will hurt like a hell, and the thumb will look like somebody is chopping it off. That's how it goes. But it is balancing. It is doing something to give you a new lease on life. Come on. You know I got sick, and I don't want you to get sick, ever. That's what I am trying to investigate. Come on! Let's do it. How many beatings can somebody take?

All right now. This is called Reverse Shock System *(see Exercise 3)*. First, listen to the science. We are not in a hurry. Create a shock system. You are in an element of surprise; you are in an element of disgrace; cut it out and then go back again. Rest the hands on your cheek and then come out with a most fantastic shock.

Everybody has to educate himself. You should have been taught these things when you were children. Play the Reverse Shock System. Just wake up like this. Wake up with a feeling of pain, horror, and whatever adversity you can play. Play it right. Imagine when something actually happens to you, and you have no way to reverse yourself. At least you are doing it now and reversing yourself. Give yourself a pattern to reverse yourself when you are hit by a shock. You understand? I think this should be the first class when you go to school. It is a therapy; just get scary! You are not scary; you think it is horrible. Get a little scary and then act normal, get scary and act normal, get scary, act normal. If I tell you to dress up for Halloween, you would do it.

These are exercises to connect the brain's neurons; they have nothing to do with anything else. The idea is to help the brain's energy so that your life has an immediate intuitive answer. This movement is totally dedicated to this idea.

Breathe consciously, and heal yourself. Do it right. It will change everything. Let the breath of life repair your system.

◆ ◆ ◆

May the long time sun shine upon you,
all love surround you, and the pure light within you, guide your way on.

Sat Nam

HOUSECLEANING III— THE KRIYA

November 19, 1988

There are no breaks between the exercises. Move immediately from one exercise to the next.

1. Eyes are closed with the hands in Ego Eradicator mudra, fingertips curled to the base of the fingers and thumbs extended. The arms are stretched forward at a 60-degree angle from the Heart Center. The hands are about 15 degrees above parallel. Stretch the arms out from the shoulders, lifting and stretching from the shoulder joint. Feel the stretch in the armpit. When the maximum stretch is reached, begin circling the arms in quick, small outward circles for **10 minutes**.

When you reach a point that you can't do it, start doing it faster. There are four mounds underneath my fingers, see that they touch. If they don't touch, it means there is a pain here, and these joints are a little brittle. My shoulders are out, my armpit has stretched. We are now empowering our three nervous systems. This armpit is very powerful.

2. With the arms still stretching from the shoulders, turn the palms toward the ground and begin crisscrossing the arms for **1 minute**.

3. Reverse Shock System: Place the hands on the sides of the face, covering the cheeks but not covering the eyes, nose, or mouth. Then quickly, with force, pull the hands away from the face. Create a shock; express surprise; create a sound—but don't rush it. Allow the hands to rest on the face and then play the hands again. Act afraid, and then relax; and continue for **3 minutes**. This exercise builds the immune system and allows one to confront adversity.

Learn what is here, in this area, and create a shock system: an element of surprise, an element of fear, an element of pain, an element of whatever it takes to reverse the neuron patterns and give you strength when actually you are in pain. You want to live? Try this! This will build your immune system; it will give you the intuitive sense to support yourself. It will help you to confront adversity. Play the Reverse Shock System. For a while it will look odd, then it will become even, then you will get confused. I am telling you the stages that you go through, and then you'll hate yourself, and then you'll keep doing it without even knowing what you are doing. That's how it happens. That's normally what a shock does.

4. Bring the Ego Eradicator mudra in front of the face, palms out. Spin the thumbs over each other in small circles. Look straight into the moving mudra. If you feel dizzy, stop; otherwise, keep going for **90 seconds**.

The idea is to help the brain's energy, the master computer, so that your life has an immediate intuitive answer—that's the idea. The faster you do it and concentrate on it, the better the result.

5. Place the left palm on the Heart Center with the right hand extending straight into the sky with the right hand's fingers spread wide. Stretch the right arm up out of the shoulder and move it in small, counterclockwise circles. (Do *not* reverse this position. Yogi Bhajan warns against practicing this with the left arm raised.) Continue for **90 seconds**.

6. Hold a ball of energy in front of the face between your palms. Play with it. Move both wrists, simultaneously twisting right and left. Look into the center of the hands. *"This exercise will improve your eyesight."* Continue for **30 seconds**.

7. Lock your hands above the opposite elbows, forearms parallel to the ground. Roll the eyes powerfully toward the Third Eye. Grind the full length of the spine in small tight circles for **2 minutes**.

Grind yourself like a pestle and mortar. You have to have that Earth balance when you move. Surprisingly it will give you spinal energy. It will correct your system so that your message system and your action system do not create a differential difference. You know how sometimes you apply the brake but you end up accelerating? Instead of the left foot, you put the pressure on the right foot. Sometimes you want to apply the brake but it takes time. This exercise is the solution. It will coordinate the motor command in the brain and the nerve command and the muscle command, all three. It will give your spine flexibility.

8. Interlock the fingers behind the neck and drop the head. Keeping the spine straight, close the eyes and try to sleep with the neck relaxed and head forward. As the gong is played, allow yourself to release with the sound of the gong for **9½ minutes**.

Take a nap, but keep the spine straight. As the wave hits you—and the strength of the wave of this gong I am playing is very, very excellent and space oriented—with every push, try to go away and away and away. The beauty is to let go.

9. Raise your head, release the mudra, close the eyes, look straight through closed eyes, and see the sound at the pituitary. Inhale and breathe very slowly in and out as the gong continues for **3 minutes**.

10. One-Minute Breath: Inhale 20 seconds, hold 20 seconds, exhale 20 seconds. Breathe consciously as the recording of *Ardas Bhaee* by Nirinjan Kaur is played. *"Breathe consciously, heal yourself. Hale and heal."* Continue for **9½ minutes**.

TO END: Inhale deeply, hold; exhale and hold. Inhale and hold. Exhale and hold. Inhale, hold; exhale, hold out. Inhale, deeper, inhale, hold; exhale, all the way, hold out. Inhale, inhale deep, hold and let the breath of life repair your system. Let it go, hold out, relax. Move your hands and shake your entire body. Jump like popcorn. Give your body a chance. Move, move, last chance, move the shoulders, neck, head, ankle, toes, knees, butt, belly, chest, neck, cheeks, forehead, front, back, and neck. Continue for **90 seconds**.

11. Stretch the hands up above the head with the fingers stretched. Toughen the arms and hands like steel. Count to **16** and then relax. Inhale and exhale quickly **5–7 times**. Then inhale and suspend the breath; the entire body should become like steel. Count to **16** and then repeat. Inhale and exhale quickly **5–7 times**. Then inhale and suspend the breath; make your body like steel. Count to **16** and then relax.

Toughen it like steel. At the count of 16, let it go. One, two, three, four, five, six, tough, seven, eight, tough, nine, ten, eleven, tough, twelve, thirteen, tough, fourteen, fifteen, sixteen . . . let it go. Very good. Now every muscle must get its share of that electromagnetic field. Tough—toughen the toe, toughen the nail on the toe. Toughen the nail on the fingers; everything should become tough, tough, tough. Tough one, tough two, tough three, tough four, five, six, seven, eight, nine, ten, eleven, twelve, thirteen, fourteen, fifteen, sixteen . . . go. Become tough as steel. Get to every part of you sitting right there, so you can feel the psyche of the electromagnetic field's energy. Every part of the body—one, two, three, four, five, six, seven, eight, nine, ten, eleven, twelve, thirteen, fourteen, fifteen, sixteen . . . let it go.

◆

Comments

We are dedicating this exercise to the central nervous system, called the shushmana. It runs between the tip of the tongue to the tip of the tailbone. There is a possibility that in certain places you may feel a sharp pain. I am not saying it will happen; but if that happens, it is just like when the train changes tracks. The ida and pingala will change the frequency, and then immediately the autonomic nervous system will adjust. It's the same mechanism as when somebody attacks us and we react to protect our self. It is called automatic response. Do you have the determination to do it once and for all to get rid of all this nonsense we are suffering? That is the kind of attitude we need today.

" The longing of the spirit, the longing of the mind, and the longing of the body are three hungers within you. They cannot go away. The body will need its nourishment, its enrichment; the mind will need its nourishment, its enrichment; and the soul will need its enrichment and nourishment. "

– *Yogi Bhajan*

HOUSECLEANING IV

November 21, 1988

*I*T HAS BEEN UNDERSTOOD BY PEOPLE OF ALL RACES. From the very first day, man understood that he gets tired. It's known that you get tired. Then man understood that he can rest, he can sleep, and by doing so, he can recuperate. It is known; it is not something I have to tell you or that you want to listen to. But man never understood that he gets mentally tired. This you cannot accept. Because accepting this means that then you have to do something, and you are not ready to do that.

You cannot get up in the morning, and you cannot do sadhana, You think those who talk to you about it are stupid. No, they are not; you are! Because you get mentally tired. Everybody gets tired, and when you are mentally tired, you do so many blunders, stupid blunders, mistakes that make life become useless, and you grow spiritually tired. The longing of the spirit, the longing of the mind, and the longing of the body are three hungers within you. They cannot go away. Body will need its nourishment, its enrichment; mind will need its nourishment, its enrichment; and soul will need its enrichment and nourishment.

Whether you want to accept it or not is not the problem. The amount of make-up and care we take just to look good? If we took just one-third of that same care to be good, we could go through anything safe and clear. We suffer losses and calamities because we are not mentally steady, we get tired, and we cannot cope. As far as spirituality is concerned, the defense mechanism of your body is very powerful. When your spirit is on, the defense mechanism of your body—the Radiant Body they call it—its light is on. When your spirit is off, the light is off, and you become vulnerable. You are attacked by situations that you just don't want to relate to.

So your life is based on three living aspects in you according to their strength. I definitely know what I'm talking about. I have twenty-four years of practical practice in becoming a yogi. I was a yogi, well-respected, internationally known. Look at it. The Golden Temple was attacked[1], then what? The Golden Temple has been attacked many times. It is the nerve center of spirituality, and when it gets attacked, lots of things happen. But for me, it was just like my altar had been plundered. I ended up with a clogged-up artery in my Heart Center—simple. If a man of my caliber can fall apart, what about you? You don't even exist. Action has a reaction, equal and opposite. If I can get emotional and feel handicapped and all of a sudden they say, "You are on your death bed, get going." Things can happen.

As far as spirituality is concerned, the defense mechanism of your body is very powerful. When your spirit is on, the defense mechanism of your body— the Radiant Body—its light is on. When your spirit is off, the light is off, and you become vulnerable.

[1]The Golden Temple was attacked by Indian Military forces in October of 1986.

When we say, "Go to sadhana," we don't say it because we want to make frogs out of you. Simply we don't want you to suffer. We don't want to suffer. You do not understand—a spiritual teacher doesn't care who you are or who you are not. His main concern is that there should be nothing that brings you pain, insult, depression, all those kind of things. A spiritual teacher lives when your spirit is bright and beautiful. But you are not willing to understand that. You think that when you are emotionally involved and commotionally into it, and all that jazz, you think you are very alive. With those gross situations, you end up with a gross situation, and then you are in pain: "I love him, I divorce him, I marry him, he is here, he is there, she is there, she is not there, job is there, job is not there." Have you ever looked at any situation and found anything other than that your switch went off? On TV the other day, they were showing a most wonderful thing. This woman was driving her car and she fell asleep at the steering wheel. The car was hanging off of the bridge. One wheel rim got stuck in the railing, that's the only thing that kept the car from going over. When they rescued her, she said, "I was just tired."

Tonight we are penetrating the most neglected area of our life—our layers of memory. We have sad memories, we have dirty memories, and we have happy memories. Man lives by perpetual memory. There is no Jesus Christ. Where is he? Perpetual memory. Whenever you do something wrong you call on him, "Jesus Christ" or "Oh, Christ." That's our perpetual memory. Moses is not here; nobody knows where he is. But he split the Red Sea. God knows he split it. You can't split it now, but the memory of Moses is there. All good deeds contain God in them, because the word "good" contains "God." Write down "she," and "he" is contained in it; write down "woman," and "man" is contained in it; write down "female," and "male" is contained in it; write down "good," and "God" is contained in it. Have you understood these words that way? You don't. You just speak; you don't care.

I believe that man is born to be happy. Fight is very simple. Fight is a single man's crusade against the whole world. I believe man is not supposed to be un-happy. There is no way that man should be unhealthy. I believe that herbs heal and God cures and doctor diagnoses. I believe in that, honestly. A good doctor, to me, is one who just delivers the doctrine of diagnosis. Once he diagnoses, then he knows what will work.

I was talking the other day to a Chinese herbalist, and it was very funny what he was saying: "Chinese formulas have three ways. Which way do you want to go?"

"What are the three ways?"

"One is for the king, another is for the minister, and the third is for the soldier."

"What do you mean?"

"King doesn't work physically, so he only needs a little to have more effect; minister works a little bit but through his head, so he has to have a different formula."

"What about the solider?"

"Load him with everything. It works anyway, because he doesn't rest."

It looks very funny, but is it not the truth? When you treat people, you have to treat them at the rate at which they physically work. You can diagnose things, but that does not mean that you can treat it right. God cures. Doctor and medicine don't; they help.

Where is God? God is under the foot, called "sole." Walk three miles regularly, do a sadhana ofabout two to three hours a day of proper exercises, and I don't think you can go wrong. There has to be a movement in order for the five tattvas to balance. It is a requirement. It is not a sexual requirement, or a stomach requirement, or a makeup and party requirement; it is the living requirement. Your five tattvas must balance once every twenty-four hours. It is a living requirement—I don't care which religion you belong to or which country you belong to.

Because I have been sick—and thank God I got sick, I am very happy about it—I found out how to beat it. I am working on it every day. It's not that I am cured, it's not that I am not upset about it; but I am going to become a guinea pig. One day my doctor put a needle somewhere, and I said, "Don't—it is creating a reaction."

"Yeah, it is the same meridian, I understand. What should I do now?"

"Balance it."

So he put a needle on the other side, and it all stopped. I mean, it's a very living body, right there. He put a needle on one side, and a red signal went on; he put a needle on the other side, and it all calmed down. That was a fascinating experience. I am very naive fellow, moving around, doing nothing, but I have a sensitivity. You have to have a sensitivity.

Memory—you live by memory. After death you live by memory. Mortal becomes immortal by memory. Guru Nanak is a memory; his birthday is coming. Lord Buddha is a memory; his celebration will be on the way soon. Jesus is a memory. Although he was born on the twenty fourth of August, they put his birthday at Christmas time because of the celebration of the Roman Empire. And poor man, Son of God, lost his birthday, that's what people do. They just put you where they want you. They feel that's the best thing.

You spend five or six thousand dollars on rebirthing—let us have one with us. Let us see what twenty bucks can do. If you can stand this rebirthing, you will never ask for it again, you will reach nirvana.

Mickey Mouse is celebrating its sixtieth birthday. Now Mickey Mouse is a caricature, a character. Character can break or not; caricature cannot break. Caricature is character solidified. Confirmed character is called caricature. That's why the Chinese language is in caricatures. When they want to write a home, they make a home. They want a door, they make a door. They don't spell things; they are very quick.

So let us see how Mickey Mouse became a caricature. During the Great Depression, Walt Disney sat down to create a character. He wanted to do something, so he created a caricature, and he started giving it a positive, funny story. Mickey Mouse started making everybody laugh. Net result: Mickey Mouse ended up with an empire, and you end up with nothing. Mickey Mouse is the richest individual in the United States. He is a billionaire in his own right, and he is expanding in France, too. He has the biggest house; and wherever he exists, his house must contain a magic mountain. Can you believe that? That's a necessity. And thousands of you proud Americans, Democrats and Republicans, you serve that guy, from cleaning his toilets to painting his castle. And that's just Mickey Mouse.

In New York, somebody had an idea to help sell clothes. He created flying reindeers and put a white bearded man called Santa Claus on them. He was a Russian immigrant who came to the States and happened to believe in Saint Nicholas. That's the story. Today Santa Claus is the best salesperson in the universe. He has overtaken everything. Even before Thanksgiving begins, he starts. He doesn't exist. Never got born, nobody got pregnant, nobody can doubt whether he was immaculately born or not. Nothing. Not a word. But do you know that Santa Claus is the most well-known saint in this universe, and he is there to profit Jews, Gentiles, and others alike? He is so powerful and so miraculous that he flies reindeers, and he walks through the chimney of every house to throw his sock full of gifts, and he never gets dirty. And he is the one and only human being who lives at the North Pole, with his whole factory and workshop. Now, am I kidding? Millions of letters are written to him every day, and the post office sorts it out. Even the post office benefits from it.

Such is also the story of Guru Gobind Singh, who was a character and a caricature in the religious world. But he made a living caricature. He created a blend of the saint and the soldier. He said, "Live like a saint, act like a soldier; that's the only way to be happy." Not that I want you to follow Guru Gobind Singh, nor do I want you to buy things because of Santa Claus, nor do I want you to visit Disneyland. I am not selling you any bill of goods. I am telling you that if you want to be happy, then there is a way. The choice is still yours.

Today is a day when we will go into our memories: bad, sad, negative, positive. This room will be filled with garbage floating all around, and there will be a lot of mental throw-ups. But when we come out of it, we'll be light, bright, and beautiful, rather than going through the sweat dreams and horror dreams of life and always having a subconscious feeling hanging over us. Do you understand that we are always walking with a ghost at our side? We don't need that. I should have taught this class on Halloween to take the ghost out of you; but it didn't happen then, so we'll work tonight, and we'll work well. Okay, ready? Let it be known that whatever happens is because we want to do it, and in the end of the tunnel, we'll see the light, we'll be happy. All right?

Plastic teeth, plastic nails, plastic face, plastic person, plastic mind, plastic relationship, plastic car, everything is plastic.

◆ ◆ ◆

Watch out, watch what comes out. Just do it for a few minutes. After the movie starts, you'll be in it. Yes, this few minutes of introduction is difficult—getting the ticket, sitting on the seat. After that "Hallelujah!" There you are—you and your ghosts. Just become a demon. Get going. Think of the ghost. I am not going to teach you rebirthing. I am going to go through the rebirthing and clean it all out. So come along with me. Go deeper and deeper to hypnotize yourself, layer upon layer, and break through. Keep going, don't stop!

Give your pains to God; let Him handle them.

◆ ◆ ◆

May the long time sun shine upon you,
all love surround you, and the pure light within you, guide your way on.

God, God, God

Sat Nam

HOUSECLEANING IV— THE KRIYA

November 21, 1988

Before practicing this kriya, drink lemon water throughout the day. You should have the juice of 5–6 lemons or limes in your system before practicing. There are no breaks between the exercises. Move immediately from one exercise to the next.

1. Make the hands into claws. Lock the molars. Roll the eyes strongly upward. Bring the hands in front and just to the sides of the face, palms facing each other. Tense the body until you shake. After **3 minutes**, close your eyes and shake even harder. Shake the anger out, and follow the guided meditation. This exercise should last **7½ minutes total**.

Guided Meditation

Whatever you don't like in your life, whatever you won't like about tomorrow, and whatever you want to get rid of, get rid of it now! Get angry—at anything you hate in your life. Figure out something. That girlfriend who didn't call you back, that boyfriend who didn't write you a letter, that husband who cheated on you, that man who didn't send you the bill, the father who didn't pay for the child support, whatever. The marriage that didn't work, the husband who is impotent, the wife who was frigid, think about anything. There must be something to get angry at in your life. Now close your eyes and concentrate on that and shake hard.

Shake this anger out! Is it something particularly American that we do not know about? Are we so shaken that we can't shake ourselves? This whole hand and finger movement is changing the brain pattern; it's a science. We are doing thousands of years of known science. Get out of it—you can cry, you can weep, you can laugh, you can do anything, but you must shake. Get to the saddest and most negative and angriest thing in your life and attack it. Attack it with a bear claw. If you don't attack it today, when there is such a pure energy around here, it will attack you.

You are working for yourself, not for me. I'm not asking you to do the impossible. Just make your hands like a bear claw and shake your body. It's okay just to go crazy; we are crazy anyway.

Beat it up. Everybody's eyes are closed, nobody is looking at you; so don't worry, it is all private. Attack the most penetrating, painful thing in your life and attack it hard, attack it severely. Because the next time that we ask you to do a subconscious release, if you have not done this before, then you will have a terrible difficulty. You will look like a fake. But if now you just go and sweat and warm up and make the patterns right in the brain, then the neurons will adjust, and things will be very easy. Harder, harder! Attack the most painful thing in life. There are lots of things we can't even share with a psychologist; we cannot share with a psychiatrist. What does it matter if you have to yell, scream, and cry? Go ahead. But get it out and attack it.

2. Place the hands on the Heart Center, one hand resting on the other. Be calm. Inhale and exhale quickly 3 times and follow the guided meditation:

Guided Meditation

Feel that you are an egg and spermatozoa. Come along with me exactly as I say. Feel that you are conceived. Feel you are conceived, feel you are conceived, feel you are conceived. Feel consciously that you are conceived. There will be a tremendous opposition to it, but feel you are conceived. Feel you are conceived, feel you are conceived, feel you are conceived. Feel the womb, feel you are conceived.

I am not going to teach you rebirthing. I am going to go through the rebirthing and clean it all out. So come along with me. Feel you are conceived, you are conceived in the womb, the womb, which is a female, and you are conceived. Feel you are conceived. You feel, you feel, you feel you are conceived in the womb, in the womb. You are conceived in a womb, you are conceived in a womb. Hypnotize yourself; there is no better hypnosis than self. Hypnotize yourself to be conceived. You are conceived. Hypnotize yourself. We'll carry you through the previous lives on a voyage beyond you. The conception as it has been repeated, conception as it has been repeated, conception as it has been repeated, conception as it has been repeated. We'll take you to all the conceptions that have been repeated. Please feel conceived. Feel conceived, feel conceived. Feel the Heart Center, the ribcage where your soul is at this time imprisoned, and feel conceived. Please go through the experience. Feel conceived, feel your soul in the ribcage. We'll take you to the yonder past to feel hypnotically the conception that has taken place before. It has no reference to reality. It's a personal, private knowledge.

After 5 minutes, the gong is played. Continue the guided meditation.

Go deeper and deeper to hypnotize yourself, layer upon layer, and break through. We are with you in pure energy. Wave after wave, we'll help you. Get into the depth of the space. It is all true. Go back and watch your own incarnations. It is all true. Believe it or not, it is all true. Go back, deeper and deeper. Feel your soul and your conception. Feel your past conceptions. All your previous bodies are lined up now in your aura. Don't miss them; feel them. Go through this journey. Your soul is traveling. Keep going, don't stop! Concentrate!

Know your own story. Pass through as many spaces, beings, lands as you can. Keep the journey going. We are going to pass through a very emotional storm. Now we are picking up the altitude. Resistance will be less and the deeper you will go in self-hypnosis. You can go into the deeper levels where you have not gone before. You can touch the frontiers that are not reachable. Concentrate and dive deep. Pick up the higher altitude to see all. Watch the world like skydivers. We are going through the crosswinds. Stand by.

Tiny, tiny, tiny, tiny, tiny, tiny light. Turn yourself into a tiny, tiny, tiny, tiny light. Little star, tiniest of all. Let the pain go, let the pain go. It was a mistake. You have already "missed the take." Let the pain go. Let the pain go. Let it go! Let it go. Give it to God. Let the pain go! Give it to God! Let the pain go, give it to God. Let the pain go, give it to God. All things come from God, all things go to God; all things come from God, all things go to God. Let the pain go, let it go to God.

*This exercise should last **30 minutes** total.*

3. Keep the mudra and begin singing *All Things Come from God* sung by Awtar Singh. (Gong continues for another 2 minutes.) Sing it. Sing it from heart for **8 minutes.**

Sing louder, right from the Heart Center. Give your pains back to God; let Him handle them. Right from the heart, sing it loud. Sing—it will cleanse you. Sing; copy the sound. Sing it hypnotically, and it will take away your pains. We all have pain. Give it back to God. Sing it hypnotically.

4. Bring your hands to your throat, one on top of the other. Let the neck sit in your hands and touch it. Keep your eyes closed as you concentrate and sing *Flowers in the Rain* by Gurudass Singh. Sing for **5½ minutes**.

5. Bring the hands to the forehead with the fingers crossing each other. Cover the forehead and sing *Walking Up the Mountain*, recording by Gurudass Singh and Krishna Kaur, for **7½ minutes.**

(See lyric sheets in the Appendix.)

6. Interlace the hands on top of the head. Look up at the palms of the hands through closed eyes. Copy the sounds and sing the *Narayan Shabd* sung by Guru Raj Kaur Khalsa, for **3 minutes**.

TO END: Inhale deep and hold for **45 seconds**. Exhale. Inhale deep and suspend for **60 seconds**. Exhale.

Look upon the sahasrara, the thousand-petaled lotus. Make a beautiful aura of your own hands, lock them. Please do it for your sake, not for mine. You are a saint; hypnotize yourself and speak through a hypnotic meditative voice—that's the voice you should go through. Look at the palms of the hand through closed eyes. Look up. Inhale deep, deep; through the closed eyes, look into the palms of your hands and rewrite your destiny as happy as you want to. Why don't you write what you want to read in your own hand? You are divine.

7. Place both hands on the Navel Point, left under, right over. Press. Press deeply and chant with the Kirtan Kriya melody for **1 minute**:

SAA   TAA   NAA   MAA
RAA   MAA   DAA   SAA
SAA   SAY   SO   HANG

TO END: inhale, exhale; exhale deep, exhale deep, exhale deep, pull the navel in! Exhale, pull, exhale, pull, exhale, pull. Inhale and relax.

" If your subconscious is totally cleared and clean, you'll be doing totally different things, and you will be a lot happier and more effective than you are today. "

– Yogi Bhajan

REMOVING YOUR SUBCONSCIOUS BLOCKS

November 24, 1988

I know you are American, and you can do crazy things, but a stinking subconscious blocks every happiness in life.

ALL RIGHT, THIS IS WHAT WE ARE GOING TO DO. Class is very tough and harsh; you either want to take it or not. It's your choice, but don't leave in the middle. If in the first few steps you don't tune in with it, get up and walk away, that is what we prefer. But if you want to stick around, then stay and stay like people. I know you are American, and you can do crazy things, but a stinking subconscious blocks every happiness in life. Your whole thing is in your subconscious. If your subconscious is totally cleared and clean, you'll be doing totally different things, and you will be a lot happier and more effective than you are today. I am sick and tired of this stupidity. I am not supposed to teach today, but my idea is, "Why be totally useless while one is breathing?"

That is how a man becomes a lunatic. "Lunatic active"—it is not a foreign land, it is not a foreign language, it is English. Lunatic active is an idea. This is how we start. We are born as children; we all get born. Then sometimes mother likes you, sometimes father likes you, sometimes you are a chum of A or B. You desire things, you want things, you know things, and you keep all these desires and wants and whatever else in your subconscious. It's a hidden you. When the reality of life hits home and what you want is not there, then what you have is not enough. What you want is not there and what you have is not enough and your subconscious is full of insecurity, fear, and anger. Knowing what I know, the fact that you are alive is a miracle.

You have to act insane, you have to act out of commotion. Sometimes you all don't think, sometimes you just jump out of the window, you lose your nervous control, you are temperamental, you are moody. There are so many names, but they are just names. And maybe it is true that there is a psychiatric or psychological or counseling treatment, but this doesn't work. Neither will it, nor has it, nor can it. Period.

Subconscious is subconscious, and what the subconscious holds, goes. That's why man found religion, dharma, faith—in order to deny the storage of subconscious. There is absolutely nothing that you have been told so far that isn't a lie: you'll find God, you'll be happy, religion will give you this or that. All of this is absolutely a white lie, it has no truth. The fact is that once you get to some reality, some religion, some fundamentals, then you do not overload

the subconscious—that's all the problem is. And once the subconscious is over-loaded , well . . . You know, some people get rich and they are unhappy; some people are very happy and spacey, but they are not rich, they are poor. They go this way, and you can go that way. The fact is, wherever the subconscious leads you it leads you. You are not in one piece, together.

People in Kundalini Yoga and Tantric Yoga are happy because we unload the subconscious once in a while, one way or the other. We teach that. We under-stand that pain is not in an empty stomach, pain is not in weaker nerves, pain is not in having no sex, no chemistry, nothing. All these sciences that you talk about don't make any sense, and your relationships don't make any sense ei-ther. Relationship is when you cling to each other for emotional satisfaction. But if you look at it wisely, it doesn't make any sense. Why? We have a tremendous amount of fear. What we decided to have and what we have do not match, and this creates in us a state of insensitivity. Now, insensitive to what? Insensitive to opportunity, insensitive to intuition, insensitive to our projection; when you have all three messed up, think—who are you? Think about it.

Somebody in the heavens went to another guy in the heavens and asked, "How are the humans on Earth?"

"Well, they are painted ducks."

"Could you explain what happened that God has changed all humans to painted ducks?"

"Yeah, all they do is make up and quack, quack, quack."

That's what you are if you look at it. A guy in the heavens can't lie.

◆ ◆ ◆

We are going to unload the subconscious, but not totally. If you get totally unloaded, then you are not that disciplined and you won't come through. So we'll do a little bit—enough that a couple thousand dollars of counseling can do, but not enough to make you saints. Because you have to walk on this Earth tomorrow, and you should not feel that you have grown wings tonight in your arms and that you are flying. Plus, you do not know where the Earth is, so you would look crazy to others. All right?

This is a heavy class, by the way, so if you are not in a rush to do something with me, that door is open. Collect your money outside and out. That's how ef-fective I am. I am not even willing to teach those who are not very eager about it. But if you want to do something for yourself, go ahead.

This first exercise is a circulatory movement; try to keep it circular. *(See Exercise 1.)* Don't make any corner or edge. It will affect the neurons in the brain and their patterns. In a couple of minutes, you will feel miserable; it will be difficult.

Well, I know the effect! We are using the upper sciatica nerve to pressurize the brain's energy in the gray matter to reorganize. The moment you start organizing it properly, it will start defying you, totally defining its own orbit. It will start offending you, and that's where you will goof up.

Just draw a huge circle in front of you. You have never done this before, I understand. You may look crazy to yourself. Inside sometimes you say, "Are you crazy?" You'll hear it. In a couple of minutes, inside your own self, you'll feel like a lunatic because the left neurons and the right neurons will try to understand what you are doing. Here, in the brain, there is a split. It keeps asking, what is next? Because the brain has never done this before. You understand? You have never needed to do what you are doing right now. You understand? This is not your modus operandi.

This is not the way you act. So every exercise will be almost out of the blue, totally lunatic, and the left side of the brain and the right side of the brain will try to negotiate because they both want to help each other. Whereas the motor in the brain is telling you to keep on doing it, because that's the way you are doing it. Keep on doing it. You'll go through a lot of pain and a lot of weakness, but that's how it is working. Inside, when the work starts, outside you will think, "Stop it! I don't want to do it." But that is the stage when you should make the circle absolutely round.

Now, whatever you have started, don't stop. If you have started clockwise keep going clockwise; if it is counterclockwise, keep it counterclockwise. Just make sure you draw a circle in front of you like you are trying to make a big hole in the wall in front of you or to make a big hole in space. Then have courage and see that it is exactly round. Don't make it with jerks and corners—that is what, in your life, makes a mess.

You might be thinking that it's a three-minute exercise. But, no, we'll go a long time. I am reading you very clearly. Somebody just now decided, "Well, let me do it for a few minutes. After a while, it's going to stop." No, not that way. I want you to keep on going.

You pay five or six hundred dollars to go to some stupid person who reads all your past lives and all that jazz, and you spend another five hundred dollars to buy a bunch of those tapes—and it's all about your past. You were a pigeon, you were a deer, you were a snake, and you have a married life and you have legs, four legs and six hands. What does any of that mean? Let us see whether now you can even make a circle or not—and how fast. You will start seeing your entire life within a couple of minutes, but first, let us reach it. The hands should become like a hammer and make a full circle. Keep on doing it. As bad it looks, it will work. Good.

Oh, my God! You machos who want to challenge the whole world, you can't even draw a good circle. Move, move, move powerfully! The movement has to be a blessed one—both hands, where they are joining, should look like heavy-load hammers. Move them like a hammer. Have you ever had a hammer with a big wooden handle? Move. Does it nauseate you? What a simple scientific thing. Move, move, move.

Now cross your arms and put your hands on your shoulders. Move left, right, left, right, left, right, left, right *(see Exercise 2)*. There is nothing slow here. We have a lot of miles to go. You look like you are doing those Tai Chi exercises where you move in twenty minutes to one side and twenty minutes to the other side. You have a long journey to do. These are all trigger points. *(See Exercise 3.)* These exercises do nothing more—just trigger. And that trigger is heavy; it gives the power to immediately release the load of the subconscious. It's a matter of stealing the stuff that you have loaded in for years. You didn't consult me on that.

We are just asking five fingers, five centers, five antennas to send the brain a very polite signal. Something is going to happen; the brain doesn't catch up sometimes. *(See Exercise 4.)* Your will is more powerful when directed; it has a strategy to think what is next. But don't give it a chance, move fast. Now, move your toes also, and your feet, too. I wish things could be easy, but you know . . .

Think pain, find it, attack it, and eat it *(see Exercise 6)*. Karma will be paid right here if you do it correctly. Find out the pain in your being. Touch your forehead at the proper place and the Navel Point and connect both chakras. Do it right.

We'll give you the energy of the Creator, the sound of the Creator, the gong. Attack your own fear, your own pain.

◆ ◆ ◆

May the long time sun shine upon you,
all love surround you, and the pure light within you, guide your way on.

Sat Nam
My prayers are with you and God bless you.

REMOVING YOUR SUBCONSCIOUS BLOCKS— THE KRIYA

November 24, 1988

There are no breaks between the exercises. Move immediately from one exercise to the next.

1. Extend the arms directly in front of the body. Interlace the fingers with the Jupiter (index) fingers extended and the palms together. Circle the arms upward in a clockwise direction. Make a large circle with the arms and move at a moderate pace: approximately 3 circles every 10 seconds. Make the circle absolutely round. After **4½ minutes**, begin to quicken the pace and then move as quickly as you can, approximately 2 circles every second. Move forcefully. **8 minutes** total.

If you start in the opposite direction, continue in that direction. The object is to make a perfect circle; direction is secondary. Come on, come on, come on, elbows straight. It is a simple science. We are applying pressure in order to confuse the reaction of our own brain. Our own brain has a computer. When the reaction starts happening, naturally it is going to tell the subconscious what is next. What is the pattern of this guy? Now, the subconscious doesn't remember any time in your whole life that you have made a hole in the wall like this. Have you? So please, keep moving.

A little faster, little faster, and little faster and really faster; get wild but keep moving round and round, round and round, and stop for nothing! Make as big a circle as you can. Don't cheat; just keep doing it. Try to add force to it and try to make it rounder and rounder and try to be a little faster. Go at your maximum speed, 55 miles an hour.

2. Place the hands on the shoulders, with arms crossed over the chest; right over, left under. Begin to twist left and right at a very fast pace. Continue to move at a high velocity for **1½ minutes**.

You should be moving 20 sides every second—that high of a velocity is required. Move at high velocity. The body will become a little taller, a little more real. It'll crack up. Hallelujah, saints are moving on. Come on. Hurry up!

3. Bring the hands to the shoulders, fingers in front and thumbs behind. Move the elbows up and down. Move fast—fly for **1½ minutes**.

Move up and down. But it has to be fast. It can't be slow. That's the point. The motor system and the nervous system must not coordinate. You should be that powerful. Break through that deadlock.

4. With the elbows bent at the sides of the body, bring the hands in front of the chest, wrists relaxed. Circle the hands outward—right hand clockwise and left counterclockwise, with the fingers extended; move quickly. After **30–60 seconds**, begin circling the feet, too. This exercise is **1½ minutes** total.

5. Bring the hands into Gyan Mudra (thumb and Jupiter finger touching). Lift the hands to the level of the ears, with palms facing forward. Keep the hands 6–9 inches away from the head. Close the eyes and look down toward the Navel Point through closed eyes. Begin chanting:

SAA	TAA	NAA	MAA
RAA	MAA	DAA	SAA
SAA	SAY	SO	HANG

JUPITER   SATURN   SUN   MERCURY

as you move the mudra, as in Kirtan Kriya—that is, use the traditional sing-song melody (not monotone) as you move the mudra from the Jupiter finger to the Saturn (middle) to the Sun (ring) to the Mercury (pinkie) finger and chant the mantra one syllable at a time. Always begin with the Jupiter finger (the syllables that begin on the Jupiter finger are **bolded** for clarity). There is no pause in the mantra. Chant steadily, at a brisk pace, with no pause in between the repetitions.
31 minutes.

TO END: Inhale deep, suspend the breath, and stretch left and right. Repeat twice more.

Keep the eyes closed and from the closed eyes look at your absolute Navel Point, deep down—not at the tip of the nose, but deeper than that. Concentrate. Keep up. Deeply meditate. If it goes wrong, don't bother. Jump. The trick is this: You'll do it wrong, that is a known fact. There is nobody so perfect who can do it right. Once in a while, this finger will become that or that will become this. It is automatic. But that's when you have to jump. Don't feel guilt, don't feel the pain—that's the trick.

6. Rest the fingers of the right hand on the Brow Point. Bring the fingertips of the left hand to the Navel Point. Both hands are slightly cupped. Connect the chakras. Close the eyes and relax. Listen to the following visualization. After **3½ minutes**, begin the gong meditation. **11 minutes** total.

Guided Meditation

Relax deeply, relax inwardly, relax mentally, and reduce yourself to the first day of your being a child. Please return consciously into the womb. Relax, relax, reduce; relax, reduce, relax, reduce, relax, reduce, keep on reducing until you reach that first day of being a child.

Now please relax and think of pain and attack it! Eat it like a lioness eats the deer, that's the food. Think pain and attack it, eat it. Think pain, find it, attack it, and eat it. Think pain. Karma will be paid right here if you do it correctly. Think pain, find it, attack it, eat it.

Find out the pain in your being. Now, find the pain in your life, wherever you can find it, and, like a lion, attack it and kill it. Chew it and laugh and go for the second and the third and the fourth. When you finish this incarnation, go to the previous ones. Attack your own fear and your own pain. Attack and kill and win.

TO END: Inhale, suspend the breath for **30 seconds**; exhale. Repeat twice more. Then inhale and exhale twice quickly.

7. Place the hands on the Heart Center, one hand resting on the other. Sing *Flowers in the Rain* by Gurudass Singh. Just copy the words. **5½ minutes**.

8. Maintain the mudra. Inhale and suspend the breath for up to **30 seconds**. Concentrate on the tip of the nose. Exhale. Repeat 5 times, then begin the visualization. During the visualization, the breath is suspended up to **30 seconds** on each inhalation:

Guided Meditation

Inhale deep, hold, concentrate deeply. Look forward through the closed eyes. See the blue pearl. Exhale. Inhale deep, concentrate, and go for the frontal burst of light, a star, darkness, red and blue. Try to penetrate into the twilight zone, exhale. Inhale deep, concentrate, and penetrate please. Everybody should do it before dying, because at that time you can't do if you haven't practiced, you won't know where you are going. Concentrate, penetrate, exhale. Inhale, concentrate, and penetrate. Train yourself to die on command. Exhale; inhale, concentrate, and penetrate in the frontal void. Go through it. Sometimes it will be red, sometimes black and dark, and sometimes blue. Keep pushing beyond and beyond, keep on practicing. Exhale; inhale deep, hold tight, penetrate, project. Each time do it a little better. Exhale; inhale deep, each time penetrate further. Project further, do a little better. Exhale; inhale, hold tight. You won't be the same again if you do it right. A little further, penetrate. Exhale. Inhale deep, project, penetrate, exhale. Inhale deep, exhale.

After **6 minutes**, begin chanting along with the recording *Sat Nam* by Guru Ganesha Singh. Copy the words for **4 minutes**.

TO END: Inhale deep, project forward, penetrate through the space in front of you. Concentrate into the dark, blue, yellow, pink, red. Whatever the arcline needs in order to be cleansed—penetrate through it, go beyond, concentrate, exhale. Inhale deep, project, concentrate. Penetrate, project, concentrate. Relax.

This exercise is approximately **15 minutes** total.

9. Talk and socialize. Sing for **5–10 minutes**.

"This rhythmic situation is a meditation to cleanse the deposits that you created in your first eleven years. The cycle of life is eighteen years; the cycle of consciousness is seven years; and the cycle of intelligence is eleven years. Every eleven years, your intelligence starts developing differently."

– Yogi Bhajan

A RENEWED SELF-CONCEPT

November 29, 1988

*W*ELL, FOLKS, SUBJECT TO GOD'S WILL AND HEALTH PERMITTING, I am going to do this last bit. It is called rhythmic meditation. It is very difficult to teach, let alone to do it.

You came with the idea, "Well, let's go. He is teaching class, it is going to be good, we are going to be spaced out." Yes, you are going to space out, but it is going to clean you out no matter what you do. You won't be the same person, because that person is an enemy made up of self-constructed fear. Not natural fear; natural fear is what your parents give you and what the mother gives you when you are in the womb—that cannot go away. You live with it. It is like a cancer, a disease. It sits with you, it develops with you, and the mother gives the child this fear from the one hundred and twentieth day to the seventh month. After that, whatever the mother does is ineffective. So any damage that the mother has gone through, which damages you in that period—that stays. That sticks with everybody. But that is not the subject today.

Second situation is the concept—you build a concept. That is what you are; and when you don't achieve that concept, remember one thing: Nobody is bad enough to be bad, and everybody has a concept. But when you do not achieve that concept, you not only get bad, mad, and sad, you also become a rat. People call it depression; people call it psychological problem; then they call it sociological problem. First, it starts as a sociological problem, then psychological, then psychiatric, and finally, they bundle you up in that straitjacket.

I was joking with a well-known psychiatrist and asked him, "Well, what is psychiatry?" He used to study with me at UCLA. He laughed and said, "I can tell you; let me describe it, Yogiji, so that you can understand. Psychiatry is nothing but making a man believe that he can sleep so long that he gets tired of sleep, so then he can wake up. That is all it is."

"How do you do it?"

"Well, we give them tranquilizers, space them out. When they come back, they feel like enjoying the world."

But all these approaches are temporary things. Let me tell you one thing: There is nothing that God can do for you. You will be sorry to hear this; but you can do everything for God and yourself both. That is how superior and powerful you are. Do you understand what I am saying—this image?

This is going to clean you out no matter what you do. You won't be the same person, because that person is an enemy made up of self-constructed fear.

I am a Catholic, so you'll have to excuse me. This Catholic image of "I am wrong and God is right" is in me most of the time, and it still shows up. That is basically my training, but my realization is not that. I am very lucky that I started as a Catholic. I am also very fortunate that I experienced beyond it. You can always do for yourself and for God what you want to do. Are you hearing me? That is a very powerful statement.

Somebody once asked me, "What can I do to be rich and happy and healthy and holy?" I said, "Just one thing: Believe within you and without you that there is only God—and that you don't exist."

So this rhythmic situation is a meditation to cleanse the deposits that you created in your first eleven years. The cycle of life is eighteen years; the cycle of consciousness is seven years; and the cycle of intelligence is eleven years. Every eleven years, your intelligence starts developing differently.

Tonight we are starting with the first step. We are giving you a meditation in a rhythmic way so you can realize certain things within you. I expect that at some point you will feel supernaturally afraid or supernaturally ugly or supernaturally whatever, those kinds of things. I don't mind that; it's just a passing phase. But I am not saying that in this meditation some of you who have a good practice will not go into self-hypnosis and find something, or those who have a good flight will have a height. But even those who are the worst and who do not want to experience a thing, they will be much lighter when we finish. All right?

Anybody who wants to leave at nine o'clock for an appointment, or for a boyfriend or girlfriend you are going to meet on the corner, please raise your hands so I can understand. Anybody who has a babysitter and has to go back because their babysitter will leave? Something like that? Anybody who feels they are trapped in the class? Feels they should not have come?

All right, let's get to the business as fast as we want. Let us cut it all out, okay. Right, folks?

◆ ◆ ◆

If you develop this pattern, which I am giving you—(*see Exercise 1*)—you can divert all eventual destructions that come toward you by using your intuitive, meditative psyche.

Meditate on the tip of the nose, please. When you do it, just say, "Oh, my God," or something to relate to Infinity. Glands are the guardians of health, and we need those juices to get to the next stage.

The second exercise is very funny. Take your hands like you are holding water. (*See Exercise 2.*) It is a very simple exercise. All you have to do is stretch your hands and let it flow. Come back, grab it, and stretch your hands. It is a heart-centered movement. It is not a big deal. We are using the nerve in the two central channels, which are the trigger points. They will conflict with the left and right hemispheres to adjust them. And naturally, because the left and right parts of the brain are not adjusted, you will feel the revolt. Just don't worry about that. We get it, and we go up, and then we let it go. And we come back here, and we go up, and we let it go. Just like a peace offering. Close your eyes, concentrate at the tip of the nose within the closed eyes, and just offer. We are tuning the rhythms in the brain. Remember this: it is a very powerful self-service. Therefore, do it automatically so that it can serve you much later in life.

Now please fill up your hands with all your anger, your attachment, your pain, and then let it go. You are ready. I am very pleased with your auras. You look very beautiful. I have never taught a class where in a few minutes you can reach that point, that color. So now just fill up your garbage—it can be attachment, it can be disease, anything that is bothering you. Fill it up and just let it go into the space. Don't let that thing go that you need tomorrow, though, because what you are going to let go of today shall be gone. Don't take this lightly. Pull out of your subconscious all the painful events. Get them in that very hand and just offer it to the space, please. Everything you remember from day one to the eleventh year. I would like you to do that.

Say to yourself, "The day I remember the first time I felt hurt, or everything that as a child I received, I will take that day and I will go then day by day and week by week and month by month and year by year. I will use my memory. I will go into the storehouse of my memory, and I will just do it and just offer it all to the space." A lot of things you can remember; a lot of things you can't. But whatever you remember, do this with it. Other thoughts and memories will come. Pick them up, do it again.

Let me tell you in a simple way. This is a purely physical and mental combination in action. Do it very saintly, very graciously, and in an absolutely human way. You have to cover eleven years—from the day of memory to the eleventh year. God is everywhere. God shall receive it. It is our right to give back to God the pain we had. Offer it to him. He is big; He can take it. He can consume it; you can't. All your pain and all your disease and all your discomfort and all that has upset you in the past came from God, give it back. Just say, "Hey, big guy, here it is, thank you very much." Really, honest to God! You will be surprised. Even if you follow this blindly, see what it does. It will do you so much good, you can't

We have the right to live in peace. We are in the image of God. God gave us life. There is nothing wrong with it. There is no need to suffer. As they say, death waits on the next corner. I tell you that good luck also waits on this very corner!

believe it. This therapy has been used by man for centuries. It works. But now people grab it and subsume it, put it under their religious, skid-row situation. You have to be irreligious to do it. Well, why not? Why not be irreligious to do it? They need it to be more than religious.

Take it from your memory. Fill it in your hand. And just offer it to the space. All ugly memories—we will clean house, our house. We have the right to live in peace. We are in the image of God. God gave us life. There is nothing wrong with it. There is no need to suffer. As they say, death waits on the next corner. I tell you that good luck also waits on this very corner! Please try. This is one opportunity you should take full advantage of. We know you can't complete it all today; we are going to do it tomorrow, too. But we want to cover as far as we can go. Pick up your own pain, in your own hand, and give it to the space. It is exactly, in the Western language, called forced self-hypnosis. You can do it right. If you do it right, you will start feeling much more and will really get a lot out of this. Recollect yourself and reconnect yourself.

Just remember anything you can remember and let it go. You must start believing that you don't have to suffer. You must start believing that you don't have to be in pain. Nobody advances from or gets richer or feels better when they are in pain. Just remember that. You can't keep pain in the memory and live with it, because pain makes you numb to reality. You have one last minute. Exercise your right!

Please open your eyes and look at both your hands. Just start looking at the lines of your hands, kind of studying your own hand. Microscopically study your own hand. Do nothing else. (*See Exercise 3.*) Microscopically study your own hand. Now block your face with your own hands. (*See Exercise 4.*) Absolutely block it. With closed eyes, try to see into infinity. Block your face thoroughly. Block your face thoroughly, and from that try to look into infinity. It will be difficult to do; it is not your practice. But there will be enough energy in this room that soon you will be able to do it better. Simply concentrate your focal point.

Try to understand—God has not gone on holiday. God has given you all the opportunity within your mind and scope to totally clarify. Now look through it to the infinity. Penetrate. Different colors may appear—green, black, yellow, nothing, everything. Different patterns will come up. Become your own doctor and diagnose yourself. Make your own herb and heal yourself and God shall cure. It is always true; always will be. Doctors diagnose; herbs heal; and God cures. All you have to do is just concentrate. Hold on steady. Concentrate deeper; concentrate on infinity, and you will gain a lot of perks and lose a lot of tragedies. It will be a help in the future; that is why we are doing it.

Now the sound and the rhythm you have to follow is the five words, five sounds: *Har Hare Hari Wahe Guru* (*pronounced Har Haray Haree Whaa-hay Guroo*). It is a simple systematic sound. Three in the rhythm and Wahe Guru has three sounds in it; but if you just go in the rhythm of it, it will deal with the tattvas and with the aura. Remember that. Let me start and you follow: *Har Hare Hari Wahe Guru.* Feel it in the ribcage. Feel it in the ribcage. Whisper. Whisper strongly, individually. (*See Exercise 5.*)

We need now a *Har* circulation in the brain area and circulatory system. Just bend down. This will also cure your stomach ailments and your circulatory problems. It is a very healing thing. Normally babies sit in this position. It is a very polite pose. It doesn't affect you badly. Stretch your hands as hard as you can. Stretch your hands forward as hard as you can and very slowly, millimeter by millimeter, try to get up. Close your eyes. Don't open the eyes. Don't damage your eyesight; please keep your eyes closed and rise up with your hands stretched out. They go up all the way, as tight as they can be, in absolute prayer.

Now, come on, you know how to shake things. You shake the whole universe. You made one atom bomb and shook the whole Hiroshima, you know that? Shake, shake, and get ready to be shaken. California is getting ready to be shaken. You know what I mean? I don't say anything. It is all top secret. Shake, shake, shake, really well. Shake it off.

Now sit down and relax. Take the power of the pranic force into the entire being of your body. Hold the breath graciously and let the breath of life circulate. Give it a chance. You live by the breath of life; you can heal by the breath of life. (*Gong is played lightly.*)

All right, now we have asked you to take vitamin C today—you might have heard or not. I would also like you to take some when you come tomorrow. I want you to be heavily loaded with vitamin C. Vitamin C in these meditations is required. It is a requirement—even in India. There we don't use Vitamin C; instead we put a man on an orange fast. All he has to do is live on oranges for seven days before coming to this meditation. He has to drink lemon water and eat oranges. That is his diet for seven days, and then we give him eleven minutes of this meditation step by step and finish it in twenty two days. They are very systematic. I think they have more time. You don't. I don't know.

◆ ◆ ◆

May the long time sun shine upon you,
all *love surround you, and the pure light within you, guide your way on.*

Sat Nam
Bless you, bless you, bless you.

◆ ◆ ◆

Tomorrow we will meet again to do our part. We can't do too much at one time; just little by little. We will continue this rhythmic series; it is just a beginning. It gets a little tougher and tougher. You will have more space here because fewer and fewer will come. Well, I mean to say, it is not for everybody. I went through it myself as a student. I know what it does.

We don't want to be not miserable. We don't want to be rich. It is true. What I am saying you don't believe. We don't want to be rich. We don't want to be powerful. We don't want to be straightforward. We don't want to cut short the garbage in our life. We want to keep all the junk. Really, those who take syringes and do it, they are not junkies. They are an epitome of junkies. But we are all very heavily junky, multijunky people.

I mean, sometimes I am shocked. There is from corner to corner a church, synagogue, gurdwara, yogis, swamis, priests, padres, God knows. All this garbage is going on, and people are still unhappy. It shocks me. Because a priest looks to you, what are you going to give him? He could just say, "Hey, my son, come here, you idiot. This is wrong. That is wrong. Do this, this." But no, they do not. "God bless you. God is going to come next Saturday." Nobody waits for that. So what we have done is, we have borrowed and purchased even the wisdom. We don't want it.

We want the wisdom that we want. And we are junkies. We have so much mental junk with us. Do you know if you let your mental junk go what will be left of you? A very bright, beautiful being. And you all have the same right because you have the same manufacturer: Made in God. Nobody else made you, and God cannot go wrong. It is the overloading of the junk that has done to us what it has done. I know, in my case, why should I listen to you; I listen to myself. I junked myself, traveled every day on the plane, here, there, this, that. You know, upside down? So what happened? Two years I couldn't even move. Now I am just trying to do something that is nice.

Somebody asked me today, "What is the best thing to become fulfilled, happy, rich and fantastic?" I said, "Very simple. Just you sit and let God act. Let God act. Let God act." Very difficult—the most difficult thing your ego can tolerate, but great. Twenty years I have been in America. You know when I came, I didn't have a shoe. My foot is very wide. No shoe fits me. I was walking barefoot on this land. That is why we had Shakti Shoes, that factory. We started making natural shoes. You know where the Shakti Shoe idea came from? We saw all kinds of shoes in the world, and we all know that under the foot, there is a sole, and that the sole gets hurt. That is why you are all crazy in one way or the other. It is all those shoes. Then we designed the Shakti Shoe—natural. And we did everything to do it. Lucky people wear it, unlucky don't. I am not saying everybody should; but that is where it is. You do not know that seventy-two thousand meridian points are in the foot, in the sole of the foot; these shoes rub and stimulate and act and overact, and the action and reaction is in the neurons of the brain. Can you believe that? Your entire life is controlled by the third and fourth vertebra in your lower back. You don't breathe. The diaphragm *helps* you to breathe. You breathe from here. It's going to take about two thousand years for the doctors to know everything. Slowly and gradually you are going to find it out.

The mystery of the brain is going to come out in a big way. Then you are going to find out! "My God, I was saying this to people. I was saying that to people. This is wrong, that is wrong." What are the herbs? Herbs heal. Why do they heal? They send the message to the neurons to computerize and change the rhythm. Everything that God has made around you is just to help change the rhythm. When your rhythm of the brain and the neurons go off, that is all it is. Meditation is nothing but to concentrate and consolidate the cleanliness of the rhythmic brain. Meditation is nothing but to change the biorhythm of the brain, magnet to magnet. Everything is magnetic energy. In polarity, it holds X. If you are uptight and surround yourself with stress, you will not have any opportunity.

All you have to do is for one week say nothing but negative words to anybody you meet, and you won't have any friends. I am not kidding. If you want good luck, just smile one week, see what it does to you. With one frown, you can lose the world. With one smile, you can win it back. So, why can't you do it? Because we are tremendously filled with mental junk; garbage is totally our base. We have got to get rid of it. No more, no less. That is as good a priority as you can find in life. So, thank you very much and relax, and we will meet you tomorrow.

Do you know if you let your mental junk go what will be left of you? A very bright, beautiful being. And you all have the same right because you have the same manufacturer: Made in God.

A RENEWED SELF-CONCEPT— THE KRIYA

November 29, 1988

There are no breaks between the exercises. Move immediately from one exercise to the next.

1. The left hand is on the Heart Center (fingers pointing to the right). The right hand begins behind the ear with the palm facing the space behind the ear. Eyes are closed. Meditate on the tip of the nose through closed eyes. Inhale deep, exhale deep 3 times. The right hand comes powerfully toward the face, as if you were going to slap yourself, and just as you approach the cheek, divert the direction of the hand so that it just misses the cheek and ends up palm facing forward. **6 minutes.**

Keep a constant speed, neither too fast nor too slow. You are commanding the motor system and asking the defense mechanism to protect. It can give you a powerful immune system. Understand that everything in you is controlled by the brain. All glandular secretion is also commanded by the brain. When you do it, just say, "Oh, my God," or something to relate to infinity. Glands are the guardians of health and we need those juices to get to the next stage.

2. Eyes are focused at the tip of the nose. Gather the hands together in front of the chest, as if cupping water, and then bring the hands up to the throat and extend the arms, as though pouring the water from the tips of your fingers. **15 minutes.**

Fill up all your anger, attachments, and resentment in your hands, anything that is bothering you, and then let it go. Pull out all the pain of the subconscious, and fill the hands with it and offer it to the space. From day one to the eleventh year, all the pains of your childhood, day-by-day, month-by-month, year-by-year, bring it up and give it to the space. Pay homage to all the sick, ugly, dirty, painful, neurotic memories. Just let them go. People think it is stupid to do this; but it is real. Once the mind is cleared and the subconscious is cleaned out, you don't have a problem. All you have to do is grab the opportunities and get well. If you are suffering with a disease, if you have a problem, if you have pain in a relationship, if you have a monetary problem, if you are poor—I don't care what your major problem is. Whatever it is, start pulling it from the subconscious memory and start offering it to the space.

3. Bring the hands in front of the face and look at the lines of your hand. Study your own hand. **5 minutes.**

Read your own palm. Try to look at it again and again and again. Read your own palm. Read it very thoroughly. You will be surprised what you can know. Very microscopically.

4. Cover the face and eyes with the hands. Try to see into infinity through your closed eyes. **15 minutes**.

Block your face thoroughly, and from that try to look into infinity.

5. Cross the hands at the Heart Center, right hand over left. Inhale deep and hold. Exhale. **3 times**. Chant:
Har Haray Haree Whaa-Hay Guroo. **5 minutes**. Then, whisper strongly for **30 seconds**.

Create a systematic sound. Pause between each syllable of the mantra. Done in a monotone without music. Addresses the tattvas and the aura.

6. Bend forward and place your hands on the ground. You may come into Baby Pose if you prefer. Anahata Choir version of *Ardas Bhaee* is played. Yogi Bhajan plays the gong lightly & intermittently over the recording. **11 minutes**.
TO END: Stretch your hands forward as hard as you can and come up into Exercise 7. Keep your eyes closed.

7. Stretch the arms above the head in Prayer Pose. Absolute prayer. Create your own profile in prayer now. State your intention; who you want to be. Make a profile. Not a prayer—profile in prayer. This is what you want to be. **3 minutes**.

Guided Meditation

Now do your prayer—absolute prayer—whatever you want to pray. If you don't want to pray, don't say it. Whatever you say, say it now. Whatever you want to ask, ask now. Whatever you want to be, be now. Whatever you say now shall be your basic, identified factor to make the rhythmic change so that your life can go around. So please make a profile. Profile in prayer; not just, "God give me, give me, give me." God has no time for that. Make the profile. I want to be this, this, this, this, and this. You have the choice to be good; you have the choice to be bad; you have the choice to be neutral; but you have this choice now! It is in your aura. Make the hands tense. Stretch the elbows. Put the hands together. And with absolutely folded hands, make a profile. A profile—not a prayer—a profile in prayer of what you want to be.

8. Shake your hands vigorously. Shake your whole body. 30 seconds to **1 minute**. Sit and relax.

9. Wave your hands in front of your face and eyes to clear your eyesight. Just a few seconds.

TO END: Close the eyes and inhale deeply. Take this prana into every part of your body. Let the breath of life circulate. Exhale. Inhale deep. Hold it tight. Circulate it throughout your entire being. Exhale. Inhale deep. Suspend. Feel the pranic energy from the tip of your hair to your toes. *(Gong is played lightly.)* Exhale.

◆

Comments
Yogi Bhajan suggested taking vitamin C to prepare for this meditation.

"Humans are a guiding light of time and space and now. You don't have to be comfortable; you are supposed to give comfort. Do you understand what our duty as a human being is? Our job is to show light, give comfort, elevate, and come to the need of those who need to be uplifted. For that we need courage. "

– Yogi Bhajan

LETTING GO OF THE PAIN OF THE SEVENTH YEAR

November 30, 1988

NOW, IN THE CIVILIZED WORLD, WE HAVE FINALLY DECIDED to understand Aristotle for the first time. Aristotle made a statement—"Man is a social animal." He didn't say man is a social being; and nobody understood what he was saying. Everybody complains that the philosopher called man a social animal and that animals are not human beings. Yet, animals are alive, they are well, they have feelings, they have commotions, they have reactions—and so does man. In those days, we never used to say man and woman separately; we just used to say man, which included woman in those days. Sorry, it's not my fault. So man is a social animal. Everybody quotes it, everybody understands it, everybody talks about it, everybody brags about it. But what Aristotle said is, "Man is a social animal." He didn't say man is a social being; he didn't say man is a social person; he didn't say man is a social ape; he didn't say any of those things. He simply said man is a social animal, which means you have social action and reaction; you have social fear and phobia; you have social complexes—inferiority and superiority; it means you are a social animal.

What is a social animal? Do you know? When a dog is braided in a society, it is called a social animal. It is a very old custom. You decorate your dog and put it on a leash and parade it through the street. It is called socializing the animal. Another way to socialize your animal is to take your pet to different friends' homes. That's what Aristotle said—you are animals, but you are decoratively braiding your personality. That's what he said, and people thought, "My, God!" He said such a good thing when he directly abused and slapped the face of the entire human race to be quoted as a philosopher. He didn't say man is a social angel. The word philosophy is based on accepting us just as a living being—that's the tragedy. We are not living beings; we are humans. Humans are a guiding light of time and space and now. You don't have to be comfortable; you are supposed to give comfort. Do you understand what our duty as a human being is? Our job is to show light, give comfort, elevate, and come to the need of those who need to be uplifted. For that we need courage. We have taken drugs, they didn't work out; we have taken a lot of magic pills, they didn't work out; we did a lot of stuff that didn't work out. We don't know why things don't work for us.

*I am, I am. No facet of
life, no circumstances,
no rituals, no rights,
not even death can stop
me from being me.
That's God.*

Things don't work for us because we are not simple. We are extremely complicated people. We complicate our self, and we entangle our self in lots of different directions. We cater not to our wisdom and consciousness but to our commotions. Our neuroses are our self-created fears. Our depression is totally our own, it's self-induced; it's nothing from the outside. You may not believe me, but sometime when you wake up and say to yourself, "Hey, is that me? Am I that stupid? Did I do that? How can I be part of this?" You can't believe it, you can't. Nobody can.

One day a daughter asked her father, "Dad, I want five hundred dollars."

"What for?"

"I want to go to beauty school."

"What is that?"

"It is a school where they teach girls how to be beautiful, attractive, sexy. They can do anything."

"Better you go to a karate teacher to learn how to defend yourself. You don't have to be pretty, darling. You are already very pretty. Instead, just learn how to defend yourself and kick whoever wants to destroy you."

You all want to be beautiful and successful. You all want to be happy and never tire. You always want to move up and up. People who worked with me today know that I started at seven o'clock, and I've been working nonstop until just a few minutes before I came here. Now that I have come here, I can work another eight hours, maybe. I could have a heart attack, but I don't care because that damn heart is not me. My brain may fail, but I am not that brain. My body can fall apart, but I am not my body. My identity can be insulted, but I am not my identity. I am, I am. No facet of life, no circumstances, no rituals, no rights, not even death can stop me from being me. That's God.

God doesn't mean anything at all—and religion doesn't mean anything at all. If your horizon is narrow, if your vision is small, you are exactly garbage—garbage qualified, garbage stamped, and garbage understood—and you stink. As long as you are an animal, and as long as your vision is small, narrow, selfish, you are absolutely a pain in the neck. You are an asset neither to you nor to anybody. And a majority of the time your troubles are for you; your troubles are not for anybody else. Others just get dragged into it because they sympathize, because they love you, because they know you, because they want good things for you.

I was talking to a young woman the other day, I said, "This won't work."

"I am going to take the risk."

"Goodbye, thank you. God be with you and may He help you, may it work out, may your words come true."

"Why don't you say that it'll work out?"

"That I can't say because I know it is not going to work out. Don't involve me."

"How do you know?"

"I read the words on the wall. Where did you meet him?"

"In the bar."

"What did you do with him?"

"Absolutely everything."

"So why do you think he is going to be a saint now?"

"Everything can change."

"Winter is winter. Have you seen summer come in the middle of winter? No. Winter will go away, but in the middle of winter, there is not going to be ninety-two degree weather when you are living up north in Ottawa."

You can't live in Ottawa, the capital of Canada, and expect to warm it up just because it is the capital. You know what people say there? "Oh, Ottawa is beautiful; it is always crisp and white and clean." Yes, because it is the most freezing city in the world. California is beautiful and warm, but it has the worst smog. It is the capital of smog, next to Tokyo. That's how things go. There are things to do and things not to do; but we do not understand the basic yogic principles, the do's and don'ts.

Somebody said to me, "I am an Indian Sikh."

I said, "Then what's your problem?"

"I cannot do yoga."

"That's all right; don't do it."

"But I want to be nice."

"Don't do anything. Yoga has do's and don'ts, just do that."

"Is that enough?"

"Yeah, that's all Guru Nanak said."

"Don't you do *pranayam*?"

If you do *pranayam*, you'll stimulate your own energy. If you do *asan*, you can confront death. If you know *pratyahar*, you can always be mentally above everybody. If you know *pranayam*, you can always grab the impossible and make it possible. If you have *dharana*, you can totally have intuition and penetrate before it hits you. If you have *dhyan*, you can always know what happens to others in relationship to you. If you have *samadhi*, there is nothing that you don't know and can't do. You have to do nothing; everything will be done for you. These are the eight facets of yoga: *yam, niyam, asan, pranayam, pratyahar, dharana, dhyan, samadhi*. They explain everything.

If you want something, you have to create something. If you love a great man, never speak a word. If you meet a small man, never shut up. Because a

There is a price for everything, a cost for everything, an action, reaction, and interaction for everything. Those who cannot match the price and cannot pay it, cannot handle it.

man of low caliber needs to be expanded, and a man of higher caliber cannot be contracted. If you marry a beautiful girl, hire a security guard. If you have a most beautiful woman and you ask her to take a cab, one day you could lose her. There is a price for everything; there is a cost for everything; there is an action, reaction, and interaction for everything. Those who cannot match the price and cannot pay it, cannot handle it. You know American cars and German cars? The German cars are still running, ours aren't because we never change the oil, we never tune up, we don't know what the word maintenance is—it's not in our dictionary. We do not believe in *avagavan*—that's recycling. Our basic philosophy is out, dump it.

Once there was a house, and the owner furnished it beautifully and threw a party. Everybody came, but the new sofa was ruined. He threw it out and furnished the house again. He was planning another party when a friend asked, "What are you doing now?"

"The first time I furnished it, I wanted to let everybody see it, but it got spoiled. I am trying a second time."

"It'll just happen the same way. The first time all your friends came and got drunk and vomited all over everything. The second time they'll do the same thing. The fault is not with the sofa; the fault is with your friends who drink too much and vomit."

"You mean to say I should not have a party?"

"Yeah, you can have a party; but it should be like a receiving line. They should come in, see your sofa, and get out. Pay them ten dollars on the way so they can go to a fast food place and eat their fries. Because the kind of friends you have, man, whatever kind of sofa you want to have, they are going to ruin it."

We have a problem. If we are not what we should be on the inside, things will happen to us again and again and again and again. Once you are set on that recording of again and again and again, on the fourth again, people will start noticing, on the fifth again people become alert—they'll say, "Wait a minute." On the sixth again, they will say, "Am I wrong?" They may be totally rotten, but on the ninth again you don't have a chance.

Any relationship, doesn't matter how thick or thin it may be, has nine chances. You must understand; don't be stupid. There are only nine figures: one, two, three, four, five, six, seven, eight, nine, and after that is what? Zero; the egg must hatch. You are done. A man can commit nine mistakes in any situation, direction, or circumstance. In life, your entire system can stand only nine mishaps. There are nine governing stars, there are nine jewels—the *nav rattan*, they call it—to affect your life's sun energy. There are nine precious stones that can change your life's energy and direction. Your system, your glandular system, changes on the eleventh day; on the ninth and tenth days the changes begin, and on the eleventh day it changes and begins again.

Monday is the moon's day, which is why Shiva, the Lord of Death, has a half moon in his hair. We think he got decorated. Forget it! He doesn't need it. It is symbolic. Monday, the moon's day. Whatever you do on Monday will cause your life or death. It's a foundation day. If you trace it back, every stupid thing you've done, which you confronted terribly, you started it on a Monday. It shall never be Tuesday, because the electromagnetic field in your brain doesn't work the other way. Monday is a moon day; Monday is the mind's day. Monday is an intrigue day. Monday is going into the center of the Earth and picking it up and lifting it to the top of the sky to look at it.

Tuesday is Mars day. Every fight you've ever won or lost was planned on the martial day. Wednesday is Mercury day. Your thinking communicated how to entangle and wangle, how to come through or not, how to have an edge or a grudge; it is always done on Mercury's day. These are very subtle forces that are not evidenced in black and white. But are we subtle enough to understand? Thursday is Guru's day. Thursdays have absolute wisdom. Even a fool won't make a mistake on that day. Take the county blotter and see how many murders are committed on Thursday. You'll be shocked to know it'll be zero. The proportion of crimes on Thursday is much, much less than other days. Friday, the day of Venus, we call it a loony day; everybody runs about. Sitting home on Friday is impossible; you can write it down in pen. Saturday you always try to do everything, but you always find it very hard. Sunday you want to do a lot, but you wish you could do nothing.

What are those other days, beyond the seven? Ninth, tenth, and eleventh—moon's head and moon's tail, also called dragon's head and dragon's tail. Tenth and eleventh are the most trying days of the month. On the eleventh day, your body's glands secrete over secrets; that's why in India, even today, even the most foolish man will go on a fast on the eleventh day. On the eleventh of the moon, if you tell reasonable Indians, "Eat something," they will say no. They live on water that day. I asked a businessman once, "What's your problem? You eat all the time. What's wrong with the eleventh day?" He said, "It covers everything." There are stars in the sky. Just because they look little, does that mean they are little? If the stars look so little according to us, then God, who we cannot see at all, must be nothing. This should not be. We cannot see God, agreed; but we cannot see our own mind either. Our mind plays more games with us than

anything. Anyway, we are going to straighten the mind out today. We are going to go into the seventh year of pain. It is called the seventh step of the child. It is a very mysterious phenomenon on which people make sacrifices in order to re-attain and re-atone their mind.

◆ ◆ ◆

Let us do the first exercise. (*See Exercise 1*.) You'll feel puzzled, but don't worry, you'll fix it up. When this five opens, two comes down. Two fingers of the left, five fingers of the right. When five opens, close the two; when two go down, open the five. That's it. Simple exercise. If you feel confused, I don't mind. The total is seven either way. Understand that you are doing the most difficult thing when you open the five and you close the two with it. Can't your mind respond to it? It is a principle of life: open five times, be closed twice. You'll always survive. You close five times and open twice, you'll be dead in no time. It is a first law of life. Your horizon should be wide five times and narrow two times.

The moment I see the aura change colors, I think you are ready for the next; jump into the next. (*See Exercise 2*.) Just understand, with this exercise, with this breathing, you are controlling the neurons' rhythm, and that's the most important thing in life. Once you have the neuron rhythm under your control, you can be anything you want to be. There is no limit.

You are in a very good mood today. I think the vitamin C is working. Now, this next exercise is a little difficult, but if you do it right, we will reach what we want to reach very fast. Then we can meditate and get out the seventh year; a lot of problems in your life will be solved. This is what the hummingbird does (*See Exercise 6*.) Stretch it out as much as you can; it can stretch about an inch and a half if you really want to stretch it out. Then move—not big, but move heavily, fast, and tense. It will affect the aura, which should turn blue very quickly—that's what it does. It's actually the armpit, where three nervous systems meet and recombine; that recombination with this movement must re-create the energy. You create a lot of fire, a lot of blue.

Move with majesty. Remember this: "So shall you sow, so shall you reap." Now you are in a position to experience the seventh year, the first constituent change. Put your hands in your lap and sit straight. Meditate on seventh year. Think about seventh year; repeat every moment of it. Look at it, read it, adjust it, judge it. Concentrate—if you concentrate on the seventh year, you can get rid of a lot of problems. (*See Exercise 7*.)

Look, for the last time, at the seventh year of life; look down at it and forgive it. Good and bad, forgive it. Let it go. Meditate deeply on the breath. (*See Exercise 8.*) Whenever you breathe consciously, it invigorates your body and makes your mind clear and strong. Breathe as slowly as you can and with conscious control.

◆ ◆ ◆

May the long time sun shine upon you,
all love surround you, and the pure light within you, guide your way on.

Blessed is my life
and my soul within my life. Blessed is the peace and the environments, the intelligence, the consciousness, the gift of God. Blessed is me within my own contained Self; the Supreme Lord presides within my heart and the glory of God surrounds me. May the peace prevail, may all mankind prosper, may I serve Thee, oh Lord, in the light, bright, and beautiful Self.

Sat Nam

◆ ◆ ◆

I have never believed in God; I trust in God. My theory is different. I don't love anybody, and I don't want to say, "I love you." I say it as a commercial situation because that's what you understand. But my love is my merger. I can vibrate, I can intercourse with the psyche of anyone I want to, and I can uplift. I believe in grace. I don't believe in richness and poverty; I don't believe in sadness and depression. I don't believe in what you believe in.

I have only one faith: everything will be lost but the grace, and I have no race against it. It doesn't matter how much the other person may be ungraceful or ungracious, nor does it matter how powerful and monstrous the other may be. Just understand and have the attitude that you are of God. If God confronts you, don't let your grace go. Forget about agreeing or not agreeing, doing or not doing, being or not being, successful or not successful, lonely or seven times married, twenty times divorced, and thirty times kicked out. Who loves who? Are you kidding? You people don't understand. Nobody loves anybody. Nobody knows what love is. People are attracted by the energy. As the radiance increases, it propels people toward each other. They feel attracted to each other; emotions, feelings, desires, expectations, behaviors, manners, social attitude, etiquettes—all are there, but do you really know what love is?

*One smile can win
the world, and one
frown can lose it.*

Love gives you one thing: an understanding of the other person's grace. When you are in love with yourself, forget about the other person. You shall not try to tread on him because our sole is under our foot, and we do not crush things with our soul. Spell it sole or soul—that's your problem. Sole is a soul—don't walk on others. Carry others. You want to know the key to success? Simple—don't walk on others. Don't step on others' toes. Carry others, carry people with you, above you; God shall carry you.

Some people ask me, "How do you know the answer to everything?"

I said, "What is there to know? You know everything anyway."

You only need to know one thing: anybody who approaches you, just put him one step higher than he is. The job will be done, and you'll be blessed.

Once a teacher came to his Master and said, "Master, I am in a lot of trouble."

The Master said, "What's the problem? Why are you yelling and screaming for me? What's your problem?"

"You sent me to the city to teach, but everybody is just yelling at me and calling me a fake."

"They come and abuse you?"

"Many people gather in the morning, and they are just mad."

"Oh, you are on a very successful note."

"Master, none have come in; none have come to learn from me; no one has come to say hello. All they do is yell and scream abuse at me. They shout and ridicule me."

"You are a great success. That's all I wanted to hear."

"But what should I do about it?"

"Go and stay there. When they come in the morning, smile; when they yell at you, smile; when they throw eggs at you, smile; when they throw stones at you, stand erect, with discipline and smile—keep smiling. Let us see what happens."

He went, and people came, and they yelled, screamed, made faces. And he just smiled and blessed them. He stood as they threw vegetables at him and dirt at him and shoes at him; and he kept smiling, saying, "Thank you, thank you." Three days they continued. On the fourth day, they gave up and came and sat down. On the fifth day, they started abusing him again, but then stopped and looked at each other saying, "What are we doing?

They decided they should go and apologize to him. So two thousand people from the village came and told him, "We are very sorry; we never understood you." He still smiled. They said, "Are you not happy?" He still smiled. "It doesn't mean anything to you?" He smiled. Finally they said, "All right, give us the one final answer: Why are you smiling?"

He said, "What else is there to do? Let us pray and meditate—that's the meditation. Smile."

One smile can win the world, and one frown can lose it.

They asked, "Why were you smiling when we were yelling and screaming?"

"I was smiling because you were angry and neurotic."

"But now why are you smiling when we are here with you and we are listening to you?"

"I am smiling at how stupid you are that you have nothing to say."

Just smile at adversity. I tell you it runs away. Two things cannot live together: adversity cannot remain where a man is smiling, and prosperity doesn't live with those who are frowning. The face is an index not to the mind but to the soul.

You see people who are very unsuccessful—what do they do? When you start telling them many things, they lean in; they listen. There is no vitamin C that can stop them. That's how they are. You must understand when somebody talks to you, if you are not willing to hear them out, you are foolishly going for an unsuccessful future. The first principle of success is, when somebody is talking, hear it. Don't interrupt. Let him complete the sentence; hear him properly. When they are done and you are asked to speak, do not answer the question if you cannot uplift the person. If your answer uplifts that person, you shall be prosperous.

Somebody once went to a very successful man and said, "I want to hire you."

"Your intuition must be great; but what do you want to hire me for?"

"I want to invest my money in real estate, I want to buy houses, I want to develop properties. I want you to be in charge of that department."

"What shall be my salary?"

"As you want, whatever you want; I can give you partnership, I can give you part of the profit. I can give you a reasonable salary, whichever you want."

"That's it? Anything more?"

"If we make a good profit, I'll see that you enjoy everything in life."

"And if I make a bad judgment?"

"That's the last you'll see of me."

"I see."

"Are you ready to accept the job?"

"I am ready, but you should know I'm not a thief. You are not ready for business; you are only ready for profit. Business is profit and loss. Business is not profit only. You are not mentally ready for business. I do business; I am not sure of profit and loss. I do my best. But you have one condition, you just want profit."

Life without being consciously graceful is not worth the risk—and what is consciously graceful? When somebody is most disgraceful to you and you smile. That's called courage.

"What do you expect me to do?"

"If we want to do business, then sometimes we will lose and sometimes we will gain; somewhere we will build, somewhere we will totally demolish, somewhere we will redevelop, somewhere we will reconstruct. There are many facets to life. We want to see if we can succeed in the end."

"I do not understand. What do you mean by succeeding in the end?"

"If we build goodwill, after a while, that will pay all the bills."

Just remember: when, as a human, you shall be consciously graceful, prosperity will kiss your feet. I not only said it, I vouch for it. Can you repeat—consciously? Being graceful doesn't work. By being graceful, you are preparing to be cheated in broad daylight. I don't believe in being graceful, being nice, being kind, being honest. It doesn't work—that's what you don't understand! Life is only decided by consciousness and unconsciousness. If you can consciously be graceful, you shall be prosperous. If you are unconsciously graceful, you'll be ruined. That's the difference.

If you drive a Rolls Royce unconsciously and you say you won't have an accident, who's going to believe you? Life without being consciously graceful is not worth the risk—and what is consciously graceful? When somebody is most disgraceful to you and you smile. That's called courage. "It's not the life that matters, it's the courage you bring to it." When somebody says to me, "Sir, you can't; no more." I say, "No, this is the start." Hazrat Abraham, the father of the Judeo-Christian-Muslim-Bahai religion (they are all in a lineage that started with him) was just a simple truthful man—that's it. He was the chief and a truthful man.

God gave him a son, and he gave a sacrifice. All this cutting of the hair, circumcision, the whole story, happened because he told his wife the truth. I'm not going to go into it—that history. But Hazrat Abraham made one promise to himself—he should not eat unless he also feeds a poor man, a hungry man. Just remember this story:

One day he waited, but nobody came. Later in the afternoon, somebody appeared and said, "How is the house of the Abraham clan?

Abraham replied, "I am Abraham."

"Would you mind feeding the hungry?"

"Oh, God bless you, you are most welcome. I am more hungry than you. Come on in."

So he told the household to give the guest a bath, they dressed him up, and they placed the food on the table. Hazrat Abraham sat down and thanked God.

He thanked so heavily that he meditated. After thanking God, he saw that half of the food was gone; the guy had eaten almost everything.

"What are you doing."

"I am eating."

"I won't eat with you."

"Why not?"

"You don't even have the courtesy to thank God. You couldn't join with me for even two minutes to thank God? Why should I eat with you? You are just scum—that's no good. There is nothing more to say—ridiculous."

"Ha, very good," the old man said and stopped eating.

Abraham asked, "You have nothing to say for yourself?

The old man had chicken in his mouth, but he said, "Wait, wait, wait, let me eat."

"Forget it. I can't sit and eat with you—you don't accept God, you don't thank God, you don't do anything.

Then God spoke from the sky. He said, "Abraham, this guy is 80-something years old, this guy has never thanked me, it is not his religion. In fact, he religiously abuses me; he has never ever thanked me. But I have always provided him better food than this low-class feast I'm sorry to see you have given him. But I don't understand, he never thanked me for 80-some years, and he always gets from me. What's wrong with you? Where's your patience, your tolerance, your clarity, your cleanliness, your higher Self?

Abraham replied, "God, what did I miss?"

"Consciousness."

After a minute, Abraham saw that God was sitting before him, and He laughed, saying, "You couldn't see me? You are supposed to see me in everything." They say that after that, Abraham never ever thought that anything other than God ever existed. That's why we call him Hazrat Abraham, the father of the divine tribe. I just thought this story would be good for you, if you remember it.

You should never believe that God will act in one certain way. God has many, many colors—but beyond all colors there is one color, which is the color of all colors—white. See clearly that the light of white is God; God is in all, and God is not small. Even in small, all is in it. So please, go home, enjoy yourself, I shall meet you in spirit. God bless you and thank you.

LETTING GO OF THE PAIN OF THE SEVENTH YEAR
— THE KRIYA

November 29, 1988

There are no breaks between the exercises. Move immediately from one exercise to the next.

1. Bring the hands in front of the chest, palms facing each other, about 12-18 inches apart; the right hand is open and the left hand is in a fist. As the five fingers of the right hand fold down into a fist with the thumb on the outside, the Jupiter (index) and Saturn (middle) fingers of the left hand open up and the thumb folds over the ring and pinkie fingers. As the five fingers of the right hand open up, the Jupiter and Saturn Fingers of the left hand close down toward the palm, the thumb releases. Continue the movement. Move quickly.
2 ½ minutes.

It is a principle of life. Open five times, be closed twice; you'll always survive. If you close five times and open only twice, you'll be dead in no time. It is the first law of life. Horizon should be wide five times and it should be narrow two times.

2. Inhale deeply and suspend the breath as you continue the movement between the two hands, 7 times, then exhale. Repeat one more time. Inhale and increase the repetitions to 14 and then 21. After these four cycles, continue inhaling and suspending the breath with 14 repetitions of the movement. Exhale and repeat.
4 minutes.

I know this is difficult, but let's do it. This is very important for energizing our gray matter in the brain in order to consolidate our own inflow. It's all meridian points; it's just like acupuncture, nothing more. It's not an automatic breath; the breath is under your control.

3. Arms are up at 60 degrees, elbows gently bent, palms facing one another. Movement: Bend the thumbs into the palms of the hands, then make a fist with the four fingers over the thumb, tighten the fists and pull the fists down in front of the chest. "Milk the cosmic cow." Keep the hands in fists as you lift the arms to their original position. Release the mudra, opening the hands and repeat the movement. To practice, inhale deeply and complete 7 repetitions on the held breath. Exhale and continue. **2 minutes**.

4. With the eyes slightly open, look at the tip of the nose. Bring the hands in front of the body, palms facing each other. Bend the thumb and then make a fist over the thumb, alternating, left and right hands. The fingers cover the thumb and then release.

Chant **Har** as you make a fist in each hand. Pace is fairly quick: two times per second.
6 ½ minutes.

One side will hurt and the other won't.
*Utter the sound **Har** from the heart.*

5. Put the thumbs on the Mound of Mercury, at the base of the Mercury (pinkie) finger. Place the left hand on the Heart Center and place the right hand over the left, forearms parallel. The fingers of the right hand point toward the left; the fingers of the left hand point toward the right. Inhale deeply and exhale completely, suspend the breath out and mentally repeat the mantra**, *Har, Har, Har,*** and listen. Hold the breath out for 15 to 30 seconds. Inhale, exhale and repeat. Continue for **5 minutes**.

Practice living without breath. You are controlling death; you are without breath or movement.

TO END: Inhale deeply and relax.

6. Extend the arms out to the sides, from the shoulders; stretch from the shoulder. Move the arms up and down, from the shoulders, 4-6 inches. Move quickly. Keep the arms stiff. Move like the hummingbird—fly! Breath will automatically change. After **2 minutes**, close the eyes and continue the movement as the visualization and Gong Meditation begin. **2 minutes**. **4 minutes total**.

Guided Meditation

Meditate on the seventh year. Meditate on the seventh year. Look at the seventh year. Concentrate; look at the seventh year: seventh year, not before, not after. Keep the arms straight, parallel to the ground, keep flying. You must understand, whether you are black or white, thick or thin, tall or short, it is the seventh year of life which is holding you here. All the pain, the tragedy, push it out. Seventh year, nothing less, nothing more. Please dare to move.

7. Gong continues. Bring the hands into the lap, palm up, right hand resting in the left, thumb tips touch. Sit straight and continue the guided meditation. **11 minutes**.

Guided Meditation

Meditate on the seventh year. Think about the seventh year. Repeat every moment of it. Look at it, read it, adjust it, judge it. Concentrate, if you concentrate on the seventh year you can get rid of a lot of problems.

TO END: Silence the Gong. *Inhale deep, spine straight, chin in, chest out. Suspend the breath and look, for the last moment, at the seventh year of life; exhale. Inhale deep again and look down at it and forgive it. Good and bad forgive it.*
Exhale and immediately move into the next exercise.

8. One Minute Breath: Begin to breathe long and deep; consciously and slowly. Inhale slowly, suspend the breath, exhale slowly; 20:20:20 is ideal, that is, 20 seconds in, 20 seconds suspend, 20 seconds exhale. Or, start with 10:10:10 and slowly build up. Music: *Flowers in the Rain* followed by *Walking up the Mountain* sung by Gurudass Singh. (*See lyric sheets in the Appendix.*)
11 minutes.

Whenever you breathe consciously it invigorates your body and makes your mind clear and strong.

9. Bear Grip with Breath of Fire. Grip the fingers of the right and left hands; right palm faces the chest, left palm faces away from the chest. Pull the fingers away from each other. **1 ½ minutes**.
TO END: Inhale, suspend the breath approximately 20 seconds and exhale and suspend the breath approximately 20 seconds. Repeat this sequence two more times.

10. Relax and shake the hands and move the toes. Shake the whole body. Shake. **30-60 seconds**.

◆

"I am fifty-nine years old, and I have not yet met one person who wants to be unhappy, unhealthy, or who wants to suffer. You understand what I am saying? But we do suffer. We don't suffer because we want to suffer; we suffer because we want sympathy, apathy—misery needs company. "

– Yogi Bhajan

GHOST KRIYA
CLEARING THE GHOSTS & OPENING INTUITION

December 5, 1988

*H*ELLO. ARE YOU READY FOR TONIGHT? If I were you, I would not have come to class. I am very truthful about it. I didn't ask you to bring Kleenexes and all that, but we are going to go through what we call "disoriented memories" tonight. You have to understand that, as a human being, you have a problem. No person from any category or caliber, from any religion, from any country, is supposed to suffer. Our suffering does not come because of the environments or because people want us to suffer or because we want to suffer. I am fifty-nine years old, and I have not yet met one person who wants to be unhappy, unhealthy, or who wants to suffer. You understand what I am saying? But we do suffer. We don't suffer because we want to suffer; we suffer because we want sympathy, apathy—misery needs company.

I met someone and thought she was very nice and very beautiful and very mannerful. But she said, "I am shit." And it was like somebody had just punched me in my chest. There was no explanation. But that is how people feel. There must be some moments in your life when you feel like shit. But when you clean out this business called "shit," you feel very easy and clean, and that is the way you will talk in life also.

Everything to you is one word—a four-letter word—and that is it. I have never seen the human race so decisive as you folks are now. People used to think, people used to talk, people used to go to great lengths. People used to understand the pros and cons, people used to wait, people used to understand what they wanted and why. They consulted this and that. But the institutionalization of the idea that we have the right to be our self is gone. It is gone. The individual has totally become just a four-letter person, isolated from their self and from others. What has that done to us as a society?

The entire society around us has totally isolated us. In society, there was never the need for a great relationship; everybody could relate to everybody, and the flow was very effective and smooth and basic. Now it is not. You need three, four types of friends. One type you can go to lunch with. One kind you can go to dinner with. One kind you can visit and cry on their shoulder. One you can make each other miserable. Lots of things; lots of types of relationships. Yet, you are lonely, you are isolated, and you have lost communication and confidence. This has not happened to an individual; this has happened to the whole human race!

The institutionalization of the idea that we have the right to be our self is gone. It is gone. The individual has totally become just a four-letter person, isolated from their self and from others. What has that done to us as a society?

Living needs discipline. You are dismal without discipline. Discipline is that grit, that strength, that organization in you, for you. People think, "Why do I have to meditate?" I say, "To clean your subconscious." Why do you have to take a bath? Because you don't want to stink. You meditate so that your mind won't stink.

We used to be tribal—little tribes helping each other. Then we became ethnicities. Then we became states. Now we have become the world. Now there is nothing. Everybody knows everything, and nobody knows anything. It is a very fascinating world today.

This world is a jungle. But how do we survive? There are two ways to survive. Survive as it comes: use the power of money; use the power of sex; use the power of sensuality, creativity; play the games; lie, cheat; get the quick buck; be a politician; be power hungry. No, that life itself can only pass time; it is not living. Passing time is not living. Remember, living is totally different. If you only pass time, you cannot live. Living needs discipline. You are dismal without discipline. Discipline is that grit, that strength, that organization in you, for you. People think, "Why do I have to meditate?" I say, "To clean your subconscious." Why do you have to take a bath? Because you don't want to stink. You meditate so that your mind won't stink. A beautiful person can spend about three hundred dollars to dress up, but you look at her, and you know there is nothing in it. But do you understand that the mind needs makeup, too? And the mind's makeup is meditation.

It is a very selfish thing to meditate. Do you think your relationship will carry on? No. No relationship will carry on. No relationship will live. The only relationship that will live is one that has a foundation. Can I put a roof on this house without any foundation? No. A relationship needs a foundation; you need, for yourself, a foundation—your foundation, your discipline for yourself. Sometimes people think I became religious because I wanted to be religious. Not at all, my dear. I became religious because I wanted to know my own reality. And when I found out my reality, I started helping people. That is why I am happy to be slow, cautious. I have a lot of knowledge. There are no problems for me. I can play with myself or play with my sickness. I play with everything. But that is fun to me. I am alive. As long as I am alive, I must know that I am not just passing the time; I am enjoying it.

Please don't misunderstand me or believe that I do not know what richness is. On the carpet where as a child I pooped and peed, there was a big emerald, four by four inches wide and four and a half inches thick. So I have seen richness that you will never, ever see. And I have seen poverty—such that I stood with no undershirt and only underwear at a railway station, thinking and feeling that somehow food would come. And what food came? Grams. What do you call them in this country? Chickpeas! And they were very hard. My family was very young, but I was a responsible person. You know how I softened them? I softened them with water from the locomotive engine—that steam. So I have seen poverty; I have seen richness. I have seen friendliness such that when I walk through the street,

everybody enjoys saying hello to me. And I have seen isolation.

But I am successful, I am fulfilled, I am happy. Just as you feel you have to make an effort to be happy, I make an effort to feel unhappy. I act very well; I am a good actor. I am a better actor than all of Hollywood. Because when I come to a student, I have to act unhappy and miserable, like an idiot, so that the person can at least start talking. If they remember that I know everything, they will never talk to me. Never! Why should they talk to me? They will sit down like this: "You know everything. Help me." And then I have got another zombie. But that is not human, you know what I mean? That is not human. We can create miracles, but we do not pretend to create miracles. Miracles are miracles; they will happen. People have to understand one thing—one thing that is very positive and that you must all have—you must have self-confidence and your organic natural beauty, natural purity, natural nobility, your natural self. You must understand that nothing can substitute for God; no makeup will substitute for the beauty of God; and the beauty of God comes out of you in exactly nine seconds.

If you cannot solve a problem in nine seconds, then you cannot affect a person in nine seconds, you cannot establish a rapport in nine seconds—nine seconds is all you have. Otherwise the combination of neurons in the brain will never support you; it means you are handicapped within yourself. The total time limit is nine seconds. That is the way we found the measurement of time—a second. We found it from our own brain. It was not thrust upon us. Nobody knew what a second was. We knew up to nine; then it is a zero. Correct? Is that true? Within nine seconds, you must know the answer, and you must have the strength to act, grit to act, courage to act, intelligence to act, consciousness to act—you can call it anything, I don't care. But all you have in life is nine seconds. You miss anything within nine seconds; on the eleventh second, you cannot make it. Remember this. This is why we are miserable. This is why Nanak said, *Naanak dukia sabh sansaar, so sukhia jis naam adhaar.* Nobody understands the meaning of it. "*Nanak, the entire world is in pain. Only those who live off the holy word are happy.*"

What does a holy word do? A holy word does not put you in the hole. It keeps you alive. It keeps you living. It gives you intuition. Intuition gives you everything. Before anything else happens, intuition allows you to react in three seconds, and that is all that Kundalini Yoga is about. Kundalini Yoga is not a thing; it is a science. It is not something that can be sold or hired or measured.

So in tonight's class, we have to act. Am I clear? Hello? Did you come here to dance with me, or what? Look, I am a teacher: I am a teacher after my death; I am a teacher to begin with; and I am a teacher when I was not even born. I believe in

Deny your love to nothing, deny your charity to nothing, deny your grace to none, deny your nobility to none. Share it, and God will give you an abundance.

one thing—compassion. I don't believe in kindness; I am just one step ahead of it. I believe there is no "No." Those who believe in Nanak say "no" to nothing. Deny your love to nothing, deny your charity to nothing, deny your grace to none, deny your nobility to none. Share it, and God will give you an abundance.

But tonight you have to work. Spell "work" and spell "out." By the end of the class, you are going to have a workout. Are you ready? I won't ask much. I have to press a few trigger points in kundalini, and I'll ask you to work yourself. I want to see the result, because I don't feel satisfied if I do not deliver one hundred percent more than what I expect to deliver. That's my range. I am sick and tired of seeing people unhappy—it makes me very sick; it is something I cannot stand. Man, born in the image of God, suffering? Come on. Okay, all set? Mind clear?

Have you been to Disneyland, all of you? Have you? Is there anybody who hasn't been to Disneyland ever before? If you go to Disneyland, you will see there is a haunted house. Have you seen that? In the haunted house, they have created the images of souls. You understand? Ghosts, right? Have you ever watched their movement? No? They have a circular effect. In us, this movement will affect the motor; the motor will affect the patterns; and the patterns in the brain will refuse, because patterns in the brain do not believe in ghosts. Did you know that? Anything that you don't believe in becomes fear for you. Anything you do believe in is fulfillment for you.

Our brain does not believe in ghosts. We don't. But whenever we start feeling, believing, and understanding that a ghost, or a perpetual fear, is real, then we lose fear. There are many human ghosts—being unsuccessful, being poor, being sick, being divorced, being married, being in love. Oh, a terrible ghost is being in love. It's a hell. You know when you are in love whether it is going to work out or not—it's "Oh, oh, oh, oh." Oh, God, it is so funny. How people in love ruin their glands—you can't believe it.

◆ ◆ ◆

So, how do ghosts move? You know, there is a light—double light they call it—that moves like a figure eight. It is a very scientific exercise and cannot be done as a joke (*see Exercise 1*). It's kind of like a figure eight in the air. This moves the body in a certain pattern. Close your eyes and meditate. You will freak out in a couple of minutes. The body's temperament will not accept it. This exercise will also hurt your head, I know. Ghost is nothing but a permanent host on Earth. A soul that is a permanent host on Earth is called a ghost. It is very gruesome to be attached to Earth for the rest of your lifetimes.

Find a space somewhere and start moving and somebody will adjust you. That's God's way. When a baby is born, he doesn't know whether there will be a crib or not. He gets it anyway.

Somebody once asked me, "Why have you come to America?"

"To teach."

"There are a lot of teachers here."

"I know."

"Then what are you going to do?"

"I am going to teach."

"Well, they have already come."

"I know."

"Well, what are you going to do?"

"I am going to teach because I don't know who has come and who has not come—all I know is to teach."

"Why do you want to teach?"

"Because I have learned."

It is simple. Move in the *akashic eight*. Close your eyes and meditate and become ghosts. How can you go into the previous lifetime? We have to just set up the space, and then we'll go to the next and the next lifetime, and then we will meditate and get rid of a lot of garbage. We are full of it. Really! Our misery is proportionate to our clarity, and our clarity is proportionate to our discipline. Keep moving. If you have been to that place, that haunted house, just feel light and feel you have no body—you are just a soul.

You think ghosts are bad? Become one now. Meditate and become delightful ghosts and shed off your karma; become lighter and lighter. But keep moving in that eight—that subtle eight—higher, higher than your shoulders. That cantaloupe that you are carrying on your shoulders does a lot of work, so please move. Become ghosts.

You spend five to seven thousand dollars on rebirthing, and you go to a psychiatrist and psychologist, and they call it group therapy. You try three hundred different kinds of things to just be normal. I am telling you more than that—you can get rid of your ghost today. The best way to get rid of the ghost is to become one—and to sweat.

It is called rhythmic space. Keep moving in your own style and your own space, but please go through it. Help your brain relax and release. Help your consciousness unload the garbage. For God's sake, let it out! What are you sticking with? Problems? Clogged-up heart is no good, clogged-up liver is no good, clogged-up belly is no good, clogged-up consciousness is no good, and clogged-up subconscious is absolutely no good. Move, move, move at your own rhythm. God shall never abandon you. Fly above the clouds. Please help yourself. Move.

This exercise depends upon your sincerity, your participation, and your being. If you get into it, everything you want to get out will get out. Make yourself delightfully light above the clouds. Keep moving. It will automatically unload a lot of nonsense that would normally take a long time by talking and doing things and helping. It is a simple thing. It is a very beautiful energy; it will take care of you. All you have to do is partici-

Our misery is proportionate to our clarity, and our clarity is proportionate to our discipline.

pate and just heat up. The body needs a little more heat, that is all. Create that heat, and things will be fantastic. Keep the rhythm going, keep the rhythm going. Lots of tears, lots of smiles, lots of life; go through it. Unload.

We don't want to be restricted. You have come here, spent ten dollars; don't leave with nothing. Come on! Make a hundred out of it. Come on, work hard. The class is called "Ghosting." But I didn't mention anything about that, because I said to myself, "If I would have said it is a ghosting meditation, they would have said, 'What is he going to do with us?'"

Be kind to your beauty. Be kind to your bountifulness, your blissfulness. This movement will help you a lot if you stretch out your arms and open up your armpits—that is all that is needed. Go into the cycling of moving in that subtle eight. Moving the body, giving the spine the rhythm it needs. Let the armpit force the brain to work it all out, forcing the subconscious to unload. What a system. Come on! Enjoy it now.

The idea is that this money you have paid tonight, it won't come to me. What comes to me is the satisfaction that I have done a good job. You understand what I mean? So don't be dishonest with me. I do it out of love. You are just doing it out of misery. Do it happily. I know you have been a ghost. Everybody goes through it.

You can spend three hundred and fifty dollars and get twenty five previous incarnations. What a joke! Then what do you do with them? Listen: "I was born in Egypt. I walked through the sand. I didn't have food. I was a beggar on the corner, and the Pharaoh picked me up." And all that. I hear them. Some people bring these past incarnations to me. I enjoy it. One guy spent three hundred fifty dollars—poor scoundrel gave his own blood and money minus taxes; you know, it must have been about five hundred dollars. And he comes out with a bunch of tapes that have nothing but his own ridiculous imagination. Here we are doing something practical. You are getting a highly elevated self of a ghost. You remember? Come on, ghost. Come on, you ghosts, beautiful ghosts, American ghosts. See one hundred American ghosts going through the top of the mountains. Just imagine.

Have you seen those people fly and catch their hands and keep moving? Have you seen that? Remember that? I understand; I have done it for years. Stretch out your shoulders, keep that movement, and force the brain to release the thoughts, the fears—all the fears that are haunting you. Let us end the haunting. Let us become our Self, the hunters. When we really do the work, time becomes slow sometimes, and sometimes it becomes very fast. But for ghosts, time is always very slow. You have become a real ghost. With your power, the watch is moving pretty slowly, but it is all right. You will make it.

Keep your hands in your lap, right over left, palms facing up. Sit with a straight spine and go back to your school days from year one, standard one, or class first, and go class by class. (*See Exercise 2.*) Go through those moments in detail, in perfect detail; because ghost knows all, so you know all. And as you remember, your ghost will eat it up, and you shall be free.

Now start breathing through the nostrils as slowly as you can, but keep your mouth open. (*See Exercise 4.*) Listen: if you give your mind a higher altitude, it will change your attitude of life for happiness. These are priceless kriyas. Do your best. Go on the wavelength; we are sending you the wavelength.

Good and bad—you are all good, you are in the image of God. You are the light of God, you have the praana of God. When you get up tomorrow morning, get up with this sound—*Rakhe rakhanhaar*. (*See Exercise 5.*) Let me tell you what these words are. These words are very beautiful. You can get the translation in English, but when you stiffen the tongue and utter the word by copying it. . . I notice that many of you do not know the meaning of these words. I know that you do not know what you are saying. I know you know that. You do not know what you are doing. But all you have to do is press the tongue against the palate on these sounds; you will be unloading your difficulty, pain, and disease. Look, nothing has worked in the world better than the word of God; and there is nothing more successful that man learned how to do than put the permutation and combination of sounds to get results. That is all it is. I am trying to explain to you that these sounds are nothing but a combined permutation and combination of the tongue and the palate. That's the game.

Rakhe. It is a Western girl[1] who sings it. It is Western people who are singing it, exactly like you and me. They can copy the sound; you can copy the sound. I want the tongue to be tough and stiff. Each word has to be conscious. I don't want these memories you have unloaded to come back. I want to get rid of them forever. That's my genuine effort. Your genuine cooperation can create the result.

Thank you very much. You have been very good.

What we need is the tough tongue. I have done it myself. When I was very seriously sick, there was nothing much to do, and it was a very tough situation. You know when there is spaghetti all around your body, and every vein is punctured, and something is going in-between and out, and they tell you, "Try to sleep and rest," and they come and poke a big needle and tell you, "I am taking blood. I am giving you medicine. I'm doing this." And you don't know what you are going through. At that moment, I chanted with my tongue. I couldn't chant loud, but with a tough tongue, I created this sound. It has a tremendous healing sound, healing self, and it gave me a lot.

This music was made on a cup of decaf at the St. Louis airport. The rhythm was there. I started playing with the cup and started chanting, and I said, "Let us make the music." And that is what this music is about; it is effective. Let this music play the whole night. Then, when you get up in the morning—if you are free and your man or your woman permits it (don't pick a quarrel on my behalf)—first

[1] Singh Kaur

thing, open your mouth and with a tough tongue, repeat for a few minutes these words. Then judge that day, watch that day, supervise that day. See what you do that day. One day. The first day.

Well, my dear ghosts, you have ghosted yourself very well, unloaded very well. I am very happy; extremely pleased. Tomorrow we would like you to understand that you are coming to a workout class. We don't expect you to come here and get nothing. I believe in nothing except one thing: If a man can have a clear subconscious, he can have a clear conscious; even if he acts unconsciously, it shall always be profitable, right, beautiful, bountiful, and blissful.

Look, I am a yogi. I have studied everything, I have read everything, I have seen, I have practiced. And I have come to conclude one thing: Happiness is man's birthright. We are very stupid if we are not happy. Somebody asked me, "Are you happy?" I said, "I teach it." And what is yoga? Yoga is not for body, mind, and soul. Yoga is when the pair of opposites do not affect you—when happiness does not make you crazy and when sadness doesn't make you dead. Whatever happens, if you remain you, that is what you really are.

Tomorrow we have to give the mental altitude and latitude to see our mental attitude, and we have to widen the horizons, and we are going to do it right here in this room. So if you come, come prepared—come with a grit, come with a courage, and come to do something for yourself. This is what you have done for yourself.

God is very important. Guru is very important, wealth is important, health is important, everything is important. But there is nothing more important than you. If you are not important, everything means nothing. I think we will ask to prepare a drink tomorrow, and we will serve that exotic drink tomorrow, not today, because that is the food of the ghosts. So I think you will forgive us today, and you can go home. I would like you to go home quick. I don't want you to stop on the way. Do you hear me? Am I clear in English? I would like you to get in the car and get home to your bed. I want you not to be on the road within the hour. Is that understood?

May the long time sun shine upon you,
all love surround you, and the pure light within you, guide your way on.

Sat Nam
and thank you very much for coming.

GHOST KRIYA
CLEARING THE GHOSTS & OPENING INTUITION

December 5, 1988

There are no breaks between the exercises. Move immediately from one exercise to the next.

1. The chin is slightly up so that the Moon Center (at the chin) does not cross the vertical. Bring the arms up, with the palms facing each other. Stretch the arms up and move the arms together in a figure eight; move lightly, keeping the arms stretched up. Open the armpit. Rock the torso forward and back in concert with the arms. Close the eyes and see the darkness. Continue for approximately **30 minutes.**

Guided Meditation

It is called rhythmic space. Keep moving in your own style and your own space, but please go through it. Help your brain relax and release. Help your consciousness unload the garbage. For God's sake, let it out! What are you sticking with? Problems? Clogged-up heart is no good, clogged-up liver is no good, clogged-up belly is no good, clogged-up consciousness is no good, and clogged-up subconscious is absolutely no good. Move, move, move at your own rhythm. God shall never abandon you. Fly above the clouds. Please help yourself. Move.

This exercise depends upon your sincerity, your participation, and your being. If you get into it, everything you want to get out will get out. Make yourself delightfully light above the clouds. Keep moving. It will automatically unload a lot of nonsense that would normally take a long time by talking and doing things and helping. It is a simple thing. It is a very beautiful energy; it will take care of you. All you have to do is participate and just heat up. The body needs a little more heat, that is all. Create that heat, and things will be fantastic. Keep the rhythm going, keep the rhythm going. Lots of tears, lots of smiles, lots of life; go through it. Unload.

It is going to automatically relax you. Don't worry. Don't sleep, don't feel sleepy. Keep going. The pattern of the neurons, the working part of the brain, will refuse to conduct itself. That is the way it is. Move, move. Close your eyes. See the pitch darkness and create the light and keep moving. Stretch the shoulders. Keep the hands stiff and create that beautiful, subtle eight in the air. The body should move with it.

Meditation continued next page

Guided Meditation — continued

Become ghosts. You can get rid of all your inner ghosts if you do it right. The best way to get rid of the ghost is to become one. Get into it! Become it! Feel you are a ghost, flying in the air across the dazzling light. Now start flying through the scorching heat of the desert; flying through the Sahara; start going through it. Go through the heat and the vastness of it. Move with great strength. There is a huge desert that you must go through. You are creating a field of your own psyche—the absolutely delightful, transparent body is that of a ghost, and you are going through the depth of all the deserts in the world: Gobi, Sahara, and so on. Wherever your memory or subconscious takes you, get into your own vast desert! Move in the rhythmic eight of the subtle self.

Now enter a lush, green rainforest. This is how it was taught; this is how it was written. Enter a lush, green rainforest. Make your way through. Powerfully stretch your shoulders out; open your armpits. Lush, green rainforest—go through it, swim through it, fly through it. You are a ghost. Ghost through the rainforest, the lush green rainforest. Maybe you have never been to a lush green rainforest. But go today. Please cool yourself through the rainforest. You understand?

After about **15 minutes**, stretch the arms up even higher, toward vertical, and continue moving. Keep your armpit completely stretched and open.

Guided Meditation

Fly above the clouds, directly beneath the sun. You have a lot of cloudiness in life, and you must get rid of it. Fly above the clouds! Work it out! Keep on ghosting yourself. Unload the cloudiness. Unload the tears. Now, please enter a lush, green rainforest. Be kind to your beauty, your bountifulness, blissfulness. This movement forces your subconscious to unload. Be happy; do it happily. Cool yourself through the lush, green rainforest. You can clear out your previous 25 incarnations. Now move into a long range of mountains, totally filled with snow, white and bright and shining, where there is calmness and quietness, where sound resounds a million times. Move in that most beautiful eight of the subtle body. It will help you; it will cure you.

Fly over the mountain, you ghosts. Remember, beneath you there is a white, shining—absolutely shining—very beautiful snow, 50 feet of powder. If you fall, nobody will track you down. Come on—keep flying. Don't touch the snow; it is cold. Now keep going, keep going from the top of one mountain to another. Huge glaciers, beautiful mountains, high peaks, top to top. American ghosts are on a journey. Keep ghosting and keep flying. Keep the movement, keep the armpit open. That is the only secret to it. Keep ghosting. Keep flying. Let us end the haunting! Move!

First ghost is a ghost on Earth; then he is in a desert, and that is purification; then he gets the lush green, and that is a further purification. And the finest is to go into the lowliest sound of the mountains, valleys—where you said, "I wanted to come." Move in that most beautiful eight of the subtle body. Please, it is required. It will help you. It will cure you, really. It is a very good movement. Sincerity is required. Commitment is required. Discipline is required. Courage is required. Grit is required. Doing is required.

Have you seen those people fly and catch their hands and keep moving? Have you seen that? Remember that? I understand; I have done it for years. Stretch out your shoulders, keep that movement, and force the brain to release the thoughts, the fears—all the fears that are haunting you. Let us end the haunting. Let us become our Self, the hunters. When we really do the work, time becomes slow sometimes, and sometimes it becomes very fast. But for ghosts, time is always very slow. You have become a real ghost. With your power, the watch is moving pretty slowly, but it is all right. You will make it.

TO END: Inhale deep and stretch the arms up and become wide, become big. Exhale. Repeat.

2. Exhale the hands into the lap; do not open the eyes. Keep the hands in your lap, with the right hand resting in the left, palms up. Sit straight and meditate as the gong is played. Continue for **14 minutes**.

Guided Meditation

Go to your school days—from first grade on. What did you think you could be? What did you want to be then? What was the most imaginative profile of yourself in the first, second, third, fourth, fifth, sixth, seventh, eighth, ninth, tenth, eleventh, and twelfth grades? Review it in detail. As ghost knows all, you know all. As you remember, try to be that person, and your ghost will eat it up, and you shall be free. Give your memories to the ghost. Give your memories to the ghost. There are good memories; there are bad memories. There are happy memories; there are sad memories. Give them all. You need to be free. You need to be free. We are creating a space—three motions, direct strength wave of the sound of the creative gong. It is a very special sound I am playing. Please use that energy and keep going. Be completely honest; your experience depends on your honesty—first year, second year, third, fourth, fifth, sixth, seventh, eighth, ninth, tenth, eleventh, and graduation.

3. Open the mouth and begin breathing heavily through the mouth. The teeth should not touch. The gong continues. Continue breathing in this way for **2 minutes**.

Breathe heavily with mouth open as if you are giving birth to a child. And the teeth must not touch. Disconnect the meridians by opening the mouth. Don't let the lips or the teeth connect with each other, otherwise it will create a nervous system short circuit. We don't need that.

4. Breathe through the nostrils as slowly as you can. Keep the mouth open; the teeth should not touch. The gong continues. Continue for **3 minutes.**

If you give your mind a higher altitude, it will change your attitude of life for happiness. These are priceless kriyas. Do your best. Go on the wavelength; we are sending you the wavelength. Go on the wavelength. Good and bad? You are all good. You are made in the image of God. You are the prana of God. The light of God.

5. Sing with the mantra *Rakhe Rakhanhaar* by Singh Kaur. Copy the sounds. Chant with the tongue. Consciously use the tongue. Press the palate with the tongue. Sing for **6 minutes**.

Even though many of you may not know the words, all that needs to happen is to press the tongue on the upper palate. When you stiffen the tongue and utter the word so the tongue is pressed against the palate with these sounds, you can unload your difficulty, pain, disease. Nothing has worked better than the word of God. These sounds are a combined permutation and combination of the tongue and palate. I want the tongue to be tough and stiff. Each word has to be conscious. I don't want these memories you have unloaded to come back; I want them to be gone forever.

6. Wake up in the morning to the sound of the mantra *Rakhe Rakhanhaar*. Repeat with a tough tongue for a few minutes. Watch that day. Observe what happens.

Rakhay rakhanhaar aap ubaarian
Gur kee pairee paa-eh kaaj savaarian
Hoaa aap dayaal manho na visaarian
Saadh janaa kai sang bhavjal taarian
Saakat nindak dusht khin maa-eh bidaarian
Tis saahib kee tayk naanak manai maa-eh
Jis simrat sukh ho-eh saglay dookh jaa-eh

God Himself is looking out for me,
Gives me the light, and takes care of my affairs.
God is merciful, and never forgets me.
God guides me, giving me good people to help me.
God does not allow any harm to come to me.
I take comfort in the thought of God.
When I remember God, I feel peaceful and
happy and all my pain departs.

◆

"We integrate a lot of garbage in the fantasy that we are very happy. When, in truth, our enemy is not our tragedies; our enemy is our happiness. There is a lore—that's the only word that can be properly used—a lore of happiness, a lore of friendship, a lore of this, a lore of that."

– Yogi Bhajan

CLEARING OUR SUBCONSCIOUS STORIES

December 6, 1988

ALL RIGHT. WE DID A CLASS YESTERDAY, and we are going to do a class today. I am very adamant to deliver what I have to deliver. But you have to cooperate with me a little bit. All right? We are reaching today into the fourth level of the subconscious. We are crossing our conscious fears, which we carry from our previous lifetimes. We integrate a lot of garbage in the fantasy that we are very happy. When, in truth, our enemy is not our tragedies; our enemy is our happiness. There is a lore—that's the only word that can be properly used—a lore of happiness, a lore of friendship, a lore of this, a lore of that.

We walk a tightrope. You know? Imagine there is a cliff, a mile-long cliff, and you plant the stakes and you place the rope and you walk. If you jump, what do you find there? Just big cold air; that's it. You know what you did? It can't be your home, it can't be your place. But that's what humans do. Humans have a subconscious lore. Unfortunately, the science about the brain is not being taught, studied, or understood. How our brain works we don't know. We think there is a brain, and it works because we tell it to work. But that's not true. The brain tells us to work; we don't tell the brain to work. The idea that we tell the brain to work is a fantasy: We believe we'll all be happy, we'll all be fantastic, we'll all be aboveboard. But we have to have a rhythm, contained rhythm, within ourselves. We can't be intoxicated; we can't be allured by our own fear or by our own happiness.

Now, this is what happens to you as human beings: The fear confronts you. Are you with me? Fear confronts you, and you simply create the other side of the coin. You get allured into productivity in order to create happiness and to get rid of the fear. You don't go and face the fear and kill it. No, you won't do it. None of you will do it. Do you know what that means? What I am saying? I, Harbajan Singh Khalsa Yogji, Siri Singh Sahib Bhai Sahib, chief of Kundalini Yoga, whatever, certify that you can never be happy; it doesn't matter what you have. The first thing a human must have in order to be happy is the ability to confront and challenge fear and kill it. But we humans are taught not to do it. Instead, fear has been used by our mother, our father, our neighbors, our schools, our television, and our society. You know why? To direct us: "Don't go out in the dark. Don't this, don't do that. Don't go to the neighbor's house." What do we do? When we gather together a lot of don'ts, we go out and do just the opposite. Do you understand that? "All right, you have told me all this, shut up! Now I am going to do the opposite." Your

This is what happens to you as human beings: The fear confronts you. Are you with me? Fear confronts you, and you simply create the other side of the coin. You get allured into productivity in order to create happiness and to get rid of the fear. You don't go and face the fear and kill it.

Humans have nothing to worry about if they can challenge fear and kill it, conquer it, rather than storing it in the subconscious.

brain does it for you automatically. You are worse than an animal, and you call yourself human.

This dichotomy, this duality, this action and reaction, this conformation exists in every human being. Nobody is above it. Because whatever your challenge is, whatever you are scared of, you have to create an opposite pleasure, an opposite happiness, to balance it. Do you understand that? Do you understand the theory? If you say, "We don't," then in your life, when don't, don't, don't becomes too much, you just say, "All right, shut up. We are doing this, and this, and this." Then, you see, you feel very released, liberated, free; you are happy. You call it independence, freedom, something like that. But the question is, you don't do it. In the end, you say, "Well, I did it anyway; it's my job."

In your brain, there is a survival technique that will not challenge fear. Life is like a river. When a river hits a hard stone, the river makes a turn and goes through some other way. That's why rivers and people and spermatozoa move in a zigzag. It's called snake walk. The snake is considered very important because the thought wavelength is like a snake. In science, we understand thoughts as wavelengths and frequencies. But in the past, we only knew one simple thing—a man's snake strength. So today we say, "What is his frequency?" In those days, we would ask, "What is his snake strength?" So you have a problem as a human being, and you are born with it—and nobody is an exception to it. Whenever you feel challenged, pained, or irregular, you create an opposite. Everybody has a death wish, because you all want to go Home, and yet you get so attached to the play of the world that you don't want to go Home. You want to go Home, but you don't want to go Home.

This class will be very good. So, come on; let's do it and finish. I have a moral obligation as a teacher, and I won't fail. Now, right here, let's put the split. This is my left side; this is my right side. The left is my foundation. The right can never be a foundation; never will be. So whatever I have to do, I have to do by my left side. What I have to achieve, I have to achieve by my right side. Remember this. Also remember that no class out there exists to teach you how to confront and conquer fear. As long as this is not being taught as a course within human schools of knowledge and life, there is no way that humans can be happy.

Fear is automatic, and we do not want to confront fear; we want to avoid fear. Why would we take on fear when we can avoid it? But remember, avoided fear simply gets put in the subconscious. Whatever we avoid consciously becomes garbage in the subconscious, and whatever garbage exists in the subconscious is alive; it needs an alternative. So the fear that somebody is going to steal my things, the fear that I am going to lose something—that's not going to go away. Fear of love has destroyed more lives than love itself. When we are afraid of love, we create love, but it's never natural, never organic. And then we blow it; it falls apart.

Humans have nothing to worry about if they can challenge fear and kill it, conquer it, rather than storing it in the subconscious. Who gave us fear on our first day? "My baby, my boy, don't go out." First fear: "Don't go out." We are not children of kangaroos; we don't have that bag to rest in and jump with the mama all the time. We can't. We are human, and it's our tendency to explore. But we are told we can't explore. Second, woman is born of the basic situation called egg, so her movement will be oval. Man is born of the basic situation called spermatozoa, so his movement will be zigzag. It cannot change. A woman cannot be a man, and a man cannot be a woman. They can be intermediary; you can call it anything you want, but they can never meet in thought form, in their thinking. In the world, power is in how you think, not in how you act. Your basic blueprint is how you think. When you are not thinking right, you cannot act right, and your thinking can never be right. You can think to be successful, you can work to be successful, you want to be successful. But in the end, you'll find you have failed. Why? Because you have stored so much fear in your subconscious that it affects you; it steals away your real capacity.

Meditation actually does nothing. I mean, it's the biggest hoax, the idea that meditation does anything. Meditation only does one simple thing: It cleans the subconscious. People don't even know how to meditate. Honest to God! I have listened to all the holy men, right? Lots of people with lots of status. They think I am a Yogiji, so they brag about their meditative experience, and I know they lie. I know it, but I don't say it. So basically, either I am a coward, or I am a deceitful achiever. But I don't want to offend them; I don't want to tell them, "You have wasted your life. You are good for nothing. You are useless." I just want to be a good guy. So I am also not real. You understand how we lie to each other?

They come and lie before me. They know I am the Mahan Tantric; there is no doubt in their mind that they are talking to God. That's why they want to brag. A child only comes and shows his achievements to somebody he considers higher. So naturally they come and they brag: "I had this experience and that experience." And I say, "Yeah, yeah, that can happen, good, thank you very much, let's talk about something else. Have a cup of tea. Or get out of here."

When you start meditating, garbage will begin coming out—that is the start of meditation. What's meditation for? To clean the subconscious. All your garbage:

how many times you masturbated, how many times you wished for a woman, how many times you stole, how many times you wanted to steal, how many times you wanted to just punch somebody. I mean to say, the dirtiest details of your life—which only you know—they start showing up. That's called stage one. Stage two: You are in the actual grip of everything you've resisted, everything you've desired *not* to do. Now, even things that you have never thought of—that's all stored in your subconscious. God, if you understood that garbage, you wouldn't even believe it. The Playboy Channel isn't that pornographic at all compared to what comes out of the human mind; it's unbelievable garbage. Third stage—I am giving you the stages of meditation—third stage is all about your projections of the universe and the mastery thereof. You want to be on top of the universe, not under it; and those nightmares and those thoughts and those dramas come out during this stage. Now, how many things have I told you, three? Right? In the fourth stage, you actually experience physical intercourse, you taste food, you live; and sometimes you live a few lifetimes in thought; it's known as living in meditation. Sometimes you die from an entire life that you were to live, but you lived it in just seconds. Sometimes the practical and virtuous nightmare is only nine seconds. In nine seconds you have been born, you have lived, you have died, you have had your funeral, you have left your children crying, you have done the whole thing—takes nine seconds. In this universe of the man, at least where the brain is concerned, there is nothing beyond nine seconds. Everything is in nine seconds. It acts, it affects, it cleanses—it does the whole thing.

Today we are going to hit the third stage of the subconscious, the real storage of our antique dirt. You know what I am saying? You know when you get angry what you do? You remember this movement? Have you done this? (*See Exercise 1.*) There is nothing inhuman. Yoga is what we normally do. You will start feeling it in a couple of minutes. Just keep on moving. This is a first stage. We'll develop it stage by stage.

Sometimes I wonder—I learned all these things, and in spite of all the handicaps, life is smooth. But think of those who don't have this, how pressurized life would be. Just imagine. Imagine going to New York without a car and walking on foot. That's how our life is because of this heavy load in our subconscious. Now close your eyes and move faster; move so fast that your whole body shakes. In this first stage, you will get angry. First degree burn, they call it. First degree burn, second degree burn, third is serious, right? Now get first degree angry. Close your eyes, meditate, and get really first degree angry.

I can't do much today, so I am very calm and quiet; but I think you'll understand and you'll do it. It will do the same thing as if I were to yell and scream. You are tied into me. We are in a network now. So don't worry about it and get really angry—first degree angry. I want to see your aura, and I want this aura to be red—not pink—I want it red.

Today we are doing everything anti-God. So if somebody comes from church, he will say, "Oh, my God, Yogiji has gone mad or berserk. God knows what he is doing." But this is what we have to do. We have to face the devil, our own subconscious. You must go stage by stage.

The second stage is very funny, so I just want you to cooperate. Get angry; not hungry, angry! Yeah, get angry! It's fantastic! Don't miss it. It's fun, just do it for fun. Get angry to the first degree. Pretend you are not afraid to see how limited you are. I am limited tonight.

Now, if I read your auras right, you have a ton of it, and you are losing only by square ounces. The question is, why don't you for once just get into it and say, "May I please ask you, Almighty God, who do you think you are? You did me this wrong, you did me that wrong. What the hell do you think, why did you create me?" That's why He is Padre; He is a father. Get mad at that fatherly God. He can't do anything to you, I tell you. Today He is sleeping. Get onto Him; get even with Him. Remember everything you went through and just tell Him, "We worship you, Almighty God, but you didn't make the rain. You did this to me and that to me; you made my mama spank me and my governess spank me for not reading three pages of the Bible every morning. God, what the hell are you?"

Today, even if you are a Jew, get Catholic; become a little bit Catholic and lay the guilt back on God. The subconscious will help you remember, but only if you get into the action. You need a little phobia just to get going. You can't do it in a sane condition. Become a little loony, be a lunatic, and just personify God. Being a lunatic is a good idea. Philosophers, lovers, and lunatics—they all belong to the same category. They are very one-pointed.

Come on, use your force; you have muscle don't you? Your motor system must freak out. As long as the motor system is consistent, the conscious is not asking the subconscious to help. Remember that. Speed up.

Now, listen to me. You see these hands? You see this? This is not a human way to punch; this is actually the Tantric Punch. (*See Exercise 2.*) Imagine that God has come to tell you, "Don't you call me names." And punch Him once, and then again and again, until you are exhausted.

All right, now please put both hands on your heart. (*See Exercise 3.*) Think that there is a God, and you are going to totally take Him in. You are going to suck Him in. The mouth has to be very wide and open, and then you breathe out through the nose. Make the nose like this. Have you seen those Tibetan *Thangkas*? Actually, that's what we are doing. It's very special and effective; they call it a prosperity kriya. Make your nose hard and your mouth big, and inhale God. You'll feel like

Happiness is a fulfillment within one's own lotus of the heart. Head has nothing to do with it.

those shaktis in all those paintings. Big eyes—they go very big and wide, and the nose goes violently nasty, and when you inhale you just inhale the whole God.

All right, now inhale deep. Be calm, quiet, peaceful; inhale deep. Be calm, be quiet, be peaceful. Let the breath go. Concentrate under your hands and bring all the energy to your Heart Center; feel a lotus open. (*See Exercise 4.*)

Now let us concentrate in our heart and let us copy the sound from our Heart Center. (*See Exercise 5.*) Let the petals of the lotus create the sound. Copy the sound with a hard tongue. Use the tongue, hard—tough tongue.

◆ ◆ ◆

May the long time sun shine upon you,
all love surround you, and the pure light within you, guide your way on.

Sat Nam

Well, you have unloaded a lot, but you have more in store than you ever thought. You thought that perhaps doing it once would be enough. Well, anyway, whatever you go through is fine. Now just enjoy your life and have fun! Everything is all right; we will work it out and see you sometime in the near future. Is that a safe statement?

Thank you very much for your cooperation and participation and for not jerking me around. You did a wonderful job. You were all beautiful. It was a heavy thing. You won't understand right now, but somewhere in the middle of the night, we'll meet, and we'll talk about it. Don't worry. It's just a beginning. We are trying to become real American yogis. We are trying to practice the principle: Self-help is the best help. There is a science; there is a procedure. I know sometimes you don't do it one hundred percent; but, you know, what can I do? I can tell you what to do; but the performance is your part, and proportionate performance will get proportionate result. That's the beauty of Kundalini Yoga and Tantric Yoga—it produces on the spot. There is no tomorrow. You don't wait, you don't meet God, you don't think about it. In fact, you can't wait.

All we want is a simple thing. If everything goes wrong with me, just remember what I am telling you now. I have come to conclude two lines, and they are the foundation of everything: Man wants neither God nor religion nor anybody; what man wants is happiness. Happiness is a fulfillment within one's own lotus of the heart. Head has nothing to do with it. But until the storage here is emptied, this cantaloupe that we carry on our shoulders will continue to fill up, because it releases thought forms powerfully and continually and gets us into lots of

situations. We cannot confront even one thing. We keep saying, tomorrow, tomorrow, tomorrow, until the file is full and life goes totally dumb. We make our life so insensitive that we can't even relate to our self, much less to others. We want friendship, we want to love, we want to talk to others, but we can't. Are you kidding?

Happiness—God is happiness. Love is kindness. God is happiness, and the total reality is compassion. Give as a flower gives its fragrance; it obeys no boundary. Giving should not obey any judgment. Flower never says, "You have smelled me, now pay me twenty cents." Does it say that? Never. You spend billions of dollars on fragrances, trying to impress people. If you would just create your own fragrance of compassion and bound not your boundaries, you would be very successful, rich, prosperous, loved, and fulfilled.

What I saw when you were dropping all that garbage, it looked like there was a garbage collector's strike going on for a long time! It was beautiful to see human beings becoming a little subtle, gaining a few feathers and flying, and feeling a little better, feeling good. Some of you say, "I am no good. What am I doing? I didn't . . ." And in spite of that, you were doing it. I mean, that was a beautiful experience, and I enjoyed it. Enjoy that sometime, that *Mahabharata*, that big fight you have with your ego and with your self. When the self wins, that's all—that's the only purpose. Once self starts winning, life becomes happier.

There is no nobility more than self; there is no reality more than self; and there is no God more than self. If God could have created anything better than you, God should have, must have, and would have. The guy didn't know better—that's it. God could only create you. You are neurotic, you are rotten, you are bad, you are this, you are that, but that's what He did. If He did a bad job, then what's the problem? He did His job, and you don't have to worry about it. It's not your job; it's not your problem if you are bad.

Please, like a flower gives a fragrance, give yourself a chance, just a chance. Trust yourself, love yourself, and be yourself. Repeat those three things.

I trust myself, I love myself, I am myself. Come on, you know English. You take a pledge in Chinese? Raise your right hand and put your other hand on your heart. Close your eyes and become really good. Say it for your own sake.

Students: I trust myself, I love myself, I am myself.

I believe you. Thank you.

CLEARING OUR SUBCONSCIOUS STORIES
—THE KRIYA

December 6, 1988

There are no breaks between the exercises. Move immediately from one exercise to the next.

1. Bring the hands up in front of the body at ear level. Extend the Jupiter (index) finger of each hand and "wag" the fingers. The movement is generated from the wrist; alternate the hands, left and right. After **2 minutes**, close the eyes and begin moving faster; move so quickly that your whole body shakes. Get angry!
Continue for **11 minutes total**.

Guided Meditation

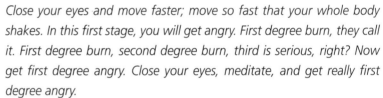

Close your eyes and move faster; move so fast that your whole body shakes. In this first stage, you will get angry. First degree burn, they call it. First degree burn, second degree burn, third is serious, right? Now get first degree angry. Close your eyes, meditate, and get really first degree angry.

Get that anger out! Just point at God Almighty, "Hey, You, the Big One!" The object is to hit the Highest One, and God is highest in our thoughts, so get to Him. This is what we have to do. I am translating the scriptures now: Imagine Almighty God around you. Close your eyes and become a light, bigger than God, and tell Him with your index finger, the finger of Apollo, the finger of Jupiter, what the hell He is and that you don't care. You have to do it consciously. I am sorry to have to teach you this. It's not a very good thing for the believers, but that's how the subconscious works.

Personify the whole universe, the creation of God, and just say, "What the hell are you doing?" Don't get angry at little people: human beings, brothers and sisters, neighbors, creatures. Instead, try to effectively get angry at God and pretend that you are not afraid. Pretend you are not afraid. Pretend you are not afraid, and you don't care what God can do. If God kills you, then still you are within God. If God doesn't kill you, then you are within God as well. God is within and without; therefore, pretend powerfully and project forcefully and get mad! Get angry. Get it out. You will release so much garbage that you can't even understand. It's a simple theory. It has nothing to do with me and you. It is a simple physical act. If you perform better, it will do better; if you perform slower, it will do nothing.

God is a Father; get mad at that fatherly God. Get even with Him, get angry, get really tight. Pretend to be very, very, very mad. There is no better hypnosis than this self-hypnotic state in which you have to create your own God—huge, bigger, biggest, Infinity—and you, the little finite creature, are going to tell Him off. I mean, really tell Him off! "Why did you do this to me? Why did you do that to me?" Get on with it! Get even with Him! Today is the day, through all incarnations, through all Samskaras, through all karmas, to get friendly with confronting God and to forget about fear. No fear! Get even with Him today, doesn't matter what. Remember everything you went through and just tell Him: "You created me, you didn't give me this, you didn't give me that. What kind of God you are? Who the hell are you?" Come on, let's go.

Remember everything that God did to you and get even, period. What you will get is a clean self, with no fear. Can you believe how beautiful that will be? Let me tell you, God is so big, He won't mind. He won't! He is very big, huge, very compassionate, kind, compensating. Come on. Get even with Him and face Him. "You gave me a dirty brother, you gave me a dirty mama, you gave me a dirty papa, you gave me a dirty dog, you took away my blue dog and my pink dress and God knows what." Whatever has hurt you, get even with Him today. Really get even. This is the day. "'Why did you make me a girl? Why did you make me a woman? Why didn't you make me this or that? Why didn't you do this for me? Why didn't you come to my rescue?" Do Him in. Remember everything—everything that can make you angry— and make God responsible. Lay the guilt back on God; the subconscious will help you remember. But you need a little action, you need a little phobia, a little fury and a little madness, a little anger to just get going. Ask God why He did to you what you don't like. "What's wrong with Him? Why couldn't He give the lottery to everybody and have fun? Why couldn't everyone get twenty thousand dollars a day and the matter ends? Why does anybody have to be poor? Why did He even create a belly? Why do I have to eat and get fat?"

Just keep on moving: heavy, strong, authoritative, and authentic. Act as though you are really doing it. Don't act like it's just an exercise—that's the problem; in exercises we say move your fingers, but I didn't say that. I said, just do it as normally as a human being can. With your hands, just tell somebody what is what. Use the left finger, right finger, doesn't matter. But just keep on doing it. It will be effective, and you will start feeling the weight of your fingers. It is all in the magnetic field, that's how the brain will start evaluating it. Your motor system must freak out. As long as the motor system is consistent, the consciousness is not asking the subconscious to help.

2. Tantric Punch: Close the eyes and place the tip of the thumb between the Jupiter (index) and Saturn (middle) fingers. Begin punching, alternating left and right in a moderate to quick pace. Use force for **2½ minutes**.

Guided Comments

Imagine that God has come near you to tell you, "Don't call me names." Give Him one punch, and then the other; get going until you are exhausted. It will immediately start relaxing your body. It will give you a kind of relief. Punch Him. Punch Him for all the injustice, all the unwanted action and reaction, all those sad and bad memories: the lover who did not take you to dinner, the husband who didn't come home, the letter that arrived late. It will give you a beautiful relief.

3. Place the hands over the Heart Center, left hand over the right, thumbs extended up, fingers parallel. Right fingers face toward the left; left fingers face toward the right. Inhale through a wide, open, rounded mouth with a look of surprise on your face, eyes open wide, brow lifted. Exhale through the nose. Crinkle the nose as you exhale with an angry expression on the face. Eyes and mouth remain wide throughout the cycle of the breath.
Continue for **4½ minutes**.
TO END: Inhale deep and suspend the breath for 10–15 seconds. Be calm and peaceful. Exhale. Take a few quick deep breaths.

In Tibet, this is a prosperity kriya. Inhale the whole God. Eat Him up, gulp Him up, get Him all in. Exhale and make a very nasty, angry nose. It will give you a lot of relief. It will give you a different state of mind and attitude. Get Him all in and get the anger out.

4. Maintaining the mudra, concentrate and bring all the energy to the Heart Center. Begin the guided meditation. After **12½ minutes**, begin the gong meditation and continue the guided visualization for **12½ minutes**. This exercise is **25 minutes total**.

Guided Meditation

Feel a lotus flower open at the Heart Center. Concentrate and find what color your flower is. This flower will have a color; it is the color of your personality. Every person will have a different color; it cannot be dictated. Whatever that color is, that's your gemstone, that's you. (Not gemstone in the sense that you are going to go out and buy it to-morrow, but just your gemstone.) In your heart, imagine hypnotically, through thought form or through meditation, a flower, a bud, opening up into a blossom; a bud opening into a blossom, and it has a color. Which color is it? You should see it. It can be any color, but it shall have one color. Concentrate. Don't worry about failure; the number of times we have failed in life doesn't matter. The important thing is to just succeed once. Just get to it, concentrate. If you have any technique to do that, do it.

Close your eyes, concentrate your energy, close your eyes, concentrate your energy, close your eyes, concentrate, concentrate, relax, relax, relax, relax, relax, relax, relax, relax like the dead.

Relax. Open up the lotus of the heart, open up the lotus of the heart, open up the lotus of the heart, open up the lotus of the heart. All your tragedies will go away, all your problems will go away. Your reality, your best, will come out of you. All the best in the universe and the Mother Earth will come and serve you. Opportunities will come to you. Open the lotus of the heart, open the lotus of the heart; concentrate, recognize the color.

Everybody can do it; just concentrate. Just a little bit, a little bit more. Feel it. Think about it. Meditate on it. Open the lotus of the heart, open the lotus of the heart. The bud will start opening, and your state, your attitude, your mind, your luck will start changing right under your two hands—the miracle right under your two hands. Give yourself a chance; one chance, one chance. Open up the lotus of your heart. Today every man will sing and pray, and in that prayer just open the lotus of the heart; see its color for yourself. Concentrate.

It is there, don't ignore it unconsciously; see it subconsciously. Close your eyes and go into your Heart Center and use your subconscious. Open the lotus of the heart, concentrate. I pray for you, you pray for me, we pray for all, all pray for us; but it's all a matter of heart. Open the lotus of the heart.

continued next page

Guided Meditation — continued

If you have never meditated, never concentrated, still do it. There is no chance for failure, just concentrate; it will all happen. Please try it sincerely and open the lotus of the heart. Forget everything; relax from everything. You have to live—you need the friendship, the strength, the fragrance of the heart. Any flower that does not bud and blossom has no fragrance. Remember that rule. Nature has its own rule. Blossom. Open the lotus of the heart. Open it up. You have to have a substitute. You have unloaded so much subconscious fear, now you have to give it a beauty, a joy, and an everlasting happiness—create it. Go through it.

Please. Give yourself a chance. Don't let your mind play games with you. Don't let it divert you. The subconscious is under attack. We want to clean out all the garbage; but it will start playing all its tricks. It will take the body into different directions. It will itch, it will hurt, it will make you nervous, it will get cramps, it will do anything. Don't be part of that. Just open the lotus of the heart.

Under your hands feel the burst of the sun, burst of the sun, vast blue shining skies and a huge burst of the sun—the light, the warmth. Like fragrance from the flower, we are now going to fly away. In waves, in waves, we'll give you the supporting strength of the wave, one and one quarter circle into seven is the rhythm. We'll give you the wavelength, and the fragrance of the flower moves on that wavelength. Please start flowing with the fragrance of the flower.

Gong Meditation Begins

Like little ghosts full of fragrance and light—transparent—fly there in wavelengths. Touch the frontiers that you can't even imagine. Go as far as you can, space to space, galaxy to galaxy, millennium to millennium, beyond the beyond to yonder land. Come, my love, to infinity. Become the fragrance of the flower of the heart. Smell your flower, your fragrance, with your physical nose. It's a reality—smell it. Give, like the flower, your fragrance to all. Smell the flower of your own Self. Like a shining spirit in the breeze, let the blossom float away. Smell it, enjoy it, get intoxicated in it.

Let your flower get the smell, taste it, feel it, enjoy it. Let your memory release, memory release, memory release, memory release the fragrance. Let your memory, your memory, your memory release, release, release the fragrance. Let your memory, memory, memory release, release the fragrance. Let your memory, memory, memory release the fragrance. Let your memory, memory, memory, memory release, release, release the fragrance. Let your, let your, let your, let your, let your, let your, memory, memory, memory, memory, memory, release, release, release, release, the fragrance. Fragrance, fragrance, fragrance.

Now sit in your own heart, the moving, pulsating heart. Vibrate, vibrate, vibrate, vibrate, vibrate, vibrate, vibrate, vibrate, vibrate, vibrate, vibrate, vibrate, vibrate, vibrate. Penetrate. Vibrate.

5. Maintain the mudra and begin chanting with *Rakhe Rakhanhaar* by Singh Kaur. Chant with the sound. Gong meditation continues over the music for **4 minutes**.

Let us concentrate in our heart and let us copy the sound from our Heart Center. Let the petals of the lotus create the sound. Chant with a stiff tongue.

TO END: Inhale and suspend the breath while the gong is silenced. Exhale.

**Rakhay rakhanhaar aap ubaarian
Gur kee pairee paa-eh kaaj savaarian
Hoaa aap dayaal manho na visaarian
Saadh janaa kai sang bhavjal taarian
Saakat nindak dusht khin maa-eh bidaarian
Tis saahib kee tayk naanak manai maa-eh
Jis simrat sukh ho-eh saglay dookh jaa-eh**

*God Himself is looking out for me,
Gives me the light, and takes care of my affairs.
God is merciful, and never forgets me.
God guides me, giving me good people to help me.
God does not allow any harm to come to me.
I take comfort in the thought of God.
When I remember God, I feel peaceful and
happy and all my pain departs.*

Affirmation

After the kriya and The Long Time Sun blessing, Yogi Bhajan taught this affirmation practice:

Like the flower gives a fragrance, give yourself a chance, just a chance, to trust yourself, love yourself, and be yourself. Repeat three times: "Trust yourself, love yourself, and be yourself."

Now, close your eyes, raise your right hand, and place your left hand on your heart and take a vow: "I trust myself, I love myself, I am myself."

◆

" Seeing you, who I love—seeing you small, seeing you suffer, seeing you not use your capacity, your capabilities, seeing you not take care of your life, seeing that you do not have the vastness and the strength to deal with life is more painful than living. "

- *Yogi Bhajan*

ANGELIC GHOSTING

December 11, 1988

THERE'S NO QUESTION THAT I WANT TO TEACH, but neither is there a question that they don't want me to teach for medical reasons. There is a risk involved. I agree I am not well; I am seriously ill. But I am not worried about that; my sickness is not so bad. I may die physically, but that's all it can do. It can't do anything more. But seeing you, who I love, seeing you small, seeing you suffer, seeing you not use your capacity, your capabilities, seeing you not take care of your life, seeing that you do not have the vastness and the strength to deal with life is more painful than living. I don't think I should be concerned. Maybe I am doing a commercial for you, who knows?

Do you know how stupid and terrible a situation you create when, as a human being, you cannot live in harmony, you cannot communicate, you cannot keep the promises you make—when you do not deliver what you are supposed to deliver? Do you think it's all a joke? No, it's not. You are the children of the commotional self. Do you know why you want to love? Do you have any understanding? We are born in love, we die in love, and we can live in love. So why is love so important to you? Why is making a trauma important to you? Why is creating a drama important to you? Why are yelling and screaming important to you? Why is getting angry important to you? Why is getting depressed important to you? Why are apathy and sympathy important to you? Why is anything important to you?

You know you are dead. You do not feel alive. That's the absolute Gospel truth. I understand I am dying, but who cares. You know what death is? Nothing. But after death, I am alive. You are dead when alive. What choice is left? After all, I am a teacher; I am not just hocus-pocus. But I cannot see my people totally depressed, anguished, and angry—all that stuff.

I don't want to blame you, because I know the reality. This is the science: a quarter-ounce weight is created by one thought. One thought is equal to one-quarter ounce by weight. And in one wink of the eye, this brain produces one thousand thoughts. Just add up the weight during the day. How much weight do you live under? It's a simple science. What do we need? We need power, we need strength, we need grit to face our life, to be real with ourselves, because reality will make us face it. What bothers me most is when you are a Ph.D. or an M.D., you are professionally successful, and you have all the money in the world, you live in a twentieth-story penthouse—but even with all that, one day you cannot get up and

You are the children of the commotional self. ... Why is making a trauma important to you? Why is creating a drama important to you? Why are yelling and screaming important to you? Why is getting angry important to you? Why is getting depressed important to you? Why are apathy and sympathy important to you?

tie your tie or put your pajamas on at night. I have seen those rich people who, in terms of money, have everything at the push of a button, everything at their command. Press the button and this will happen, press the button and that will happen. But they are such babies, such extremely emotional babies, that you hate them.

I have also seen rich people who are so afraid that their anxiety attacks have reached the point at which they're worse than a heart attack. Even somebody who has a two thousand-square-foot office in New York, all to himself, you know what I am saying? Some people do not even have a house that big. There are paintings, there are things, and there are staff and all that, but just one little thing can trigger a kind of death spell. People live, people die—doesn't matter. But not being you is more painful than anything else.

You can't communicate—you can't! To communicate, to create understanding, you need three things: a clear head, a radiant heart, and an honest trust within you. Forget about God and religion and you and your success; forget about everything, because without these three things, you do not even become a human being. The problem is with this load, this mental load. What you don't achieve, you don't achieve automatically; it's automated. Automatically you release these thoughts, and automatically you store them in the subconscious.

After twenty years of teaching, I have found that you do not meditate. It's very painful to me. Whenever I talk to you about meditation, you say good things about it. But, no, you are dead wrong. Meditation brings up absolutely all the floating garbage stored in the subconscious. Now, if you take me into a garbage pit and tell me this is the best restaurant in the world, should I believe that? I mean, you are just making a fool of me when you tell me meditation is great. No meditation can be great. Meditation means nothing more than going into the shower and cleaning your stink out. That's what meditation is. Meditation is a process. Meditation is not a religion. Meditation is not necessary or unnecessary. But your children will suffer, you are suffering, your parents have suffered, and this country will suffer, because we do not start the day with a clean mind. We only start the day with a clean body.

Suppose there is a house, and on the outside, it has very well-decorated grounds, and the fence is right, and the walls are sound. But once you go inside, it's just a pit, a big pit. How would you like that? Do you understand the difference? Imagine a person who looks very beautiful, very pretty—she opens her mouth, and after the third minute, you want to vomit. All that makeup and all that glory and all that beauty—but the moment the person opens her mouth, after five minutes, you want to run. You want to open the window and jump out. But you are wrong there. Do you know why? Because your body has strength, but your mind has nothing.

I was in the hospital with spaghetti all around me. There was not one artery, not one vein, where that needle was not in. Oh God, it was horrible. Three machines on this side, three on that side; this monitors this and that monitors that; every nurse coming by. It was fun. Later on, one nurse came to check on me to see whether I was okay. She sat down and said, "Hello, how are you? Do you know why I have come? I want to know who are you."

"Wait a minute. I am a heart patient, that's what I am, no big deal. I had a problem with my arteries, and we did an angioplasty, which freaked out and I kind of died."

"No, no, I am asking—who are you?"

"Just a human being, no big deal. Nothing more."

"I have dealt with many patients, but there is not one patient who has brought his kind of guru and his kind of music, the whole thing; and you even had it in the intensive care. Anyway," she said, "I have come to apologize."

"What for?"

"I was the one who gave you the morphine so that you could sleep that night. And you got up at two o'clock, tearing up all that spaghetti, everything got pulled out and . . ."

"I told you before you were giving it to me that it's my body's natural response. At a certain time, I should meditate. I told you don't do it, but it was 'doctor's orders,' so you stuck me in my thigh and it hurt terribly. It's blue even today."

One thing I also learned in that hospital, which I want to share with you today, is this: They want you to rest and sleep, but every half an hour, they come and stick a needle in your butt or in your veins. It's true. I was just there, and I learned what real nursing, caring, and loving in all your daily home needs is like. This is how you actually live! You live exactly as I lived in that hospital. That's exactly how you live. That's exactly how you fight.

You know where we betray God? God gave us this life to live, but we are just pretending to live. We only believe that we are living. Forgive me for this frankness—God knows whether I'll get up tomorrow or not. But who cares? So let me tell you in your language, because holy language you don't understand. You are just stupid stone heads, and do you know why? I'll tell you one thing: You should be very successful; you should be so successful that you make everybody you touch successful; your touch should make the difference, or you are just nothing. But the problem with you is that you don't understand that God has made us to live, and we should enjoy it.

This presumption that I have to live betrays God. You have overloaded your circuits so badly that even if you are dead or alive, it doesn't matter; you betray God, you slap His face. You talk of God, but let me tell you what religion is; let me

tell you today. You are very lucky. You know what religion is? Religion uses fear to get your money so that you can be good before God. What do we use? We push you—and get your money—so that you can be good before your self. That's the difference between this religion and everything else.

We get money, that's true; and we say, definitely, that *dasvandh* belongs to Guru and not to you. If you don't pay, you are stupid. We say it frankly, and we expect everybody to give *dasvandh*. We are not upset about it. Not that it is a good thing or a bad thing—no. We feel that one-tenth of what you earn you must pay.

If you have a head of the religion who is a stupid idiot, then that's your bad karma. If it's good, then things will grow; all right—that's your choice. But one-tenth of the money doesn't belong to you and one-tenth of the time doesn't belong to you. That's why we say meditate, do sadhana. It's not that sadhana is nonessential, nor should somebody say with pride, "I do my sadhana." Some people say, "It is my twentieth day of sadhana." I say, "Oh, my God, you should have been born in England, working in the coal mines. They never took a bath because they thought if they got their spine wet, they'd go weak. In your whole life, twenty days you clean your mind, and the rest of the time you are an ugly, dirty, stinking idiot." Have you ever lived in a house that for one year was never cleaned? Have you ever shaken hands with somebody who for the past six months never took a bath? You live in a most beautiful, decorative, motivated, and pretty body, but with a grizzly stinking mind.

I don't blame you. I know you, which is why I agree that it is not right for me to teach my wife that she will be sorry her husband is dead, or my sons that they will be sorry their father is dead, or my spiritual son that he will be sorry his counselor is dead. To hell with it! Seeing you in pain and tragedy, seeing you not going to sadhana, seeing you clogged up just like my arteries—how is that living? It is better to die as a teacher trying to do my best. So today we are not doing any monkey games. If you are not interested in this class, you can get up and leave. It's very hard, number one; it's not a child's game. It's a very hard class, and you are going to go through the hell of it. So do not blame me. But if you have any reservations, if you feel that you do not want to unload the junk, then go. Some people love it; I know that.

I know of a very, very great multimillionaire who lives in New York. You can ask him anything about himself, from the day he became Mister Somebody to this day, because all those newspapers are totally stored. He doesn't want to throw away newspapers. When I discussed it with him, I said, "Why does this matter to you? Just call the newspaper and ask for the information you want, or tie up with the entire news media through the computer's general information center and . . ."

"Is that so easy?" he asked.

"Paying rent for thirty rooms in New York just to store newspaper doesn't make sense. It looks ridiculous to me. You have some kind of phobia. What do you want these newspapers for? Your insurance has tripled because there is a fire threat; the maintenance is so difficult. You have so many, and yet you never refer to them. You store every newspaper, everyday!"

Then I thought of my students. They do the same thing. You store, contain, maintain, and keep a lot of junk in your subconscious. Well, we are going to get rid of it. We are going to get rid of certain life tragedies and certain years only. So are you ready? Can we go through it now?

Angelic is a very old phenomena. Angelic Ghosting, they call it—it is totally a Christian thing. It was my first psychology class—go, admit, confess, get re-deemed, do certain things. I mean, what is that confession? It simply relieves the burden from your subconscious. For centuries, religions have lasted because man found out that it's not possible to live happily. The purpose of life is happiness, and they believe religion has to give you happiness. But discipline gives you happiness, sadhana gives you happiness, commitment gives you happiness. We are not running a cloth shop that says we have to tie this on our head—that's not true. We don't believe God. We don't love God. We have nothing to do with God except this: We trust God in us, and we trust God in everybody. That's what this religion is about. This religion is not about jokes. It's real. This religion is simple: Live as thy higher Self. But you cannot live as your higher Self by just any method. Look, I am fifty-nine years old. I am an internationally recognized holy man, and I just want to make no hole in your life. I just want to tell you something, God is experienced by those who experience within themselves their own Self.

Today we are going to get rid of a lot of subconscious garbage. I am not going to charge you five hundred dollars for your previous life, though you'll go through it. Neither am I going to charge you one thousand dollars for telling you your future. I have no such phenomena, no such reason, to be with you. All I want you to do is unload your . . . but I am a holy man, and I cannot use that word. All I will say is unload your unwanted, is that an agreement? This class is very hard, but when you go through the unloading, you will feel such a delight that all the ice cream you could want will look like nothing. But before that, it will be nothing but green chilies roasted on the fire. Hallelujah! Let us be with it, all right?

You store, contain, maintain, and keep a lot of junk in your subconscious. Well, we are going to get rid of it.

◆ ◆ ◆

Come on, let's prepare ourselves; this is all just preparation. (*See Exercise 1.*) Three-stroke breath through the mouth and one stroke out; open your mouth. The jaw is very important. First you have to learn to open your mouth, and then you have to take three strokes. When you control the breath, your past, present, and future get into a confrontation. I am explaining the science of it so that in your life you can understand it.

This is a lotus; you have to keep it like a lotus flower. Make your hand into a flower; good, very good. Now, the hands need to become the fastest things on Earth. You have to move the whole body fast. With so many of you, this should be shaking like an earthquake. Move the whole body. Get out all the tension; don't stop! It is not crazy what we are doing; it is required. You are crazy anyway, so what is wrong in acting it today? Don't forget your trade. Do it right!

Please remember—there is nothing much you have to do here. Open your eyes and watch my hands. (*See Exercise 3.*) Just get lost. Deep, deep, deep, deep, deep, deeply relax. Come on—highest prayers.

The *tattvas* are adjusting; the body wants to sleep. I know the whole thing. I used to do it, remember? Just deeply relax, relax, relax, relax. Put your hands in your lap. (*See Exercise 4.*) Totally relax now, think nothing. Just think nothing; totally relax.

Start copying the sound. (*See Exercise 5.*) Don't sing. Copy the sound. Copy the rhythm. Repeat the sound. Exactly repeat it. Repeat the sound—it doesn't matter what it is. Feel it, feel it.

Now please concentrate at the Heart Center and use all the force to manipulate and create the sound within the ribcage (*see Exercise 6*), between the seventh and ninth ribs. The direct channel to God is between the seventh and ninth rib, from the top toward the bottom. Concentrate and create the sound from there.

Let the energy go everywhere; let it heal the system and take care of you.

May the long time sun shine upon you,
all love surround you, and the pure light within you, guide your way on.

Sat Nam

Very good. Now, we don't have beds here to sleep, but it's all okay. All you can do is go home and sleep. No intercourse tonight. I'm sorry to tell you that, because it's practically possible that tonight you will be very horny. I understand. But we'll not do it. Is that okay? I think the only thing I can request of you is to say hello to each other and smile at each other and pick up your stuff and get out of here as fast as you can and go home and go to bed. This night will take care of itself, whatever it has for you. You don't have to do anything more because you have already started. Get out and just go to bed as fast as you can.

ANGELIC GHOSTING—THE KRIYA

December 11, 1988

There are no breaks between the exercises. Move immediately from one exercise to the next.

1. With the elbows tucked into the sides, bring the hands in front of the shoulders. Make your hand into a flower. Extend the wrist so that the hand is at a 45-degree angle, palms up, with the fingers spread. Open the mouth wide, drop the jaw, and inhale through the mouth in a three-stroke breath. Exhale one stroke through the nose. The mouth will naturally close. The inhalation is very short and precise, quick and forceful. The three-stroke inhalation takes roughly the same length of time as the one-stroke exhalation. Continue for **3 minutes**.

When you control your inhalation, when you eat the breath in three strokes, your past, present, and future get into a confrontation. Then you exhale it through the nose.

2. Continue the breath pattern, maintain the mudra, and begin circling the hands. This is a vigorous, powerful movement from the elbow. The entire forearm moves while the wrist remains stable; the entire body should move as a result of the hands. Continue for **3½ minutes**.

The building should be shaking like an earthquake with so many of you. Spine, nervous system, body, organ, circulation—the whole thing—move powerfully. Don't cheat. Use the whole body; don't stop. Get the inherited tension out of your system. Get it out! Get this tension out. Don't stop for anybody.

3. Bring the hands 6–9 inches to each side of the head, at the level of the ears, palms facing forward. Look through closed eyes at the tip of the nose. Fold the four fingers down toward the palm and then open them; thumbs stay out. Deeply relax. Go at a moderate pace—approximately 25 repetitions every 15 seconds. After **3 minutes**, begin the visualization:

Guided Meditation

Start feeling the womb of the mother. Get into the womb of the mother and survey it. Feel, imagine, hypnotize yourself, concentrate, force—whatever word you want to use. Be in the womb of your mother. Look at the world around you, from within the womb of the mother, through the skin of the belly. Look at the outside world from the womb of the mother. Penetrate, concentrate, and please look at it.

Now from the womb of the mother become a ghost—a ghost of light, a holy ghost. Become a holy ghost and start planning. Create a blueprint for how you are going to live on Earth; ghost to host your life on the planet Earth. The entire teaching of the Christian church is based on the Holy Ghost. Try to become one today. Become a holy ghost. Pass through the body of Christ, up in the heavens, and plan; imprint how you want to live on Earth. That is your free will. Dream, imagine, forget what you are; be who you what to be. Dream, dream, dream, dream, dream; blueprint, blueprint, blueprint, blueprint; imagine, imagine, imagine, imagine. Pull all the records of your imagination and of your subconscious and revise it. Read it, revise it, go through it, go fast. Keep going.

Now, come back, back to the womb. Come back to the womb. Get born and start reading, reading, and memorizing. Read your memories— both bad and good. Day by day, week by week, month by month, year by year, systematic, step by step. Just read your memory.

After **11 minutes**, the gong meditation begins; continues **12½ minutes**. *We are giving you the creative sound of the gong to give you the penetration you need to get into the depth of your subconscious. Get into your subconscious, the library of the being, and read your pain and your pleasures. Read your pain and your pleasure—get to work.*
This exercise is **23½ minutes total**.

Every mother who wants a successful child should let her child, by her own mental power, see the world that he must face. She should do this for 31 minutes every day, from the 120th day to the time of delivery. None of you do that. That's why your children are born and know nothing of what they are entering into.

4. Inhale deeply and release the hands in the lap, one hand resting in the other, thumb tips touching. Totally relax; think nothing. The gong continues for **5 minutes**.

Go into the self-hypnotic stage; empty yourself. Give it away to the All, to the Goodwill, the Salvation Army, to anyone you can lay a hand on. Clean it out! Relax deeply, relax deeply, deeply relax. If you can deeply relax now, you shall generate deep roots in happiness; you can nurture yourself new. Let yourself go. Time won't hurt you; let yourself go. Space won't get you; let yourself go. Let it go. Go, go, go! Go, go, go, go! Let yourself go!

5. Maintain the mudra and begin to copy the sound of *Flowers in the Rain* and *Walking up the Mountain* by Gurudass Singh. Copy the rhythm. Don't sing; just copy the sounds. After **5 minutes**, the gong is silenced. Chant for **15 minutes total**. *(See Appendix for lyric sheets.)*

6. The hands remain in the lap. Concentrate at the Heart Center as the gong is played. After **2 minutes**, repeat the words of *Rakhe Rakhanhar* by Singh Kaur from your heart, from your seventh and ninth ribs. This exercise is a total of **9 minutes**.

If you concentrate and try to create the word from between the seventh and ninth ribs, then that word shall be listened to directly. Between the seventh and ninth ribs is a direct channel to God. If you concentrate and create the sound from there, you'll be surprised. You'll begin to understand what deep concentration and relaxation and communication you can have. Please try to concentrate and then repeat these words right from there—the seventh and ninth rib—and on to infinity.

Rakhay rakhanhaar aap ubaarian
Gur kee pairee paa-eh kaaj savaarian
Hoaa aap dayaal manho na visaarian
Saadh janaa kai sang bhavjal taarian
Saakat nindak dusht khin maa-eh bidaarian
Tis saahib kee tayk naanak manai maa-eh
Jis simrat sukh ho-eh saglay dookh jaa-eh

God Himself is looking out for me,
Gives me the light, and takes care of my affairs.
God is merciful, and never forgets me.
God guides me, giving me good people to help me.
God does not allow any harm to come to me.
I take comfort in the thought of God.
When I remember God, I feel peaceful and happy and all my pain departs.

TO END: Inhale deeply. Suspend the breath for up to **30 seconds** as you shake your body from toe to top. Let the energy go everywhere. Heal the system that takes care of you. Exhale. Inhale again, suspend the breath up to **30 seconds**, and let every part of you shake up. Move powerfully; use all your force. Exhale. Inhale again and suspend the breath for **10 seconds** and then relax.

Go home and sleep; no intercourse tonight. I'm sorry to tell you that it is practically possible, because you will be very aroused. I understand. But please don't do it. Rest.

" There is a very strange thing that I have learned by talking to some people in the past few days. They think it is the responsibility of somebody else to tell you how to be good, how to be rich, how to be nice. Forget it. Nobody told me how to be anything. I went. I found a teacher. I learned. I listened. I practiced. I went through the pain. "

– Yogi Bhajan

UNLOADING THE SUBCONSCIOUS

December 13, 1988

THE IDEA IS NOT TO TEACH YOU A CLASS; the idea is to take the garbage out. I don't care if you people come to classes or not anymore. My feeling is, I am not well, I am not healthy, and medically they warned me not to teach. On the other hand, I can't see sick people going around with a lot of junk. You are all junkies. I don't know why you have not been told that it is a mental responsibility for you to see your life through your own clarity—not what other people counsel you, not what other people tell you. There is a very strange thing that I have learned by talking to some people in the past few days. They think it is the responsibility of somebody else to tell you how to be good, how to be rich, how to be nice. Forget it. Nobody told me how to be anything. I went. I found a teacher. I learned. I listened. I practiced. I went through the pain. What is this? On one hand you talk liberty, infinity, and this and that, and on the other, me and mine. The problem I see with you people is that you have so much insensitivity; you've developed so much insensitivity.

I want to tell you something, and I want you to calculate it. You think you are great, but let me tell you how this universe works. God is funny. Anyone with a calculator can do it. Let us say the least—one wink means one ounce. We release one thousand thoughts per wink of the eye. Let me repeat—one wink releases one thousand thoughts. Each thought has a weight, called psychomobile weight. It is a physical weight. Each thought produces a psychophenomenon, which has a potential weight of a quarter ounce. A quarter ounce is the weight of the soul when it leaves the body. So a quarter ounce is the only thing Edison and all those people, those scientists, have found. Let us put it together. A thousand times a quarter ounce comes to what? We have two hundred fifty ounces per wink of the eye. And during the day, how many minutes are in a day? Twenty-four hours times sixty minutes; sixty minutes multiplied by however many seconds there are—so thirty-six thousand ounces in the whole day. No, no, I mean twenty four hours. Let's work it out.

Multiply it by a quarter ounce; how many tons does it come to? It comes to certain tons. I know. When I was taught, I knew; we used to calculate it ourselves. Okay, divide by sixteen. What does that bring? Thirteen hundred and fifty pounds. It means you produce thirteen hundred and fifty pounds of psychophenomenon without doing a thing. Without doing anything! How many miles a day do we

move without moving? What was that calculation? Without moving, you move thousands of miles. The galaxy and our star and our Earth—the whole thing is moving. So everybody moves and that much psychophenomenon you produce a day. That is the weight you carry without doing anything. Out of all those thoughts you produce, one thought perhaps becomes a feeling; and then one of those feelings becomes an emotion; and one of the emotions becomes a desire; one of the desires becomes an objective; and from one of these objectives—out of one hundred thousands objectives—you become creative; and one creative act, out of the one hundred thousand potentials, you accomplish.

Now, where does the rest go? That is the situation. The rest goes into the subconscious. It gets so overloaded that you get dreams, daydreams. You think you are thinking, but thinking is nothing but a dream: *Jagarat supat sucupat turiya*. There are four stages of mind: *Jagarat* means "awakened"; *supat* means "dream." We dream twenty three and a half hours a day. Nobody on this planet sleeps more than thirty one minutes—period. You can't. That sleep when you do not know you are a man or a woman, good or bad, alive or dead is called *turiya*. When *turiya* becomes *chittar turiya*, that is what a saint does. He sleeps. Leaves the body, goes and sees the inside world, and serves and helps, and does the job. That is called *chittar turiya*. But normally *turiya* is thirty one minutes in twenty four hours. First you go to bed, then you curl around and you read the newspaper, and you doze, and you go and sleep; and that first stage is called getting comfortable. And then you move around. You move at night between seven to sometimes seventy times to adjust a posture. I don't know. In the old days, I don't think people had to work; they were only observing what people do and how the mind works. These days nobody has time. It is an antique thing.

First, there was the carousel—the horses and ducks and elephants and dogs, whatever; that was for children, to let them know how the waves of life move. Just to teach them, to give them practical experience. That is how the carousel was first considered. Not that they were riding horses; it was just giving them that experience. Now even that experience is gone. One horse from one carousel was sold for ninety two thousand dollars. I freaked out. It was handmade, God knows. But people go crazy.

However, life cannot move. Life cannot move; day cannot move. You move on either the biorhythm or the anti-biorhythm. You do not move any other way. Your day starts when you first open your eyes, not when you finally wake up. Even if you are a blind person, you are only considered awake when you open your eyes. At that moment, you make a decision and that is your decision—not mine.

You decide whether you want to go with your biorhythm—north pole or south pole—that is it. If you start your day with a biorhythm, the day will be up and down. Vibrations mean up and down. It cannot be straight. There is no such thing as straight. So there is a biorhythm, and either you go with the biorhythm and experience a day of achievement, or you don't—and if you don't, that will be a day of deadly confrontation. You don't get to decide what your secretary told you last night or what you think today. That is not possible. That is why we meditate and we chant to God. It is a selfish thing. It has nothing to do with God. God has no time to see; He's not going to come down here and see whether you meditate or not, you are good or bad. Who cares?

What is this planet Earth? A little thing on which there are about five billion plus two hundred million souls stuffed in. What does five million souls mean? Anything? Nothing. So in the vicinity of divinity, your importance is hardly equal to one dropping of a pigeon. That is what the scriptures say. If the value of the entire planet Earth and its importance is equal to the dropping of a pigeon, one dropping of the pigeon, and the line is that you have to go through it and experience it without getting dirty in it—that is all they say. They don't say good things about planet Earth. There are other stars and other galaxies where life is very important and very possible, and the intelligence and sensitivity are much, much more than we have. But we have here a most enjoyable thing. It is called interlock of commotions. No, please understand. Interlock of commotions is the only thing that is both undesirable but most desirable. If your commotions are not interlocked, then there is no commitment.

There is a very popular saying that my grandfather used to say, which I have heard all my life. He used to say, "You don't need a committee for commitment. That is something private and personal."

I once asked him, "What do we mean by commitment?"

"Interpret it the way you want to."

"Grandpa, I am six years old. I want to know from you."

"That is what I am telling you; interpret it the way you want it."

"Please explain what you are telling me."

"The commitment—the way you want to interpret it—it has to have a frequency. Let us put it at the frequency you want it. If you give it the highest value, your commitment will become pure; then God will work for you. If you give it the lowest value, then God will spank you. But God shall not be silent in any life, because every vibration has to interlock itself with the basic, central biorhythm called God."

Between the unconscious and the conscious there is a subconscious. Conscious is good and unconscious is good, but when subconscious gets overloaded, it starts coming through. Deadly dreams, wet dreams, dry dreams, yellow dreams, black dreams... Meditation is when you clean the garbage out of your subconscious.

Religion has done the greatest disservice to God. First of all, religion has put God outside of you—that was to make money. I understand that. The church wants money. How can it get it? The church wants power. The church wants to bring people together. The church wants people to organize behind it. It is called congregation: a congested force of people, of believers, that can support the idea and pay the money. That is what it is. But beyond that, reality is what religion, or science, was about, because people want to go and explore their totality.

How do we create harmony? How do we create happiness and harmony? It cannot be created by your Ph.D. degrees, by your wealth, by being married to a beautiful man or having a beautiful wife. I tell you, everything else is just zero. It is worse than the pigeon's dropping. I tell you what makes happiness—when you have the mental capacity to create an absolute harmony with the central bio-rhythm. This universe does not rotate because you are doing it. It rotates because it wants to rotate itself. It is well-balanced. Life is given to you for happiness. Life happens for happiness—a simple law. But few can enjoy it because every action has to be rhythmic, and rhythm cannot be maintained when you are unconscious. Unconscious does not mean like when a ball hits your head and you freak out. Unconscious means your little voice, your conscious voice, which in all unconscious matters talks to you. That is called unconscious. Or we call it *drib drishti*. Or you call it what? Intuition. The real meaning of intuition is what the unconscious is.

Between the unconscious and the conscious there is a subconscious. Conscious is good and unconscious is good, but when subconscious gets overloaded, it starts coming through. Deadly dreams, wet dreams, dry dreams, yellow dreams, black dreams. There is a whole school that interprets dreams. I don't know what a dream is because I have never dreamed in my life, so I don't know. I am not going to lie to you. I don't know what a dream is. I have never dreamed. So I don't have any experience with what a dream is. But I know that dreaming is important; it is unloading the subconscious.

All of you who tell me that you meditate, just tell me that you meditate, but don't lie about it. Meditation is never a good experience. When in meditation you do have a good experience, you are actually just having a good dream. It is not meditation. Meditation is when you clean the garbage out of your subconscious. First, meditation is when all the thoughts that you think are dirty, which you reject or deny, come to you. First, those thoughts that are ugly, dirty, nonsense—those that you rejected in the past—they will come through meditation. Second, those dirty, ugly thoughts that you have the capacity to think in the future will come. And in the third stage of meditation, all that you have lived and are going to live, or that anybody connected with you is going to live, is going to come; and fourth, you can be at peace. *Chautai padme mukti pavah*: In the fourth stage, one is free.

I am a religious man. Therefore I record this with a definite humble apology, because I feel that I should not say it. But I am going to say it anyway. If, in the future, historians find it offensive, they can. But let me tell you something: There is nothing "after life" because there are no *tattvas* after Earth. Everywhere life is programmed. Here is what is called God's Will and free will. Free will is when you start wobbling. You go off the central biorhythm. That is free will. You know if we go to New York and we catch that jet stream, we get there early; but if we have the opposing jet stream, we hang in there for hours. Your day starts not when you start the day and how you start the day; your day starts when you open your eyes. And either you are ready to mentally catch onto the biorhythm, your biorhythm, and central biorhythm, or not.

Today we are doing this holy ghosting. In Christianity, in the church, holy ghosting is what the body of the Christ was based on. Or we call it angelic ghosting, unloading our subconscious. Today we are going up there—that place in the top of the house where nobody goes and where they store every leftover dirty thing—the attic. We are going to the idiot's attic in every human. *(Yogi Bhajan injects a medical disclaimer: Do not participate if you have a heart condition or any special medical situation.)*

It is you, and it is your experience. So if you come out of this experience not the same, we have no responsibility at all; because it is your garbage, not ours. We are simply cleaning. And you have only paid ten dollars, which doesn't mean a thing; it is just to help this yoga center. I don't teach for that purpose, ever. That is my problem. Perhaps that is why I am very rich. I have never taught for money, and I have never taught to initiate a student. I have never initiated one man in my whole life, because I feel that the biggest idiot in life is one who cannot initiate himself or herself, period. That is my belief.

I am not going to go after anything else. No matter how sick a person is or how negative a person is. I do not believe you have the right to decide when you are to stop being sympathetic, kind, and compassionate. I don't believe that. Certain things these days I have absolutely no tolerance for. In fact, I hate it when you tell me, "Stop here, stop there, don't be kind to this. Please look at it!" Forget it. Don't ever tell me that, because I am not going to listen to you. I believe that the worse a person is, the more sympathy he needs, the more kindness he needs, the more compassion he needs. I feel the dirtiest situation is there to test your love and your faith in God. Love is.

Love is. Law over. Law means God—over—above God. You don't know. You think love is hugging and kissing. I know. I know what that means. You have your own dictionary; I have my own. But tonight you have paid. You are caught; you are trapped, right? Understand? So we are going to do it now. All right. And

please, you are at will to stop at any time. You are also at will to leave whenever you want. There is no compulsion that you have to be here.

◆ ◆ ◆

Let us sit in a straight rule of law. (*See Exercise 1.*) You see these two fingers; this is how the Christians used to bless. You know all those people who became popes and under-popes and semi-popes. They became old and didn't give it to the young people. They started doing it like this (with the thumb released), and this became a custom. Actually, in Christianity, it's a law that you shall not bless anybody other than with these two fingers—this is Christianity—wisdom and patience. You know this finger (forefinger, or Jupiter), you know it? You know this finger (the middle finger or Saturn), you all know it? And you know this finger (both fingers in a V)—it is the sign of Churchill, the sign of victory, the sign of peace, so many signs. But the Christian sign, the sign of the Christ, is this (fingers together). "Bless you." Christ lives in heaven; Earth wants to do what it wants to.

This kriya will shake your bottom. Don't worry. You won't like it. Ask no questions. When I did it, I never asked any questions, so I don't know any answers. Don't depend on me—simple as that. When I learned this, this is what he said: Open your mouth, have three breaths, get into Christ Mudra, and keep going. Similarly, I'll say the same thing to you: Open your mouth, take three inhales, and let it go through the nose, keeping the Christ Mudra. If you do not have the energy to get into the rhythm, you will not have the experience.

We ought to get rid of the garbage, not of this breath. This breath is just to give the body the authentic power to get going. You should hear your own sound, like a crow of the wizard. There are so many crows here, and I hear only a few. Don't you want to get rid of the garbage in you?

Now you have to continue breathing exactly that way. You are keeping this mudra, but this time the mudra has to run like this (*See Exercise 2.*): Run your hands so you may experience what it is. The faster it is, the better it will be. Good, good, a little better. All I want to do is change the aura to a blue color. That's all I need. Participate, participate. It will help.

Lock your hands like this. (*See Exercise 3.*) Lock the fingers and put them at the heart and close your eyes. Don't make any noise, nothing doing. Just jump. Move, move, move like an earthquake! Hey, if some heavy earthquake comes, and you don't have your home, move to New Mexico, bring your own tent. We have been practicing bringing our own tent in 3HO for a long time. No fault of yours that they are finding a lot of faults.

There are two important words in the world: Shut up and keep up. The rest is all a joke. If you cannot keep up, shut up. If you cannot shut up, keep up. That's all. There will be no problems. Up, up! (*See Exercise 4.*) You are not trying hard enough. Pull this limp car home and straighten it out. Elbows straight—as straight as you can. Help your being. Some of you are very lethargic. I never understand that, my God.

Oh yeah, cake will be served after the class. There's a birthday—so there's a carrot for you. Come on. Come on, folks! The velocity will be half a trillion light frequency; the gong will be played in the space of half a trillion frequencies. You have to float after that. Come on, come on—just heat up your body. All right, folks, put your hands crossed like this, and put your thumbs together in your lap, and sit with a straight spine. (*See Exercise 5.*) Project with the sound of the gong and come back with it. When you float in the space, float with the tendency to balance with the rhythm. Go central, not up and down. The subconscious will automatically unlock. Open up your being with a long, deep breath. Please follow the rule.

❖ ❖ ❖

May the long time sun shine upon you,
all love surround you, and the pure light within you, guide your way on.

Sat Nam

UNLOADING THE SUBCONSCIOUS—THE KRIYA

December 13, 1988

Note: Do not practice this kriya if you have a heart condition or any special medical situation.

There are no breaks between the exercises. Move immediately from one exercise to the next.

1. Sit in Easy Pose with Christ Mudra. Hold down the Sun and Mercury (ring and pinkie) fingers with the thumb. Bend the elbows and hold the mudra at the shoulders with the palms facing forward. Open the jaw wide and inhale in three quick strokes through the mouth; exhale through the nose. The inhaled breath will sound like a crow. Continue for **6 minutes**.

The jaw has to be kept open to the max! Some of you cannot even open your own jaw. Open your mouth! Show me your teeth. It doesn't matter how many fillings are there. Come on. Take three breaths and shoot it out through the nose. I know it is very relaxing, but don't start yawning. Come on! You guys are so uptight! This is how the wise bird cries; it's called crow. Come on! Come on! Heavy-duty breath. The messenger of the wizard is called big crow. This is the sound of the big crow.

2. Keeping the mudra and the breath, move the hands in quick, small circles (initial movement is thumbs toward the body). The entire body should shake from the movement. After a minute or two, close your eyes and continue. This exercise is **4 minutes**.

We are using the circuit. It's simple if you know the Chinese system; it's just the central circuit. We are going through the central circuit. We are going through the heart and the lungs so that the heart and lungs may not fail. Your whole body will shake when you do it. Keep moving and keep breathing. Now it is for real; before was just a rehearsal. Up, up, up, up—keep up! It will help you to erase body discomfort if you apply the rhythm to the body.

3. Interlock the fingers at the Heart Center. Jump the body off the floor for **1 minute**.

Move the body, move the body, move the body. We need the energy, we need the spine, we need the shushmana—that's what we are trying to move. Move, move, move like an earthquake!

4. Bring the lock up above the head and continue jumping the buttocks off the floor for **6 minutes**.

The whole thing has to jump right from the butt. The way we are trained is to just produce the result. Come on. Move the butt like the waves, with rhythm, horse-riding, call it anything. Ride the horse, gallop! This exercise will take care of everything in you. Go in a rhythm, go in a style, go like you are riding a horse—ride Western style. Please, use the rhythm and keep up. It should feel like you're galloping on a horse. Do it in a rhythm. We need the heat of the body to go through the space. I don't want you to go cold. That's not right. Sweat a little bit; it feels good.

5. Sit with a straight spine. Interlace the fingers with the thumb tips touching. Close the eyes and concentrate on the tip of the nose. Don't let your concentration move from the tip of the nose. Inhale deep; exhale deep as the gong is played for **14 minutes**.

Guided Meditation

You are entering a reign of forgiveness. Practice forgiveness of the self. Forgive yourself. Don't fight; don't resist. You are in the region of forgiveness. This is the hemisphere of forgiveness for your self. Redeem yourself. There is nobody above you; there is nobody beneath you; there is nobody around you; only you. This is the hemisphere where you can forgive yourself. This is a very rare opportunity. Don't ask forgiveness of God. God shall guarantee. Whatever you forgive, God shall forgive, guaranteed. Go for it! Don't fight! Forgiveness eats up the misfortune. Forgiveness eats up the misfortune of tomorrow—guaranteed. You are passing through the region of forgiveness. For the sake of giveness of God, that is what forgiveness means: for-give, for-giving. The holiness of God will open up the holes; opportunities will come. Let God give you by forgiving. Those who don't forgive get nothing.

6. With a stiff tongue against the upper palate, start repeating the sound **Hamee Ham Tumee Tum Whaa-hay Guroo** for **11 minute**s.

7. Gong is played as you meditate on *Promises* and then *Himalaya*, by Sat Peter Singh.

8. Keeping the mudra, raise it above the head with the palms facing the crown of the head; stretch your arms and your spine. Breathe long and deep and slow as the music continues for **2 minutes**.

Stretch up your hands with a straight body, stretch out your spine. You have done all this for an hour and a half, only for this moment, so don't take it lightly. Stretch your hands up straight, elbows straight, interlock. Just breathe long, deep, and slow.

TO END: Shake up, please. Shake up heavy, and shake up very strongly. The only favor you can do at this time to your whole body is to shake up really good. Unload, unload. Inhale deep. Inhale deep. Open up the fingers, stretch out the palms; be very tough and strong. Put all the tension in the palm of the hand and give it to the space. Exhale. Inhale deep. Take the body, all the disease, all the tension, all that is in it, and unload it in space. The fingers should be like that of steel. Let it go. Once more; this is your last chance. Inhale deep. Deep. Deep. Stretch up. Stretch! Stretch and tough! Don't bluff. Relax.

9. Talk to each other. This is a requirement of this class. Turn around and start speaking to the next person, say anything; talk about the weather or anything.

◆

" Either you control your mind, or your mind controls you. If your mind controls you, whether you are rich or poor, tall or short, beautiful or ugly, you are done. You are useless. You will just create twisters. You will just come and go. Life is all about the control of the mind. But there has to be spirit behind it—the soul. "

– Yogi Bhajan

UNLOADING YOUR PAIN & FEAR I

January 3, 1989

W E WILL HAVE A VERY GOOD CLASS. It's a New Year you know. We will give you something to remember. Do you know what pain is? Do you? If you spell the word pain, it is "pay in." If you can pay in, then there is no pain. The question is, where is the source of pain in life? Is life full of pain? Yes. Life is full of pain, that's an evident fact. We are not going to lie about it. Pain is an essential part of life. It causes you to move. Why is there pain? The body has an automatic system that creates an SOS, a signal of stress; and stress is a disease. Stress is not a psychological or psychoanalytical or biological situation in the sense we take it. We think stress is just something that happens. No. Stress is a simple dis-ease. It makes the body uneasy, and the body sends the SOS signal—and it's called pain.

Words are very beautiful. You know the letter G? If you spell it in English, you have to spell it "g-e-e"—G. Old English will spell it "g-e"; today's English will spell it "j-i." If you put an A with the Old English, you get, "a-g-e." Now, put an S before it: Sage.

Take away the S and put in an R, and it will be rage. If the sage has the rage, he is not a sage. So you become a sage, because you relate to a *Ji. Ji* means "soul." *Ji* as in *Japji*[1]. Just understand it—the first *bani* is *Japji. Jap* means the repetition of *Ji*, the repetition of the soul. Pranic body vibrations are called Ji. Chinese call it chi energy; we call it Ji. Some people call it soul. Some people call it Holy Spirit. Call it anyway you want to call it; it is what it is. It is the vibrant reconstruction of the body's cells. Within seventy-two hours, ten trillion cells change themselves, period.

What is aging? It is a slowing down of this process. If you are on a seventy-two-hour rhythm, you will not feel anything. But the moment you go to a 10-hour difference, you start feeling it. It is just like living in New York and flying back to Los Angeles—the time zone change affects you. We have to understand that in the future, medical science must learn to understand how the cell changes and keeps its biorhythm under control. They must learn to see that the parasympathetic, sympathetic, and motor nervous systems totally coordinate—and at what frequency, at what hour?

I was talking with someone the other day. He was complaining that his medication was ineffective. I told him to take it at eight in the morning, and it would work. Why? Don't ask that question. This is homeopathic medicine; it's a medicine

If you spell the word pain, it is "pay in." If you can pay in, then there is no pain. The question is, where is the source of pain in life? Is life full of pain? Yes. Life is full of pain, that's an evident fact. We are not going to lie about it. Pain is an essential part of life. It causes you to move.

[1]Pronounced Japjee; we have used the traditional English spellings throughout.

of potency. Ten o'clock is too late. It won't have an effect. So he took the medication at eight a.m., and it worked. Medicine won't work, herbs won't heal, if the body is not in a position to receive it systematically.

Let me tell you a story I heard as a child, and it is always in my memory. Aflatoon [2] was the greatest doctor that science ever produced. He had the science of medicine and the art of healing put together in one man. A very, very old woman walked to him and said, "Master, my daughter is suffering with diarrhea, and I have come a long distance."

He said, "Lady, here are the four tablets. If by the time you reach home, she is breathing, she is still alive, diarrhea or no diarrhea, give her one pill; it will heal. However, because you have to travel a long distance, if it doesn't heal, give her the second pill. It shall heal. Suppose, unfortunately, that two tablets do not work. Give her the third one. But when you give the third, give two at a time; it shall heal. There is no reason not to heal. Diarrhea will stop; she will be healthy. Later, ask her to come see me."

The woman went away. She did exactly what he told her to do, and the girl died. She was shocked. So she told the entire village, "We are not going to bury her, no way. Let's take her to the guy because he said, 'She will heal.'" So they brought the coffin all the way to him. When he saw it, he said, "What happened?"

"The girl died."

"What did you do?"

"I gave her the first pill. It didn't stop. I gave her the second pill. It didn't stop. Third time I gave the two pills. It didn't stop; she died."

So he called all his apprentices and said, "Bring all the books of knowledge and all the herbs and pile them up in the courtyard. We are going to burn this child, this dead girl, over the entire book of knowledge, and I am going to burn with her. It's an insult."

When the disciples began working, something touched his shoulder. He turned around but couldn't see anything.

"Who are you?"

"I am an angel, and I want to talk to you."

"Shut up. Go away. No angel, no God, nothing. Simple, I am not in the mood to hear anything."

"I am an angel. Don't get crazy. Follow me. You gave four pills to the mother?"

"Yes."

"You put it in paper and wrapped it properly."

"Yes."

"If the mother's body would have touched those pills, the daughter would have been healed. But you were very nice, you wrapped them up in the paper. So fine."

[2] Aflatoon is the Persian name of the Greek philosopher Plato

"What does that have to do with it?"

"Don't yell. Don't yell! The mother opened the wrapper and put the pills in the mouth of the daughter; but she never touched it with her hand."

"What does that have to do with anything?"

"Wait. Why you are so upset? Why are you not listening?"

"Come on, quick. Tell me what you want to say."

"Here are your four pills, dry and exact."

"What do you mean?"

"Because the girl was to die, it was her time. When the mother was giving them to her, I took the pills in my hand. I didn't let her body touch them. I knew your pills were okay, but I have to do my job. Here are your four pills."

That's why I always say, "Herbs heal, doctors diagnose, and God cures." Nobody believes it. When God wants to cure, He cures, and He secures the means to cure.

There has to be a cause of death, and there has to be an opportunity for wealth. That is how it goes. You are all actors on a paper stage. You are all paper tigers. You have to do what you have to do, but there is somebody else who does everything. I am not trying to be a fatalist, but let me tell you as a scientist, in pure mathematics, root square is the root square to gamma, alpha, and beta. In a theta state, productivity can only exchange from matter to energy and transfer the energy into matter. Therefore, all prosperity, productivity, and projections are controlled by the self-projection of the neurons. Understand this: When the rhythm in the neurons, which controls the projection, starts acting within the scope of less than four seconds, man becomes prosperous—no matter how dull he is. When it starts acting within the scope of over seven seconds, a rich man will become poor; that's all it is—time. Constructive induction helps you understand the facts, and the moment the facts are induced, you shall deduce the opportunity in seconds; these are the balances.

Unfortunately, male has no right hemisphere. He is half-human. Every male is half-human. It happens during the seventh month. You get that "acid bath," and you lose the right hemisphere of the brain. I mean to say, your left hemisphere supplements and complements the right, but you do not have the right hemisphere of the brain. Thank God, because despite the fact you are stupid, you are very strong, very competing, very courageous. But basically, as a male, you are stupid. You do not have intuitive sensitivity, which woman has. Luckily for you, woman has both sides of the brain. But because she has both sides, she doesn't know which way to go, so she is always confused.

There are a lot of very important things in our life. Mind is the muscle; body is the shell. There cannot be two opinions about it: The mind either controls you, or

That's why I always say, "Herbs heal, doctors diagnose, and God cures." Nobody believes it. When God wants to cure, He cures, and He secures the means to cure.

It's impossible to both control the mind and have the mind control you. No. It is always one-way traffic; it's a one-way road. Either you control your mind, or your mind controls you.

you control your mind. There cannot be two relationships. It's impossible to both control the mind and have the mind control you. No. It is always one-way traffic; it's a one-way road. Either you control your mind, or your mind controls you. If your mind controls you, whether you are rich or poor, tall or short, beautiful or ugly, you are done. You are useless. You will just create twisters. You will just come and go. If you control your mind, even if you control only forty percent of it, you make sense. If you control fifty percent of it, you make prosperity. If you control sixty percent, you become a legend. Life is all about the control of the mind; but there has to be spirit behind it—the soul.

Don't tread on me—don't think that the sole is under the foot. You are the soul. The sole purpose of the soul is that you must shine like a star. What kind of star can you become? You can become a juggling star, you can become a yo-yo star, you can become a lot of things. Just understand this: It doesn't matter whether you are religious or nonreligious, pious or not pious, great or not great—your prosperity is proportionate to your purity. In this sense, the Christians are right. Holy Ghost, this spirit, determines the whole of life. Whenever you confront a situation, you become numb. That's one thing about fear that you can understand medically. It freezes you. Challenge is nothing but pure fear confronting your intelligence. Consciousness helps you go through it; it doesn't help you fall apart. When I went to Canada, I can't tell you what an experience I went through. The Canadian government had just begun a new experiment in education called Rochdale College. Young kids and their professors lived and worked together. They happened to somehow put me in charge there. Now, what kind of building that was or what kind of education it was, I don't know. Nobody wore clothes, every girl and boy walked around naked in every room—you could see everything, even those things you can't see on television. And nobody paid even a penny.

But I could talk to those young people; I could understand them. Where is the fault in a human? Human fault is not in his geography. Human fault is in the flow of the energy. If the energy does not come handily, readily, the confrontation is heavy, and the game is lost. When the energy is freely available, you run on it; the car is perfect, Rolls Royce, new edition, all fine. But when there is no gas in the tank, what can you do? You know when the gas starts running out what the car does? Phak-thak-thak-thak. And after that, nothing—that's it—because it can no longer suck the gas out of the tank. It starts running on fumes, and finally it says "adios."

I sometimes wonder when people say, "I don't want to meditate." In response, I say, "Yeah, be mad then." There is tremendous human faculty that has never been used in this country. I am shocked: "Oh, he is black, he is brown, he is yellow." Nobody talks to anybody as a human being. "He is rich, he is poor, he is a doctor, he is an engineer, he is an idiot, he is a half, he is a full, he is a fill in the blank." We always have a brand. We have never, ever, in the past three million years, recognized a person as a person; we never will. That pure deficiency dictates our behavior. Sometimes, when the animals look at us, the dog starts barking, birds start chirping, and things start happening, because they think a fool is coming. They communicate. To them, a human being is just a living fool who lives by his own demagogy. There is no democracy, there is no socialism, there is no communism, there is no government. A bunch of stone heads get their scene together and call themselves civilized human beings. Tell me how civilized they are?

In this world today, 1989, today is what? The second? The third, the third of January,1989. A human cannot recognize another human just as a human, just as she is. You recognize gold as it is, and then you start looking at the purity of it: fourteen carat, eighteen carat, twenty-two carat, twenty-four carat, right? That's what you do. Have you ever measured another human being or person just as a person and then related to their evaluation, their purity of the heart and clarity of the head? I am willing to say right now that every religion has failed, pure and simple, because religion is a science that creates reality. And what is reality? To find God? No. God is not going anywhere. It's a stupid waste of time to find God.

It's absolutely insane to become rich, because God is a super power, and richness is a medium power. But the question is, can you handle yourself? Can you control yourself? Can you confront a fearful situation and excel? Can you pass a truck by accelerating and pass it without accident?

Life is not whether you are beautiful or you are ugly. Life is whether you can share wisdom. Life is not to share your money. A doctor is not a doctor if he cannot share the technique to make people healthy. An attorney is not an attorney if he does not win people their rights or pursue their cases as well as justice. A teacher is not a teacher who doesn't teach properly. A teacher who looks after how much money he is getting, how many students he has, what kind of students he has—he is a stupid businessman. The most criminal and painful job is to become a teacher. Technically speaking, when you are a teacher, you are going to put your nose in everything about a person's life. It is the relationship among a stone, a chisel, and a hammer. What's the relationship? The spark.

Somebody told me once, "Yogiji, I am studying with a great teacher."

I said, "Must be very nice."

"He is so nice, so beautiful."

"Wow, God." I didn't say anything. You know what I mean? I thought, "teacher" and "nice"? I've never heard of that. If you have bad luck, then you'll have a nice teacher. "Teacher" and "nice" do not go together. How can a teacher be nice, tell me? His job is to look inside you, inside out. How can he be nice? The only thing

nice is that he may not say it to your face; he will call you on the phone. That's the greatest niceness he can do. Or two or three days later, he will say, "I met you last Sunday. What was the matter?" And you have to lie for about fifteen minutes to defend yourself; meanwhile, he will say, "No, no, actually the facts are this, this, this and that should be enough."

One who presides at infinity and teaches excellence means that the whole thing has to be absolutely A-1, mint condition—that is the job of a teacher. Teacher is not a joke; not everybody can be a holy man. Everybody can be a saint, everybody can be God's man, everybody can be just a man, everybody can be anything, but not everybody can be a teacher. The job of the teacher is to take a person, clean him out, and never let him not be intelligent. Now, how many people want to live intelligently? Emotionally, yes. Affectionately, yes. Everybody wants to be loved. I don't know what love you are talking about.

Do you love yourself? I asked somebody that same question.

He replied "Yes. I really love myself."

"In how many minutes do you bathe?"

"Two, three, five. Sometimes I take a tub bath for fifteen minutes."

"Have you taken one day, a full day, a whole day, to bathe and nothing else? Why don't you, for one day, soak yourself in water?"

"Not possible."

"Why not?"

"There is a lot more to do."

"Do you know it takes over six hours of soaking in the water for the pores to open up?"

"I never heard that."

"Do you know there is a science called hydrotherapy?"

People used to do hydrotherapy on the eleventh day of the moon, when all the glands in our body are fully accelerated. People used to go to a *Mahashnaan*—a great bath, they used to call it. They would go into the river and stand up to the neck there for eight hours. Do nothing; just get into the river, jump in, and stay; talk to each other, chant, do kirtan, the whole thing. But they would all stand in water from when the sun came to one rope—that means about an hour or two—until one rope to go down; then they would come out. They were the healthiest people in the world. They understood a science.

This body has many, many charismas and many, many majestic things in it. But you always have a pattern, and your pattern is known to all your friends. Things that you are hiding about yourself, they are always known to your friends, because your behavior has an impact—a silent, unsaid impact. Everybody knows that you are a liar or you are a thief or you are an exaggerator or you say negative things or you are positive; your basic patterns are known to everyone. Therefore nobody accepts you at face value. So don't try to pretend to be pretty or ugly; it doesn't make sense. What is the relationship? The relationship is either full of pain or it has no pain. Pay in. Pay in the attention and you will have G, and you can measure the age of the G, and you can become a sage just by not being confused.

Wisdom cannot be read and learned. Proportionate minus confusion is your wisdom in life. You understand what I am saying? I have seen people very, very wise, extremely wise. You ask them to sign a piece of paper, and they say, "Take my thumb and put it there." They don't speak or they can't speak just because they are born to speak. They can't read, they can't write. But they are very, very wise, because they are extremely simple; they are not confused. The majority of the people are confused. The sign of a confused man is that you will never find him going in one direction. You see how confused we are? You want to see that? If you want to see a confused woman, watch when she is selecting dresses.

For fifteen minutes, there will be nothing but tremendous chaos. She cannot decide what to wear. Just stand behind the mirror and watch someone put on their makeup—see how confused they are, indecisive to the core of death. Just see a woman who is ready to go to a dinner, how confused she is. Once I went to somebody's house in Hollywood. I was very shocked. The living room was fantastic, the house was wonderful. But when you entered the house, the entryway was totally mirrors—all sides, top, bottom, mirror.

"What is this for?"

"This is my wife's trip."

"What is this trip?"

"Watch."

We went in, we sat down, she got ready, she came in, and we got up to leave. Then she started dancing in that entry hall. She started going round and round and round, looking at herself.

"See what is happening?"

"How long?"

"About five minutes."

"What do you do?"

"I close the door and stand on the porch under the canopy. That's why we have a canopy, because every time, this is what she does. She goes in circles."

These are normal, insecure human beings who are not even aware of whether they are beautiful or not, real or not, truthful or not. You talk to them, and they say, "I am this and this I am, that and that."

Man cannot time his stools. He has been potty trained from the very first day. All his life, every human being has a problem clearing his stool. It's a medical fact.

Have you seen these people doing Tai Chi, that slow process to stretch the body so the gases can move, the muscles can move, the circulation can move, the body's joints can move? It's funny. In Española, whenever we have to go out, we start the car and heat it for three or four minutes. We let it run two or three minutes before we go. It's not like California, where we get in, start the key, and there you go. You kill the engine; everybody knows it. But in New Mexico, if you kill the engine, the nearest workshop is thirty miles. You know certain things can happen, so subconsciously you are very careful. Here in Southern California you know that there is a workshop on every corner, so what do you care?

But the facts are that there are rules in life, rules that can help you avoid the pain and the stress. So we are going to go through that today in our thirty-some minutes, and we are going to do a good job. Are you ready?

◆ ◆ ◆

All right. Sit down with your spine straight. Give yourself a distance. It's a very funny thing that we are going to do. (*See Exercise 1.*) Split the fingers and just move the hands. Just churn the body's upper area. In the old days, when we used to make butter, we used to churn the yogurt; this is exactly the movement.

If you are doing it honestly, you should have an automatic rate of breath; at the rate that oxygen consumption is required, that will be your rate of breath. Just become yo-yos—back and forth, up and down. Split the fingers in the center. Separate the lower body and the upper body and accelerate the mercury; that's what we are doing. We are accelerating our power of communication. We want to talk to the Unknown, that's what the preparation is. Get into the act.

Listen, either you move, or I know a way to make you move. I will give you an exercise, and you will not be in a position to be happy. I am just teaching like a gentleman; you should learn like a gentleman. Put your force into it. Your aura tells me when you are doing it; you are not doing it—that's the problem. The moment I find that the majority are doing it, then I am satisfied. Do you have a sense of proportion? Can you give your body its own right to oxygen, so that the breath can be automatically deep without your inhaling deep? You will start enjoying it when your intake of oxygen becomes automatically proportionate to your tiredness and stress.

Would you mind sweating? You really need persuasion. Come on, please. We want to make this class beautiful. The only way we can do what we want to do is if you have enough oxygen in your circulatory system. We can tolerate cheating up to twenty percent, but not more than that.

Give your body a new chance for this New Year of prosperity. Nobody is going to be poor this year. You don't have to worry—be happy. Come on, breathe. A heavy Breath of Fire (*see Exercise 4*) can break your pattern of stress—heavy, heavy! Heat up the fat you ate over the Christmas holiday; all that stuff you ate, burn it up. Don't give up. Help your kidneys. Hammer the breath.

Take the longest breath you can and meditate at the Navel Point. Touch the navel with the breath of life. (*See Exercise 5.*) Imagine you are standing on a platform, about to leap into a pond of water. Take the posture please—inhale and hold the breath; take a leaping stand and then hold the breath and leap, relax.

Please shake your hands and shake your body, shoulders, and especially the ribcage. (*See Exercise 6.*) Get rid of the stress.

We presume that you will go back home and take a good shower and go to bed tonight. Watch out for your dreams. You have released a lot, especially in the middle of the session. We couldn't push you beyond a certain point; so graduation, moderation, is the way of life.

We will have a class tomorrow, and we will go into a very factual, systematic system. But we want you to come with an empty stomach. In the afternoon, don't eat too much. Take some soup or take some fruit, and then come to class so that we can totally cook you. The idea is simple: If you have too much in the belly, then it becomes very difficult to stimulate the Navel Point, which is affected by the whole footage of the filled intestine. It doesn't make for a lot of space, and we need a lot of space. So if you come tomorrow, just be light on the food. You will be heavy on energy, and we will really do the job. As far as today is concerned, it's just an introduction.

Remember when you are in dire trouble from any sickness, if you can hold the breath and pump the navel, then you can come out of it in seconds—that's God's remedy.

◆ ◆ ◆

This is a year of prosperity; and every year there is a mantra that brings things, that makes things happen. This is the year of eight, the year of infinity. Even those who have been dead all along and soaked with misfortune and misery—luck never smiled on them, it is not in their fate—even they can be prosperous. We don't initiate people and charge sixty-five dollars and give you a secret mantra in the ear and all that. What is a mantra? Mantra is *Man-Tra*: the mental vibration, permutation, and combination in which you put your things together. That's what mantra

What is a mantra? Mantra is Man-Tra: the mental vibration, permutation, and combination in which you put your things together.

is. *Man* means "mind." *Tra* means *tarang*. *Tarang* means "the wave." To fix the mental wavelength—to prosper or to power or to control or to decontrol—that's what mantras are. *Tra* comes from *tarang*, which is the sound wavelength. When you take the string and you move it, it creates a sound—*drrrnnnggg*; that wave is called *tarang*. Water waves are called *jaltarang*. There is a music in which you put water in cups and you create the sound and you play—it's called *jaltarang*, a water harmonica.

I am going to share all this with you as long as I am breathing; I don't promise beyond that. I want you to understand that this is a year of prosperity. If anybody remains poor this year, that's how full of garbage he is. That person has not put any effort into changing. It doesn't matter what life was three days ago; that has nothing to do with it. It's the year of the eight, the year of Infinity; it's called *ashtang* year, it's a set year. Nineteen eighty-nine, right? Eight and nine totals seventeen, which in turn totals eight.

Am I right? It's mathematical. Try to understand what you are up to. You are in for prosperity, for personal power and personal fulfillment this year; this is the year. If you miss the boat or miss the bus, take it as you want to, understand? In one decade, every ten years, there is only one year. So missing it means the remaining nine years you will pay through the nose—that's all I can politely say. I am leaving no exception; I am just telling you this is the year when you can base your prosperity; leave your doubts, work hard, intelligently; and consciously fix your prosperity for the next decade. So, nine years—if you want to eat the fruit, sow now.

We are giving you the mantra of prosperity, which will work for you. If you do not know how to play it, take the recording and play it at night while you sleep; let the mantra take care of itself. The subconscious hears it anyway. All you have to do is sleep with it and wake up with it—that's what we need. If you chant and you want to be very quick and all that, that's your headache. We are giving you a way out that's simple. When you sleep, put the recording on and start chanting with it; then sleep with it. If you have any sexual duties, do them first. Or if you want to watch some TV and all that, do it. Well, I am not interfering in domestic life. But after that, sing along with the recording and then sleep and wake up with it—that's all we require. Actually, to be honest, we need you for three minutes before going to bed and three minutes when you first wake up. We need you almost six minutes a day. We are not putting any conditions, we are not asking anything, because we think everybody has the right to enjoy this year and be great and be prosperous.

Now we will play the music. If you can play with us for one more minute, it won't be very late.

Har, Har, Har, Har Gobinday

Har, Har, Har, Har Mukanday

Har, Har, Har, Har Udhaaray

Har, Har, Har, Har Apaaray

Har, Har, Har, Har Hariang

Har, Har, Har, Har Kariang

Har, Har, Har, Har Neernaamay

Har, Har, Har Har Akaamay

This was sung on New Year's Eve for 31 minutes, and it was done in a very pure atmosphere. It is very pure. God bless everybody.

◆ ◆ ◆

May the long time sun shine upon you,
all love surround you, and the pure light within you, guide your way on.

Sat Nam

We will meet tomorrow to complete what we started today. I am here for one more week. After that I have to go be with the children, and I am going to spend a month with them. They are important; they are tomorrow. I love to be with tomorrow more than with yesterday. I am selfish in my way. I never hesitate to say that, because you must understand: What is prosperity? Prosperity can be learned by one simple thing. If you take the eye of consciousness, which is called the Third Eye, and plant within it any basic element, you shall be prosperous. In citrus, the basic root citrus, when you plant the eye (the seed), you get oranges. You understand what I am saying? It's transformation. Life is not a big hassle if you just understand. The decisive outcome is proportionate to the consciousness, which you apply with intelligence.

Intelligence is a tool to apply consciousness or commotion. Intelligence works both ways. With intelligence you cannot intelligently and consciously apply commotion; it's not possible. You can use your intelligence to be commotional. But what does commotion do? It freezes your frequency; it takes away the expansion of life from you. You are really your own enemy; nobody else is your enemy, and there is no such thing as being stupid. All you have to do is fix your range of fre-

quency so that it cannot match the vibration of the universe. If not, you will be stupid, dead, absolutely unhappy yo-yos. Every human being can do that! It's not something you have to try to do on purpose.

The application of intelligence is a basic. Yet the majority of people don't even apply intelligence. I am not bothering them, God bless them. They can eat their own productivity. But those who apply intelligence with commotions are the worst. When you have the grip of intelligence, apply consciousness, and you will be on top of the world.

Somebody once asked me, "I have gone through every newspaper, I have telephoned every agency, I have registered with everybody, and still I am not getting a job."

"You want the job to come to you. Or you want to go and find a job?"

"Well, how lucky I will be if the job can come to me? I am really tired, I am lost. I just lost six hundred dollars, and my rent is twelve hundred dollars."

"The condition seems serious. And you are not finding a job?"

"No."

"Vibrate on it."

The guy was so desperate, for a whole day he did nothing but vibrate on it. Finally, at about four o'clock, the telephone rang. It was one of his friends.

"Hey, did you get a job anywhere?"

"No."

"Well, my boss was telling me that I should have an assistant, and I thought of you. Would you report tomorrow at eight o'clock?"

"What?"

"We are friends. You want to be my assistant or not?"

"What is the pay?"

"Forty-eight thousand dollars to start. I could have asked for more, but I didn't want to irritate my boss. It also includes insurance, and they will give you the company car and half of your rent wherever you are living. You will have your own secretary, and I expect you to come at eight o'clock tomorrow morning. Should I pick you up?"

"That would be best; I don't have even the courage to listen to the telephone anymore."

There is a universal mind, and there is an individual mind. When the individual mind contacts the universal mind, the universal mind contacts the entire God-dom. That we will do tomorrow.

Thank you.

UNLOADING YOUR PAIN & FEAR I—
THE KRIYA
January 3, 1989

There are no breaks between the exercises. Move immediately from one exercise to the next.

1. Split the Saturn (middle) and Sun (ring) fingers of each hand and bring the thumbs to the mound of Mercury, at the base of the pinkie finger. Extend the two arms out in front, parallel to the floor, with the palms facing each other. Pull the right arm back, as though pulling a bow. As it returns to the original position, draw the left arm back. Continue vigorously, pulling and pushing the arms forward and backward for **8 minutes**. Move from the shoulders—it has to be from the shoulder blade—allowing the upper body and ribcage to twist with the arms.

Separate the lower body and the upper body and accelerate the mercury; that's what we are doing. We are accelerating our power of communication. We want to talk to the Unknown, that's what the preparation is. Get into the act. Come on, please.

You are all here under stress. But the question is why do we get stressed? When the lungs do not have the power to soak the blood with the oxygen required, you get stressed. It is a simple thing. The whole problem starts from the breath of life. The oxygen the body needs is sometimes not available; you breathe shallowly. I am asking you to work hard and work fast and move fast so that the oxygen can have its own rhythm and your diaphragm may give you the oxygen you need. Come on, breathe for God's sake. Move heavily and breathe heavily—that's how it is. Move, move, move. Move!

2. Close the eyes and concentrate at the tip of the nose. Extend the arms out in front and make a cup of the hands. The arms are lifted to about 15 degrees above parallel, so that the hands are in front of the face. Imagine water flowing from the hands. After **2 minutes**, begin visualizing in the following way:

We are asking you to transform yourself into a fish and to start swimming at the bottom of the ocean. This is a mental exercise. Transform yourself into a fish and start walking at the bottom of the ocean. It's called lobster's walk. Sixty percent of the body is water. If the body can be balanced and in proportion, health can be resumed, fatigue can be gone, and stress will be over. Set yourself. Remember, do not take the sight from the tip of the nose and do not open the eyes. Do the experiment right and walk at the bottom of the ocean.

After **1½ more minutes**, play the gong, if available. This exercise is **5 minutes total**.

If you do the exercise right, you can lose a couple pounds. Yes, yes, I am just telling you the power of the mind over body. You start giving your body's water away. It is absolutely a mental exercise. It has nothing to do with the body, but just see what it does. Give the water away. Give water to the thirsty. Quench the thirst of the Universe.

3. Put the hands on the Navel Point, left under, right over. Concentrate deeply at the Third Chakra, the Navel Point. Bring all the energy to this point. Continue the gong, if available, for **4 minutes**.

4. Keep the hands in the same position and begin pressing the Navel Point with both hands as you begin Breath of Fire and feel the pulse at the navel. This is a powerful movement of the navel—Hammer it! Continue for **4 minutes.**

TO END: Inhale deep, hold briefly, and exhale long and deep.

Breath of Fire burns up the garbage in the body. Give your body a new chance in this new year of prosperity. If you can do Breath of Fire at this moment, heavily, from the Navel Point, while pressing the Navel Point with both hands and moving and measuring the movement as powerfully as you can, it will release for you a new set of energy in a couple of minutes.

5. Continue meditating at the Navel Point with the long, deep breath. Listen to the gong, if available. Continue for **4 minutes**.

TO END: *Inhale deep.Pretend you are standing on a high platform and are about to leap into a body of water. Take that position. How you will leap? From a height of say 30 or 40 feet into the water? Take that position, exhale.*

Inhale again; presume that you are going to leap into the water down there; take that posture and exhale. Inhale deep again, hold, and take that leaping position. Exhale.

Inhale deep again—this is your last chance—inhale and hold the breath, take a leaping stance, continue to hold the breath, and then leap! Relax.

6. Start shaking the hands and the body, especially the shoulders and ribcage. Get rid of the stress. Close your eyes. Go wild! Listen to *Walking Up the Mountain* sung by Guru Dass Singh with Krishna Kaur *(See Lyric Sheets in the Appendix.)* Continue for **4 minutes**.

Shake up the ribcage, because that's where the breath is imprisoned. That's where the dungeon is. Move, move the upper area; move, shake up. Go crazy; close your eyes. I want the spirit to be free from your own dungeon, the ribcage. I want you to move the upper body and release.

TO END: Begin clapping the hands. Clap hard to prevent arthritis in the hands. Continue for **20 seconds**.

Whistle for **20 seconds**.

Cough for **20 seconds**.

Sneeze for **20 seconds**.

Laugh with a wide, open mouth and wide, open eyes for **20 seconds**.

Inhale deep and begin pumping the Navel Point for **20 seconds**. Exhale and repeat twice more.

Relax.

◆

Laugh so that the soul cannot be tied down in the dungeon. We are releasing the ribcage. If harmony is lost, life is nothing but full of pain and stress. Where is your point of harmony? Your Navel Point. It must move to move your whole life. Your power lies in your pelvic bone. Your brain cannot work if the pelvic bone is uptight; that's your basement.

" The power and projection of the word, that's how this *granthi* works—whether consciously, subconsciously, or unconsciously will decide your luck. There is no such thing as luck; it doesn't exist. Whenever the combination and permutation between your seven chakras and your five tattvas are in harmony, your aura will be bright. "

– *Yogi Bhajan*

UNLOADING YOUR PAIN & FEAR II

January 4, 1989

UNLOADING THE PAST OF HARSH MEMORIES—THAT'S REBIRTHING. Today we will go through the layers of the mind and get rid of the pain. What I am trying to explain to you is this: Do you know how your mind is? Anybody? You must be aware. Somewhere you might have read some book or something. No? What do you mean by mind? How did this word mind come through?

Your mind has three portions. Your brain has an eastern hemisphere and a western hemisphere. Every female, and I mean every, has an active right hemisphere and an active left hemisphere. Every male has no right hemisphere. Men go through the acid bath, which turns the one part of the organ into a clitoris and the other part into the penis, period. And it is God's justice that giving you that little extra meat in the penis takes away your activity of the right brain. The male right brain becomes supplementary to the left brain; it never initiates. Just remember that. Because of this, a male has to compete to become sharp. Woman knows how to be sharp. She only becomes dull because she is indecisive, not because she doesn't know anything.

If a woman comes to me saying, "I am in pain, I am suffering." I think she is playing dumb. She is an idiot because she is trying to get sympathy. There is absolutely no woman born on this planet who can be dumb; there is no such thing, no matter how insane she can be! God gave her sixteen times more sensitivity and intelligence, because God prepared her to be a mother. She has to protect her future child; therefore, all the equipment was provided. There was no injustice. Women only suffer because they are indecisive; they wane and wax too much.

Now, comes the mind. Your mind has nine layers, and each layer has the three parts of the mind: positive, negative, and neutral. Negative comes first, positive comes next, neutral comes over it. There are two parts of the mind and then the crown over it; that's how it is. It is called a flower bud. The mind's situation is that there is one part of mind and a second part of mind and the central part of the mind. Your brain works, but your mind is a constituent of a lot of things in you. So the mind has three parts, and each part has nine layers. It's like an onion—you peel one layer, and the other layer will come; you peel another layer, and other layers will come.

Today we will go through the layers of the mind and get rid of the pain. Do you know how your mind works?

The mind has to be trained. The mind has a natural survival tendency. It is the only thing man has that is faster than time and not measurable by space.

The mind has to be trained. The mind has a natural survival tendency. For example, when God made man, man said, "I am being separated from you, oh, God. I mean, that's not fair."

God said, "What is the problem?"

"Suppose I don't like where you are sending me."

"Come back."

The mind was given. It is the only thing man has that is faster than time and not measurable by space. It's the fastest tool of infinity; and it has eighty-one total layers. You have three minds, each mind has nine layers, and each of those nine layers has nine layers; it is much more, my God. But anyway, why bother when you don't care? You don't want to know. You are Americans—that's enough. Star and spangle and that whole thing. You salute, you put your hand here, and God bless you.

Man has never tried to be real. There is a saying: "If you do not conquer your mind, you have lost your trip on the Earth." That's a known fact. This is the only *pauree [from Japji]* that describes the yoga practices:

Mundaa santokh saram pat jholee dhi-aan kee karahi bibhoot
Khinthaa kaal ku-aaree kaa-i-aa jugat dan-daa parteet
Aa-ee panthee sagal jamaatee man jeetai jag jeet
Aadays tisai aadays, aad aneel anaad anaahat jug jug ayko vays.
    —Guru Nanak, Siri Guru Granth Sahib, page 6, from *Japji*

Make contentment your earrings, humility your begging bowl,
and meditation the ashes you put on your body.
The thought of death; aspiration of the bride to be; faith in the Lord your walking stick.
Come as a traveler; All are fellow students; conquer your mind, and conquer the world.
Salutation! My humble salutation to You.
The Primal One, the Pure Light, without beginning, without end.
Throughout time you remain the same.

Guru Nanak says to the yogis, "You are doing all these rituals, and you think you are in control of it, but it's not true. If you have not conquered your mind, you have not conquered the world. And if you have not conquered the world, then what are you talking about?" *Mundaa santokh* refers to a particular practice in which they cut the sun lobe (earlobe). Yogis tear apart the sun lobe—that's why you put earrings in your ears. It is not a fashion; it is to become impotent. Do you know that? Do you know why we make a hole in the ear? This is a sun lobe. It's an old system, an enforced system, to pierce a woman's ears so that she cannot think right. It was to make a woman a slave; iron was penetrated through the ear—iron, not the earrings and diamonds that you have. That was later on, you know, when a king wanted a slave, so he put the diamond in it. Basically they used to use an iron rod to pierce the ear, and then yogis would put in this *mundaa santokh*, those big wooden things. The idea was to make the lobes hang, to tear them apart, so that you could practice being impotent. I do not call it celibacy; I call it impotency. Celibacy? There is no such thing; we never believe it. What is the use in being celibate and having wet dreams? Big deal. No, that's not reality. Reality is whether you are in control or not in control. Life has no two meanings to it.

So, they put them here and on other meridian points, too; and sometimes they put six, seven, eight. To me they look ugly, but to them that's the only way they have learned to control themselves. It's acupuncture. These days the Japanese have a little needle they put in and then put plastic over it so it continues working.

Mundaa santokh. Guru Nanak asks why you think patience will come to you? Because when you understand the psychosomatics of sex—no, it's my point of view, and I quote no scripture, I take no responsibility, I am hurting no religion when I say this, but I am telling you what truth is. The truth is, the life in you is based on the sixth sense, the creative sense, which is sex. There is nothing in the world, there is nothing in sex, there is nothing without sex. The creative sense makes you move. Now, if the creative sense doesn't become creative and effective, it becomes sexual, which is also creative. Without sex, you can't create babies—except for the saying that Jesus was born of an immaculate conception. But beyond that, you have to sexually create children. Physical creativity is sexual, mental creativity is art, and spiritual creativity is ecstasy. These are the three creativities.

The positive mind will create art, the neutral mind will create intuitive Infinity. You will know what even a telescope can't tell you; you can see it without knowing anything. So, *mundaa santokh*—the first thing in life is patience. And where is your patience tested? Your patience is tested when you hear something. Whenever you hear something, if you can control yourself and you can have patience, you will win. Therefore, those who can listen patiently can always be successful.

Mundaa santokh saram pat jholee. Your *karam*, your cover, should be *saram* and *pat*, grace and nobility. *Saram pat*, grace. *Saram, soram, sirim*—these are three words in the scripture that mean "grace," "one who gives the grace," and "one who lives in it." *Saram pat*—*pat* means "nobility." You should have *saram pat jholee.* You have to ask not for things in the world; instead you have to give to yourself two things: one is grace and one is nobility.

Mundaa santokh saram pat jholee dhi-aan kee karahi bibhoot. We put on our body the ashes. The yogis do that to curb the sensuality—the sixth sense. This is

The creative sense makes you move. If the creative sense doesn't become creative and effective, it becomes sexual, which is also creative. Physical creativity is sexual, mental creativity is art, and spiritual creativity is ecstasy. These are the three creativities.

all to help their mind. We should be intuitive through our meditation, our Radiant Body—not by putting ashes on the body. Guru Nanak advises them:

Mundaa santokh saram pat jholee dhi-aan kee karahi bibhoot
Khinthaa kaal ku-aaree kaa-i-aa jugat dan-daa parteet.

You will see some Hare Krishna people with the *dandi*—they call it *dandi*. Swamis walk carrying this stick, the flag of nobility.

Khinthaa kaal ku-aaree kaa-i-aa—this body shall be eaten by death, but the soul is always virgin.

Ku-aaree kaa-i-aa jugat dan-daa parteet—this law of stick: Spare the rod, spoil the child. That works; that's the way nature takes care of things. If things are not admitted by the Natural Law, then things are administered by what is called the Rash Law. If you don't move, there comes a stick on your butts, and you move! So this environmental pressure is always on us.

Jugat dan-daa parteet—the law of the stick. Finally, if you do not have intelligence, you will be hurt. Between your hurt and your intelligence there is a relationship; but between consciousness there is no relationship—please mind that. If you are conscious, then you are in control. But when you use only your intelligence, then you will be hurt.

Khinthaa kaal ku-aaree kaa-i-aa jugat dan-daa parteet
Aa-ee panthee sagal jamaatee man jeetai jag jeet.

Aa-ee panthee—I am, I am—it's a rule of God that has come from time, Infinite to Infinite. But when one controls and conquers the mind, he controls the entire three worlds: world of the past, world of the present, world of tomorrow.

Aadays tisai aadays aad aneel anaad anaahat jug jug ayko vays.

God has all shapes and colors through all time and space. God is Infinite by His own Infinity, and beyond Infinity, still God is—that's all it means. *Aadays* means "I salute, I salute, I salute." Ah, *Japji* is the most sacred description of Godliness, explained in as few words as necessary; sometimes it will need a longer explanation. But in that line, you will hear this line:

Man jeetai jag jeet.
If you conquer your own mind, you can conquer the whole world around you.

Let me tell you some facts. You have seven chakras. They call it *granthi*. *Granthi* means a nerve plexus, a place where the nerves combine actively, where messages come. From there, the nerves talk to the muscles; that's called *granthi*, like *agan granthi*, or fire. The lotus, or *granthi* of fire, is in the heart. The power to speak, the power of the word, is in your throat. How do you speak? "Will you please do this? What is he talking about? What? Who the hell is this?" You question and react from your subconscious.

The power and projection of the word, that's how this *granthi* works—whether consciously, subconsciously, or unconsciously will decide your luck. There is no such thing as luck; it doesn't exist. Whenever the combination and permutation between your seven chakras and your five *tattvas* are in harmony, your aura will be bright.

You have an electromagnetic field; everything has an electromagnetic field. This dead rod has a foot-and-a-half aura; birds and fish have a three-and-a-half-foot aura; but the mammals have a bigger aura. There are mammals in the sea, and there are mammals on Earth—and you are one of those mammals. Because you have the capacity of intuition, you have a nine-foot aura on each side, up and down. You're nine feet deep, from that foot of yours including your heel. Your aura in the ground is measured by the heel strength, not from the toe. If your aura down into Earth is shallow, you are poor, and you cannot become rich. I could give you the Federal Reserve Bank, and money shall still not be with you. Money is only measured by the depth of your auric root into Earth. Your aura toward the east side will give you the knowledge to grab opportunity. Your aura toward the west gives you the strength to produce the impossible. Your aura above you will give you height.

Together—to gather means to collect, to get. So it is together that is most important in life. Our entire activity is based on getting things together. Organizing, arranging, doing all those kinds of things. We are always working for security.

> *Aageh aapnee mot say, koi bashar nahi,*
> *Saaman so baras ka, pal ki khabar nahi.*
> (Traditional Punjabi saying)
> No individual is aware of his death. People can make arrangements for a hundred years, and the next moment they can be dead.

So basically, we do not work here because we have to work; we work because we love God, but we do not trust God. Those who trust God will never work. The fact of life is that when you trust God, then Mother Nature works for you. When you love God, then you should work hard, through your sweat; Mother Nature will never work for you. That's where you decide who is poor and who is rich.

Money is only measured by the depth of your auric root into Earth. Your aura toward the east side will give you the knowledge to grab opportunity. Your aura toward the west gives you the strength to produce the impossible. Your aura above you will give you height.

Tehel mehel taa ko miley jaa kao sant kirpal
   - Guru Arjan, Siri Guru Granth Sahib, page 255
Services and palaces shall be granted to those on whom a saint is happy.

That's one line that can never be untrue. Saint, or *sadhu*, means one who has completed his sadhana. What is a sadhana? After all, sadhana has to have some reason. There are three lines: *sadhana, aradhana, prabhupati*—those who do sadhana, those who do as they have been told to do, and those who become the Master of God.

You are controlling the mind; they can control God. When you read all the scriptures from all the religions, from day one to today, there are only three words; you will come to conclude only one thing—sadhana, aradhana, and prabhupati. Let me put it to you in a practical way: A gun that has grooves will hit right; others won't. That's why they make the grooves in a gun's barrel. Grooves are for hitting the bull's eye. So in your mind, you have to keep the grooves, but how do you keep the grooves? We put the grooves in our own mind by a particular sadhana.

Sadhana is the most selfish act. Why early in the morning? The answer is very simple. Why at the ambrosial hours? Because that's when the sun hits Earth at sixty degrees. Why do you go berserk in the evening? Because that's when the sun hits you at sixty degrees. It is sixty to sixty; no big deal. You can't read the sun. At three thirty a.m., it's not at your longitude or latitude; there is no Sun, but the angle is correct. You must understand that the things that have become rituals were once realities. They are still realities, but we have never read, never understood, and never explained them. We think that a bunch of stupid people get up at three o'clock in the morning, take a cold shower, sit down, and say one word—*Sat Nam, Sat Nam, Sat Nam*. We think, well, they are crazy. No, they are not. You are crazy! You who get up with a cup of coffee; you are crazy. You do not get up consciously, and if you do not get up consciously, you will not spend your day consciously. You will not work out consciously, and that day is your bad day; it is not what was read in the stars for you.

Some people tell me they love me. I agree. A lot of you love me, but I sometimes wonder do you love yourself? Some people have done for me more than I even have words to thank them for, but have they done enough for themselves?

Now, I am who I am. I am a spiritual teacher. I am supposed to teach your spirit. What shall I do? Put methylated spirits, or gasoline, there instead of your real spirit in order to make you move? You create two things, like the Earth—you have the movement around your own axis and the movement of your orbit. Your orbit is your destiny, which I can help; the axis is your problem. Your ego is your problem.

The idea behind teaching rebirthing is a very old idea that is now being cast in the United States and the Western world. The idea is to release the subconscious, the storehouse of misery. The subconscious is not a good thing. It's a good store, but when its disk gets cluttered, it won't let you move in your life—that's the tragedy of it. It numbs people to reality. Some people take up their axial pattern, and they are very rude. Some people take up their axial pattern, and they are very, very lazy. There is always one facet in your life that will govern you, and that is called the Crown Principle. We want only one Crown Principle: Start working on your mind.

Tonight we are going to work maybe a little late. How many people have an appointment or dates after nine p.m.? After that time, some of you get very itchy, your butts start hurting, and you start moving; so I start cutting down the class as much as I can. But my idea is that tonight is a very special night, and I want to work with you, and I want you to work with me. Is that agreeable? Ready? Because I don't want to do it today if you don't want to do it. I don't want to go into everybody's subconscious and take that can of worms and loosen it up if you are just going to go walking about in your life tomorrow, putting your garbage all over the place. That would be terrible. I want you to just open it up, clean it up, patch it up, and send you back. That's the way I want to do it. Is that understood? I have some moral responsibility; I am not as bad as you think. I have to do certain things, all right? Let's work it out.

◆ ◆ ◆

You all have dread in you; all you have to do is get out that dread. Remember all the previous ages when you were a lion, when you were a black panther. (*See Exercise 1.*) Why do you go and pay six hundred dollars to some idiot who is going to put you in a hypnotic state and make a tape recording and give you fifteen tapes and charge you one hundred dollars a tape, letting you know that you were this or that, you were born in Egypt when it was lush.

Sometimes I wonder why you are insecure. When you attack the psyche, you will feel weak. Your own psyche you can't attack? You want to win the world? Come on. This will go away, I can bet on that, but don't let that fall apart. If we are working, then we are working. Hey, wait! I told you that when you get to the lion's breath your hands will become weak. It is exactly reverse; it's not right. When you get to lion's breath, watch me clearly, and I can show you how it comes to be. You will find in you the strength of twenty horses and three elephants. If a dead man knows this kriya, he can get up, write his will, shake hands, and die again.

I am not kidding. Please learn that you must breathe the alternate breath, the Cannon Breath. Do it with that strength.

Hold on. Do you want to experience something, or do you just want to pay ten dollars? I am not teaching you this for my sake. What should I tell you? You don't deserve a teacher. You are just idiots! You come with your ten bucks—what are you giving it to me for? For what? You want to learn something? You want to get rid of something? Do it; otherwise, don't come to my class at all. I don't need this gathering. I simply felt the pain that you carry—this whole load of garbage in your mind. You have to be relieved of that. We can't go on analyzing ourselves and going through all this. Let us do it tonight. That's why I prepared you yesterday; so let's work it out. Understand that? It's going to be a class, and you are going to participate; otherwise, pick up your coat and your boots and out you go.

Don't let your aura change. We've got to deal and heal our self; it's a very honorable thing to do. Don't be slaves! Free your soul. Some of you are just lazy—get out.

Inhale deep, and lock your hands please, and pull. Pull to the outside, with all your strength, and hold the breath. Let the ribcage go through the creativity of it; exhale. *(See Exercise 2.)*

God took man's seventh rib and made a woman. Woman can create another man, man can't; man is a help. That's what it symbolically means. It doesn't matter that He took the bone and created a woman. Creativity is a woman, and seventh bone is nothing but the center of the Heart Chakra. So I am telling you to open up that chakra by force. I don't have eighteen years to teach you Hatha Yoga; I am going to do it in exactly eighteen seconds, so be with me.

One who cannot maintain Root Lock is not worthy of sexual intercourse; but you do it every day anyway, who cares. Perfect yourself! This is where you decide that you want the energy to go to your brain or to the other person. Root Lock decides—not you. Now they've got a pelvic muscle, then they've got the G-spot—God knows what they'll get next. They've got nothing.

Once the spine is under your control, the head has no connection at that time, and you are totally by yourself. Stronger, stronger, stronger, stronger—it gives you all the energy you need.

Creativity, new ideas will come; new opportunities will come; luck will smile at you—which is why, in our language, the pelvic bone is called luck. You say it is good luck or bad luck; they say it is good lower back or bad lower back that decides everybody's opportunity.

All right, now relax please, and sit straight. Go through your seventh year *(see Exercise 4)*, the first complete cycle of consciousness. We will only do two years—the seventh and the eleventh.

Consciousness grows by the age cycle of seven years. Intelligence grows by the cycle of eleven years. Life grows by the cycle of eighteen years. These are Earthly years; we call them sun years, not light years. The age of the stars is measured by light years. The age of the human is measured by sun years. The seventh year is your first year of conscious change—please replay it.

Now open your mouth but keep your eyes closed; don't open them. Open your mouth, not the eyes, and breathe in and out. (*See Exercise 5.*) Breathe as if you are giving birth—from the pelvis to the mouth and the mouth to the pelvis; breathe.

Now, please replay, intelligently, your eleventh year. You will get rid of a lot of garbage. Intelligently replay it. (*See Exercise 6.*)

Please copy the sounds of the chant. (*See Exercise 7.*) It is a prosperity mantra.

Now, please save your breath and just listen to this. You have eight chakras—the Eighth Chakra is the aura—eight chakras. You also have to understand your five *tattvas*. Eight times five comes to forty. When you repeat these words, there are exactly four *Hars*, and the fifth is the *Gaitri Mantra Shabad*, which makes five times the eight words of the *Gaitri*—that's forty.

Now, why are we doing this? Are we insane? No. there is one law which you cannot cross and that is called the Law of Creative Nature. Either things will always come to you or you will always go after things; it cannot be that sometimes you go after things and sometimes things come after you. It's wrong, it never happens and that's the main confusion. That's why you can't sit and wait. God is very clever. God created this world to play, and we created union with God in order to play God. So there is a direct confrontation between man and God. Don't think that you are very humble. As a human, you are not humble; you play God, and God plays you. You made Him make magpies. There are so many stories in which man has totally made God work for him. So man is no little animal, little bird, some mosquito that can only buzz, buzz, buzz. Man has done something very great. There are men who have led us to believe by experience that God works for us.

I asked someone, "What are you doing?"

"I don't know. Guruji told me to do it, so I am doing it."

"You are pretty lucky."

"Is something wrong?"

"Yeah. Can you tell your son what are you doing?"

"No."

"Why not?"

"Oh, Guruji said, 'It is only for you.'"

"Your son is not for you, your daughter is not for you, your wife is not for you, your neighbors are not for you? Since when you are living this alone business?"

Kundalini Yoga gives a human nothing but prosperity and perpetual strength, an unending strength that can't be stolen; it can't be taken away.

There is nobody who is alone. Everybody lives either with his good luck or with misery. Nobody is alone. I have never met one person who is alone, even those who complain they are alone. Just tell them where you've come from, "Oh, I just had a party;" these are alone. The game we play in life is apathy–sympathy; we do not play the game of prosperity and perpetual-ness.

Kundalini Yoga gives a human nothing but prosperity and perpetual strength, an unending strength that can't be stolen; it can't be taken away. Once you set yourself up, things will start working for you. It's ridiculous to work for everything; it's impossible. Nobody has succeeded, and everything has a limit. The president can go for four years and another four years, while a king can go for his whole life, but both are nothing but a rubber stamp. Life takes away the juice in order to give you a status. Remember this law of nature: Whenever you have a power, you have a limit.

Mantar sidh nahee, sadhana nahee, mantar sidh nahee. Mantar sidh nahee means "mental vibrations are not perfected." So are you going to do it right? Or are you just going to talk the whole day? That's not interesting. Thank you very much. I don't want you to become rich overnight! I want you to work hard for it.

My problem is simple. Take it as you like, but within my psyche, I am just mad today because you didn't do a good job. I gave you the opportunity to learn just one thing: If you can breathe the *Trishula* breath—that is, inhale ten seconds, hold ten seconds, and exhale ten seconds—then you will have enough energy to understand what I am talking about. You chant this mantra only with the tongue, which is also known as the *Gian Lingam*, the *lingam* of knowledge, the organ of knowledge. But you have to understand; learn with me and bear with me. There are two powerful plates in your whole body: your tongue and your upper palate. The rest is all bogus. Your upper palate has eighty four meridian points, and when the tongue rotates and touches those eighty four meridian points, it creates a permutation and combination that bring you opportunity. That's why if you speak a few words, you win; but if you speak a few words wrong, you lose. Words do not mean anything; it is the permutation and combination that your psyche creates that repels or attracts. You understand?

Word is not a small thing. Word is the real power. Words makes the body act and react, draw or reject; it's a magnetic field. The whole universe is a magnetic field. Nobody is anybody's friend, nobody loves anybody; it's all a bogus lie. It's a total fraud. If we create positive words, we feel love; if we create negative words, we feel hatred. The way you act with your cat, with your dog, with your friend will all be different. The way you act with people will always create hatred or friendship, whenever you want. Nobody is anybody's friend. We create friends, we de-

stroy friends; we create lovers, we destroy lovers; we create students, we destroy students; we have people, we leave people; we let go, we let come; it's all central psyche.

It's a telephone exchange system. You make a call, and they pick up, and you both start talking. In between, there are miles of difference. How can someone in Los Angeles talk to New York? He goes all the way up, and he goes all the way down; that is possible. You can go that much up and that much down, and you can communicate—it's possible. But can you possibly communicate correctly so that you can have everybody as a friend? You have to decide. I don't have to decide; you have to decide. You want to hustle and hassle for everything in your life? Is that the way you want to live? Or, instead, do you want things to come to you? That's your decision. If 1989 is the year of prosperity, I will be working with you to bring prosperity. I have a selfish motive.

Let me tell you one thing: I make a lot of money because I know how to, and I want all of you to make money, too. I pretend to be miserable; but really I am a very happy man, and I want you to learn how to pretend to be miserable but be very happy. Just understand; it's my duty as a teacher to tell you what to do. Otherwise, I don't care—whatever you do is the will of God. Sometimes I put my will into it, and that's called prayer. A teacher's prayer is very powerful—the love of a woman, the blessing of God, the virtue of the mother, and the prayer of the teacher. Your own prayer won't work; you have to work for it.

In my own life, I realized this when I was sixteen and a half years old—just sixteen and a half years old. I was a good yoga student, that's all I can say. One day I was told I have an audience with my teacher, just like that. I went and saw him. I sat down, and I was very respectful. He started looking at me and inspecting me all over. It was an unusual day. I thought to myself, you get only one audience with your teacher every twelve years. When I was twelve years old, I had one, so I thought I would be twenty-four before I get another. But I was sixteen and a half when I was called in. I went there and sat down, and all those other students, colleagues of mine, two hundred of them, were outside.

I sat and he said, "Bhajan."

"Yes, sir."

"Well, from now onward, you are a master."

"Yes, sir."

I had a habit of saying, "Yes, sir." I couldn't say, "What does it mean?" I was not an American, so I didn't say, "Why? What are you trying? What did you see in me? How am I going to do it? What does it mean to me? Please, I am not ready yet." And all that stuff. I could have said that, but I said, "Yes, sir."

Don't bother whether there is darkness in life; just create the light. It is a law: Where there is light, there is no darkness.

He said, "So be it. But there is one condition: We have to leave this country."

Now, I am a man of the crown, prince of the state, how can I? But I never said yes or no; only, "Yes, sir."

"When we go to the other country, I will be alive and so will you; but you shall not see me in person ever again, and this is an order."

"Yes, sir."

I left, and there were about two hundred fifty or three hundred people who said, "What happened?"

"Nothing."

"But what did he say?"

"I am master."

"What?"

"Sit down, everybody, and bow." And they all sat down, and they bowed. I was a master. I realized that the word has the power.

"How long do we have to bow?"

"Until I say get up."

Then I said, "Now, get up everybody and look at me for the last time," because you do not look at the face of your teacher; you always look at his feet. So I said, "Look at my face for the last time. I was one among you, and now I am the master, and you are all my domain. Now go." That's it; that's how it happens.

It happened in seconds, because the blessing of the teacher is vouched for by God. The word of the Guru is vouched for by God. Whether it's gospel or not gospel, I don't know; I am just telling you how it is. The word of a teacher is vouched for by God. The word of a man is vouched for by his honor, by his deed; the word of a woman is creative. These three things will never go away. A woman who cannot re-create life and a man who cannot fulfill his destiny of nobility and a teacher who cannot bless? I don't buy it; there's something wrong somewhere. So just understand what I am trying to tell you, whether we are few or we are many, it doesn't matter. The question is, are our values virtues, or are our values hassling? Are we yo-yos, or we are creative?

Creative is what? What is creative for an engineer? Nothing. An engineer is creative, but his wife is running away. A doctor is very great, he heals the whole world; but his own son jumps out of the window—that's not creative. Creative is when you control your entire psyche. Something that is going to be destroyed and you know it—stop it from being destroyed. Once something is not going to grow, flourish it. Your magnetic field should be creative.

Put a candle somewhere. Try this at home: Darken the house, and then take a matchstick and burn the head of a candle; there will be no darkness. Where there is

light, there is no darkness; where there is darkness, there is no light. This is a law. Create light, and darkness automatically goes away. You waste all your life and energy getting rid of the darkness. You are so stupidly self-destructive. Don't bother whether there is darkness in life; just create the light. It is a law: Where there is light, there is no darkness. Where there is "I," there is no "Thou." Where there is "Thou," there is no "I." That is a second law. Those who trust God, the universe, Mother Nature, serves them: *Ridhi Siddi, Nauniddi.*

All occult powers, all angels, all demons, all destructive and constructive powers serve those who trust God. Those who love God? They sweat. So make a choice. You know what I am saying? You can love God and tell stories about it and have fun—and misery—at your own feet. But if you just trust God, the entire nature will start loving you—the entire nature.

Once when I was riding a horse from my village to the district town, I saw a man walking. There were eight or nine of us, and we had time, so we began playing a game—riding three miles this way and three miles that way. We ran helter-skelter; we were not on a path. And during this time, I saw a snake, a big snake, running in front with a man following it. It surprised me. I said, "What is this now? A snake normally runs after man, but here is a man running after a snake." It was reverse. When that man saw me, he stopped, and the snake ran away and disappeared.

I said, "What can I do for you?"

"I have lost the way, and I have to go to district headquarters."

"Why were you chasing a snake?"

"No, the snake was guiding me. I was not chasing him. He is letting me go because you came in."

"Okay, now you want a horse?"

"No, I can run as a horse can run. I don't have to ride the horse."

"Are you sure?"

"I am very sure."

"Well, my rule is that I am the prince of this estate, and I have to take the bridle of the horse, and you have to be on it because our law says, 'Guest is a God.' Now that I have acquainted myself with you, you are my guest."

"I can't do it."

"Until we reach our spare horses, I cannot give you a horse, so you have to ride this horse, or we both have to walk. Which one do you choose?"

"Is it a custom, or you are doing it from the heart?"

"My heart and my head have nothing to do with it; it's a rule that I must obey."

He rode the horse, and I took the reins. He thought I was joking; but I was not joking, I was real. And you know what he said?

"Hey you, son, the world will obey you."

"Which world?"

"That world, yonder there, where you have not yet gone."

Can you believe it? You are head of the state, you enjoy the whole thing, but somebody is saying, We are going away to the other side. Somebody said the yonder land, and I thought to myself, "God, where is he sending me?"

But, you know, there is a mental habit not to question. "There is not to reason why, there is but to do or die rode the six hundred." Charge, charge of the light brigade. The mental power to accept is a habit, and when opportunity comes, you say, "Yes, sir." That's what Guru Nanak said in *Japji*:

> *Ketia dookh bukh sad maar*
> *Eh bhe daat teree daataar.*
> If misery comes to me and misfortune comes to me and it comes
> a hundred times, that is your gift O Lord.[1]

When you start accepting things in that way, God will never give you trouble, because He is infinite. You can kill a rooster, but it takes two hundred times the guts to kill a chicken; you can't do that. So when the individual soul starts accepting Thy Will, then the Eye of God opens up. Not your eye; the God's Eye opens up for you, and the universe starts serving you. That is the real way to be rich and happy and to multiply. That's the real way. But what happens when you start walking on the spiritual path, the path of reality? Then you start being challenged because of your firmness, your steadiness, your basement. You know, when they make a basement, they dig it up, they put the stone, they put the cement, and then they hammer it. The idea is to make the basement steady.

In Canada, I went through that basement situation. I had no shoes on my feet; I was naked and minus so much. I used to take a newspaper and make slippers out of it. There was no money, and there were no friends; the opportunity I had come for went away. I used to sing this song, which sometimes you sing, "One day the day shall come when all the glory shall be Thine; people shall say it is yours; I shall deny not mine." I just made up the verses and sang it all the time. At that time, I never knew you, and you never knew me. But I know I have come to replay the destiny. It's already there. It's already there.

Twenty years ago, an Indian from a third world country, economically poor—mosquitoes, flies, absolutely dirty—came here, and you started touching his feet. Don't you understand? Do you touch my feet? No, you touch your soul. You don't touch my feet, because under my feet is my soul, which is your soul. Nobody touches my feet; nobody has to. Why are you so beautiful and still your feet are not touched? Because you are not related to your soul. Soul is under the foot of the person.

[1] As translated by Yogi Bhajan

Once the astrologer Pandit Ram Chand, my personal astrologer, said, "Yogi Baba, please for God's sake, don't go to America. Please look at the stars. For two and a half months you will never have water, nor food, nor clothes. You will have nothing; these are the deadliest months, two and a half; only Mars is transit through your Saturn, Jupiter into this, and that is this." He totally calculated the entire thing.

I sat down and said, "Pandit, here is eleven hundred rupees. You are my friend, and you have told me the truth. I know I'll have no food, I'll have nothing to walk on. I will be absolutely dead, dread poor, right?"

"Yes, painful if you go now; but after two and a half months, everything will be fine."

"No, Pandit, if I start obeying the stars, then the stars will never obey me. Now, let me go through it. I know how to go through the eye of the hurricane. My name is Harbhajan. And hurricane and Harbhajan—both start with H. I say, 'I will go through the eye of it; don't worry about it.'"

"God, I love you; my whole mathematics will be wrong."

"It's not wrong; it will be right. But you don't understand what I am saying. You are telling me to obey the stars, and I am telling you that I am going to make the stars obey! Simple dialogue, there is no big deal. Let me go."

He was right. In Amsterdam, all my luggage was stolen. When I landed in Montréal, they told me that. They gave me twenty-five dollars to buy a toothbrush, underwear, or toothpaste, whichever I choose at the Montréal airport. They put me on the plane. I came to Toronto, which was where I was supposed to be joining the university. I was to establish blah, blah, blah, but my guide died hitting a light pole. There was nobody to receive me; none whatsoever. There I was—in a foreign country, and in minus forty-five degree chill factor, sitting in Toronto, wearing a silken robe that somebody had given to me as a special gift. I was a customs officer; therefore, the airline gave me four seats to sleep, and they were very sorry that my luggage got lost. Do you believe this? I can't go out; I was sitting there; and I don't know who to call, what to do, who to meet? This one officer, who was trained by me in Delhi, recognized me. It took him two to three hours to find someone who could accommodate me, and then he took me there; that's how I started.

The next day, somebody took away my shoes, and my feet were so big that nothing fit them. So I took a couple of newspapers and strapped them up, nothing to change into—ask my wife. I called her from the embassy in Ottawa, and she said, "How are you doing?"

I said, "Perfect but I have no underwear, and I don't know what to do about it unless you send some to me through a diplomatic courier."

My *kacheras* came because I knew the prime minister. I knew the ambassador. I knew everybody. Finally, they learned that I have no money and I have no work and I am just running around. They called me the man's commission, and still my passport bears it. The guy gave me a hundred and fifty dollars and stamped my passport.

"What are you doing this for?" I asked

"Well, because you have been asked by us to come to Canada, and you are going to be an asset to our society. We are giving you maintenance money, one hundred and fifty dollars a week—free."

"I don't live by welfare. I know how to earn; I will earn so much money that I can hire you; it's only a matter of days."

"Within those days you will freeze to death."

"But I am not accepting this money."

"My job is in jeopardy over this. You want my children to be outside in this cold?"

"Okay." So I took the check and tore it in the center and said, "That will satisfy you? You have stamped my passport and have paid me. I tore up the check and left it in anger. You can report it this way."

"God, you are a strange Indian."

"Yes, a good Indian is a dead Indian, and I am a strange Indian; I am going to live here. I am going to be here, you understand? You are a Canadian, right? I am a landed Canadian now, and I am going to live here; I am not going to ask you for money."

"Who you are going to ask?"

"The one who created the calendar; I am going to ask that guy."

"That guy has a name?"

"Yeah, he is called Mr. Generating Organizing and Destroying self, and you call him God."

Like that; I walked away from his office. My relatives asked me, "Did they help you?"

"No."

"Did they give you something?"

"Yeah, they tried to give me something, but I didn't accept it."

"Why?"

"Because I know better."

"Don't you need help?"

"Once you start getting help from people, then God has the right to sleep. I won't let this guy sleep! He brought me to Canada; He has got to take care of me, doesn't matter how."

"Are you angry at God?"

"Never. I am just telling Him to do His job right. He should do like a God, not like a crazy person."

"What are you going to do?"

"I don't do anything; everything will be done for me."

Within two and a half months, I hit the front page of the *Globe and Mail* in an article. I never looked like a Yogi; please don't misunderstand me. I used to have a polka-dotted turban, pink in color; I used to have one shirt and a pair of pants that never fit me, even to the last day. In our Sikh Dharma archives we still have a blanket that has so many holes. Five or six people used to take turns warming ourselves with that blanket. We called it a "holy blanket" because there were so many holes you could see through it. We never cared; we built up an empire and gave it away.

Earth is Earth. Earth means meaning. Planet Earth is called Earth because it has a meaning. Life here has to be meaningful. There is one Gurmukhi word called *anarth*, which is a tragedy in which you lose the meaning of life. As I told you the other day, when you add alertness to G, it becomes age; when you add sincerity, it becomes sage. These are states of "altar" consciousness, which you all can learn.

Therefore, I am asking you to take this mantra home. Sit with it, wake up with it, and sleep with it. Chant it, and when you chant it, chant with your pure tongue, so that your upper palate can send the Morse code signal to the Creator. I am very practical—my life is a science, and my actions are an art. I always put some goodness and juice into it. But just remember, you all have this year of prosperity—it's for all of us. If we don't grab it, we are going to suffer for the nine years to follow. So don't let it loose, you hear me?

Dr. Soram told me yesterday, "Sir, your health isn't fit for teaching the class. We can bail you out of it." I said, "No, dear son, I have certain responsibilities that I have to discharge; nobody else can do it for me." That's why I have come to teach these classes to you. At one thirty and at two thirty, Baljeet came to check my pulses when I was in bed. See how smart and alert I am right now! Because now I have to perform my duty, and the beauty is in duty, not in gossips, or wasting time, or pretending and saying, "I love you." It's not in pretending to live with you, not in any of that commotional nonsense. Just be alert. Just be alert, and Nature will serve you, and God will provide you everything. God is the creator of everything. Can't He create goodness for you? Heavens, what are you trying? You are just being tested. Roasted almonds are always tastier than the raw. Don't be afraid to get roasted a little bit.

That's what sadhana is—three o'clock cold shower, going to a place, doing these things—just getting roasted so we will become a little tastier.

Are you with me? So, will you chant really from the tongue so I can satisfy myself tonight that I have not failed as a teacher and that my students were at least cooperative if not conscious? Well, I am just asking for a little, and I don't expect too much. As much as I have taught and left with you, if you had practiced one hundredth of it, none of you would have any trouble. Come on.

Roasted almonds are always tastier than the raw. Don't be afraid to get roasted a little bit.

Everybody with tongue alone. Tongue is called T-square; use it. *Ang Sang Wahe Guru. Ang* means the "limb;" tongue means the T-square limb. If somebody is an engineer, you will fully understand what T-square means. You would not get any shelter or house built if you did not know what a T-square is. Am I right? Do you understand? If somebody doesn't have a tongue, what do you call him? Mute? No, you are afraid to say the real word—dumb.

If you don't hear, you are deaf and dumb. The entire psyche within you is your ENT—ears, nose, and throat. If you do not smell properly, you are always in trouble. If you do not hear properly, you are always in trouble. If you do not speak properly, you are always trouble. The tongue is called T-square; it's the basic rule of construction, isn't it? It's called "T-Ang"—tongue, in English. You call it tongue; in our vernacular, we call it *jeeb*. It's the same as *ji* and *ab*—*Jeeb. Japji*—a soul that can be presented to you now.

Jeeb, jeebhou jap de har har naam. It's called *jeebhou*; it's also called *rasna*. All the five *tattvas* and their juices can be seen and tasted by the tongue. It's a T-square, so use it, as hard as you can! I want that result! I just want to see the arcline and let you go. Otherwise we are going to sit here the whole night.

Thank you very much. It works, but you have to be good at it. It took that much to correctly pronounce it—thirty seconds, and it is all good. You are all very good; your power of prayer is perfect, but sometimes you do not trust yourself to use it. Please have a very happy week. I think we will meet you Tuesday and Wednesday, and after that I will be gone to be with the kids. You will have to wait until I come back; you have to pray so I can come back.

◆ ◆ ◆

May the long time sun shine upon you,
all love surround you, and the pure light within you, guide your way on.

Sat Nam

Everybody has a lot of facets, known and unknown. Those who are trying to show only one side (and, normally, as a human being, we show just one part) are insecure. We do it intentionally. It's not that we are crazy; we are dishonest. Every human being is dishonest. Basically we are all liars who never trust God and who show our insecurity for sympathy and empathy—and that's called tragedy.

Life is not tragic because God created you tragic or for tragedy—that's not true. It can never happen, bless you. It happens because the part you put out is insecure.

Put out that you are secure and just see how the world comes to you. Because you must understand, the yo-yo has a distance already measured on a thread, right? If you want to dance on the thread, then that's the way it is. But once you let yourself be free and trust God as Infinity, with that Infinity, you will be the happiest person. It's not just you. I have seen the most powerful people. I have met kings and queens and the president and all the great people in the world. I have also met a lot of spiritual people. Everybody is crazy.

I am fifty eight years old. Am I fifty eight years old? I am going to be fifty nine, and I am sick and tired of these people. There are people who teach how to feel secure, but they are the most insecure. The best thing is to trust God; trust God and live that way. Don't trust friends; they all have an end. Why trust something that has an end? Trust something that has no end. In twenty years, I came here and built an empire. You have been here twenty years with me, and you are still hustling. Where is the relationship? Get out and be successful. Trust God and make tomorrow yours. I am telling you the key to success! These books and philosophies and seminars at UCLA aren't going to make you successful.

Trust God. Tomorrow morning you will wake up and go and conquer the world—it is yours. You know why? Why don't you ask me how it is possible? Either trust me or question me. Anybody have the guts? It's a very simple thing that belongs to God. If you trust the one who is the Owner, the part of ownership that is you will have the governorship; that's the rule. It's called the Law of Rulership. You have not read history nor economics nor physics. I don't know what to do; you guys have to work it all out. But tomorrow, when you get up, get up with one idea in mind: Don't believe in God, don't love God; just trust God and conquer the world. Try it one day. You will be surprised how much you can achieve.

Have a nice day, thank you very much, and see you next week. Here's to the best of your health and happiness.

UNLOADING YOUR PAIN & FEAR II—
THE KRIYA
January 4, 1989

Eat very lightly before practicing this kriya. Soup or fruit several hours before practice is recommended. If you have too much food in the belly, then it becomes very difficult to stimulate the Navel Point. There are no breaks between the exercises. Move immediately from one exercise to the next.

1. Make your hands into claws. With the elbows bent, bring the hands to eye level, about 18–24 inches apart. Make your arms very stiff and strong. Open the eyes wide. After **90 seconds**, open the mouth wide, extend the tongue, and begin breathing through the mouth—Lion's Breath—fast and heavy. Don't let the hands relax with the breath. Keep the tension in the hands and the arms for another **90 seconds**. This exercise is **3 minutes total**.

Make a dreadful angry face. Become the most dreadful beast. Get the dread out. You all have dread in you. Don't tell me you know better; all you have to do is get out that dread. Get to be a very powerful, tremendous, very awful, dreadful beast! Bring strength into your claws and stiffen your forearm and attack. Attack the psyche! Now, breathe like a lion, African lion; powerful cannon breath they call it. Keep this strength; don't let the fingers go weak. Come on get rid of all that hidden anger that will destroy you. Come on, sit and make it tight and strong. Now breathe, harder; come on out, come out heavy and strong. Let us really do it—open up the chest, ribcage.

2. With the fingers interlaced in front of the face and the forearms parallel to the floor, cup the palms in the shape of a dome, facing downward—Dome Lock. Inhale deeply and suspend the breath. Pull your fingers away from each other, with all your strength, without releasing the fingers for **30 seconds**. Exhale and relax, relaxing the mudra between sequences. Repeat the sequence 4 more times. Between each sequence, take three quick, clearing breaths. Continue for approximately **3–5 minutes**.

This will open the seventh rib, the Heart Chakra, and free the tailbone. Tear it apart; you have to use the strength of two bears. We are going to change the metabolism, we are going to let the brain understand that we are the masters. I am the master of myself—that's what we are going to do.

If you give any leverage to it, the pelvis will open naturally. And the moment the pelvis opens, that little thing underneath (the coccyx) and the anus—the First Chakra—it can move (and be uncomfortable). So sit balanced, and please safeguard your tailbone. Be sure that your weight is balanced on the sitting bones and stretch the spine up with each repetition.

3. Place the mudra in the lap, palms up, and apply mulbandh. Close the eyes. Keep the lock pulled tightly. Draw the energy up as you lengthen and tighten the lower spine for **2½ minutes**.

Tighten the lower back—first, second, third, fourth vertebrae. Apply the Root Lock. Take the anus, sexual organs, and Navel Point, and pull it all upward—that's called Root Lock. If you are in the correct position, the lower part of the skull will start shaking.

4. Sit straight with the eyes closed and go through the seventh year. Replay, from day one, the entire seventh year for **3 minutes**.

The seventh year is the first year of consciousness. Whenever you were when you were seven years old, just understand and go through day one of your birth to the last of the seventh year; replay it, please. Close your eyes, concentrate, and meditate. Replay the entire seventh year by memory.

5. Open the mouth and breathe heavily, powerfully, through the mouth, as though giving birth. This is a pelvic breath. The entire lower spine must create this breath for **2 minutes**.

We are not asking for a navel breath; we are asking for a pelvic breath. The whole lower area is to move in order to breathe. Open the mouth—an open mouth will work. Heavy, heavy, heavy! Get the energy you need. Restimulate yourself. Inhale deep, exhale, close your mouth, and concentrate.

6. Sit straight with the eyes closed and replay the eleventh year. Gong is played, if available, for **5 minutes**.

7. Chant Har Har Har Har Gobinday for **6 to 11 minutes**.

Har Har Har Har Gobinday
Har Har Har Har Mukanday
Har Har Har Har Udaaray
Har Har Har Har Apaaray
Har Har Har Har Hariang
Har Har Har Har Kariang
Har Har Har Har Nirnaamay
Har Har Har Har Akaamay

Use the tip of the tongue—that is the Lingam. Use the tongue as a lingam and create the sound; copy it. This is a prosperity mantra. You all want money, you all want to be rich, you all want opportunity, you all want to be healthy. You want everything, but you cannot sow it. There are two lingams: one is the male penis and the other is the tongue. The tongue is given to male and female, both; it's called lingam and you have to use only the tongue to create this mantra. It's going to affect you; and I want that effect. The moment you can pull the central nervous system through the tongue, you can get into the state of ecstasy. Tongue and pelvis connect!

There is one law you cannot cross: It is called the Law of Creative Nature. Either things will always come to you, or you will always go after things; it cannot be that sometimes you go after things and sometimes things come after you. It's wrong! It never happens—and that's the main confusion. That's why you can't sit and wait.

So what are we doing here? We are just making a permutation and combination through the lingam. You need a penis, you need a lingam, to produce a baby. Now, this is a psychic lingam. The tongue is nothing but a psychic lingam. So if you speak exactly with the tongue and copy these four words, you will hit the upper palate at the proper point. The heavens are also called the upper palate, and that will shake; that's what you need. The moment you shake the tree, what do you get? You get the fruit. Learn this mantra as a science; don't learn it as a ritual. You have to learn to do this exactly as I'm telling you; before you leave, the tongue has to repeat the sound. Sound is there to control the permutation and combination. The movement of the tongue can be controlled so that it can hit the upper palate, and then the thalamus and the brain and the psychomagnetic field of the body and the neurons will start making the combination. The moment they make the combination, you don't have to worry about anything. You will attract everything to you. Whatever your needs are, they will be met—that's the law.

◆

"No man is yet born of a woman who has learned these three words. Yesterday is yesterday, it can never be today; today is today, it can never be tomorrow; and tomorrow will never become yesterday or today. That is all. "

– Yogi Bhajan

UNLOADING THE PAST OF HARSH MEMORIES 1

January 10, 1989

*ET ME PUT IT THIS WAY SO IT IS VERY SIMPLE: We all know, or we have been told, that we are born in the image of God. We also know that God is everywhere. And we have been assured for centuries that if we worship God, we shall be happy. We have been asked to love God and love our life. You must understand, every human being would love to live forever. That is the hidden purpose. Each one of us uses fashion or makeup to try to look as common as everybody else. The purpose of having a common look is so that it's convenient to convince other people, communicate, talk, influence, exchange ideas, and thoughts with others. These are all pluses and minuses of life.

But as I grow older, I have found through my experience and my meditation that there is no such thing as sickness, pain, and displeasure in life. If it is there, we have the capacity to become insensitive to it. But we don't work on that area, because it is very unpleasant for most people. They have money, plus they have the memory of yesterday. If yesterday couldn't teach you yesterday, it will become pain today. Do you know that? You are supposed to learn from yesterday—yesterday. You should deal with today as today, and you should deal with tomorrow as tomorrow. These three words—yesterday, today, and tomorrow—nobody has learned.

People have written scriptures, people have written books, libraries are full of them, as are colleges, universities, degrees. All those books talk about the incarnations of God and messengers and holy men and personified God. If they want to hang me for saying so, fine, but I am also the head of a religion, and what I am saying is very unreligious, sacrilegious. Still, no man is yet born of a woman who has learned these three words. Yesterday is yesterday, it can never be today; and today is today, it can never be tomorrow; and tomorrow will never become yesterday or today. That is all.

Now, tell me, if you cannot learn three words in your life, what can you learn? I don't care which religion you belong to or which country you belong to. The beauty in America is not that it is a good country. It is a powerful country. No, the beauty of this country is that it is a country of immigrants, and the insecurity of immigration doesn't leave you for seven generations. Find an American who is here seven generations and see how lazy, how neurotic, and how angry he is. Find a first-generation immigrant, how terribly poor he is, how indifferent he is to the environments, and how early in the morning he wants to get up and go to work. Somebody who stays

> *If yesterday couldn't teach you yesterday, it will become pain today. You are supposed to learn from yesterday. You should deal with today as today, and you should deal with tomorrow as tomorrow. These three words—yesterday, today, and tomorrow—nobody has learned.*

here for seven generations, however, develops a lot of anger, a lot of resentment, and a lot of pain. Our problem in life is our yesterday. It passed, it went away, and we are not divine enough, holy enough, or spiritual enough to trust God. We are not noble. We are not respectable. All this drama you see when you leave this ashram and you meet people outside of here? That is all a play, that is all public relations. Every person lives eighty percent public relations, ten percent real, and ten percent fear. Did I make sense? One hundred percent? All of you, no matter how good and bad you are, you are eighty percent public relations.

Go to the doctor's office. All the walls are filled with certificates and photos. Somewhere he shook hands with this, somewhere he did that. I went to a personal friend of mine's office, and I looked at him and said, "How many Ph.D.s on these walls are bought, and how many did really you complete?"

"Well, to tell you very frankly, it is all the work of my public relations department."

"In trying to convince me that you have so many honors and honorary degrees, and so many non-honorable degrees whatever they are, aren't you demoralizing your inner self? Why do you have to have all this outer show to convince yourself that you are wise, educated, and learned?

"Ask me a question. Test me out."

I asked him this question: "What is the value tomorrow of yesterday?"

He couldn't answer. I answered for him: The value tomorrow of yesterday is if you grow up today. Yesterday has no value. Yesterday's only value is if it gives you some encouragement today—and tomorrow has no value in your life. No value! Even with all your money and sex and muscles, all your public relations, which is eighty percent of you, tomorrow has no value for you if you are not prepared for it. A person who is not prepared for tomorrow and a person who has not acted today by learning from yesterday has not yet learned how to live life.

Life is a lie if basic truth is not found. In your life, you must understand that if you love somebody, you won't be happy; if you become rich, you won't be happy; if you sleep tonight with five hundred men, you won't be happy; if you sleep with nine hundred women, you won't be happy. There is no act in life that can make you happy. There is no God that can make you happy. There is no angel that can make you happy. What I am saying looks very strange, if not stupid, to you. But I tell you, if you do not grow up a little bit and mature a little bit today, if you do not have restraint and discipline a little bit, if you cannot control your emotions a little bit, if you do not have kindness and compassion a little bit, you are a stupid beast in the body of a human. You are a direct living insult to God, who created you in his own image.

I can say that I have had trouble in the West. I never expected that. I don't mind that trouble, but people do not have reverence here. Fifteen degrees latitude below us is Mexico. You don't like that country. You just go there to visit because restaurants are cheap and the food is good. But those people, poorer than you Americans, know one thing—reverence. Whether they are Catholic or not, and even with all their corruption, they have one fact known to them, and that is called reverence. We have not learned it. It is strange, because we are only about three hundred miles away, right from this town. It is a very funny thing they have studied—when a Mexican comes to Los Angeles, the first thing he loses is reverence. People who live here are very different from the people who live there. Maybe it is the weather that makes people behave so differently?

But what I am telling you, you who live in America, is that you have a problem: You carry yesterday in memories so deep that it becomes a very powerful gangrene in life's happiness today. Tonight I am going to put you through your garbage, and you are going to stink, but it is not my problem. I didn't ask you to fill your subconscious memory with every known memory of yesterday. You know what you do? You pile up yesterdays. They are always ready for you. But there is only one thing worth remembering. Tomorrow is going to come, and I shall meet it halfway. That is good.

So we are going to go through a stinking meditation tonight, and we are going to let our garbage float. The sun will shine, and we will be light, bright, and beautiful. When the sun shines on a garbage pit, it makes the stink even more serious.

I normally would not have taught this course, because I do not want to infringe on the income of others. I mean, I just teach you a class; whereas other people charge six thousand dollars plus nine months' commitment and make you cry like babies to go through rebirthing. To be very frank, that is all unnecessary. That is just polarizing and dramatizing something that is basically very simple. But tonight you will go through your own pain.

We will cover a couple of years of yesterdays tonight. If you bear with me through this insanity, the net result will be that we will end up lighter, we will find some little relief, and we will be strong enough to face our tomorrow. If you can face your tomorrow, you can face your God—that is the purpose of life. Those who are afraid to face their tomorrow have already denied God yesterday. Just remember that.

I do not know what I can tell you about spirituality and goodness, kindness and richness, your beauty and your wonders, and all that stuff. I do not know what I should tell you about yoga and meditation, power and release, and relief from the stress and strain of life. But simple things I do know: If you are willing to face your tomorrow with a smile, then you are already facing God, or the Unknown. And if you have faced yourself well today, then you have already faced yourself well tomorrow.

Your fear of death is proportionate to the threat on your life. Death doesn't come to a person who isn't afraid of death. Death needs an atmosphere of fear. Disease is only a vehicle; it's actually the fear of death that kills a person, just as it is the fear of poverty that actually makes you poor. I have been in Los Angeles twenty years, and I do not know how you can be poor. You might be thinking that I am following President Reagan, who says the

If you can face your tomorrow, you can face your God—that is the purpose of life. Those who are afraid to face their tomorrow have already denied God yesterday. Just remember that.

As long as those born of a woman do not know how to respect a woman, there shall be no peace.

homeless are not homeless because they want the open air. That is his explanation. He is the president of the United States. He has seven more days to go. Whatever Nancy teaches him at night, that's all he speaks in the morning. He is a very, very faithful husband. She watches him very cleverly and intelligently, but she knows.

The only way to avoid divorce in life is to just go by the fundamental word of God—that is, she contains he, woman contains the man, and female contains the male. If you ever love a male but you cannot contain him or you do not have the capacity to contain him, don't marry. Don't be friends, don't go on the first date. It will be a very painful mistake. If a woman is not willing or ready, by understanding or by education, to contain that man, I don't have to say anything. "In the beginning, there was a word; word was with God, word was God," and that is what it is. Woman can do whatever she wants. I give her all rights. I teach women to be great. I feel that if a woman is great, the entire family becomes great. A man does not need a beautiful woman or, very literally, an educated woman. A man needs a very graceful woman. A man who thinks he can be happy, fulfilled, and successful without a graceful woman is a lunatic—an insane, sex maniac animal worth nothing. Because man without a very graceful, noble woman—whether it is a mother, wife, grandmother, friend, aunt, or niece, I am not judging the earthly relationship—knows no happiness.

Sometimes people ask me what I think of a woman. If God has to take shape on the Earth, he has to be born through a woman, or he should drop from the sky; he has two choices. People ask me whether World War III will happen or not, and I tell you tonight: As long as those born of a woman do not know how to respect a woman, there shall be no peace. We will keep on building cannons and atomic bombs and threatening each other and not threatening each other. One thing you must understand: The unseen hand of tomorrow, which you call God and I call tomorrow, will straighten out all of us, because God has one powerful virtue: God negotiates. God is the biggest negotiator.

Remember, last year, when there was a big drought in the Midwest. It is funny—people who were churchgoers felt much less stress and pain than people who were not. It is a strength. Because what is going to church, what is being religious, what is being a godly person? What is all this theory? All this God business is just that people are willing to meet tomorrow head on.

I feel there are three types of people: First are those who live in yesterday, and they shall have no tomorrow, for they deny God. Second are those who live today; they will have difficulty tomorrow, because they will always be unhappy and remorseful because today is gone. Third are those who will live to meet tomorrow half way. You know what will happen to them? That Almighty God will serve them and help them face it and win, because God is tomorrow and through his own image he enjoys this world.

It is a very stupid teaching in the spiritual world that God lives through us. It's not true. God is a very funny guy. He created this Earth to be busy. And He created a word called challenge, and he gave us—his pawns—the ego to meet that challenge. That is why, by nature, we prefer to be brave and martial, and in the name of that, sometimes we are executors.

However, tonight we are going to offload our past. We will be going through a very heavy method. The normal cost in Los Angeles of this gimmick is about $6,000 and six to nine months of doing of it. I am just preparing you today and tomorrow, because this Saturday I am going to San Diego to really grind you through it, which should be sufficient to get rid of all that pain we have. But let us start today and try to deal with it as we must.

Ready? Find a suitable comfortable area, so you can sit comfortably and be firm. Whatever posture you adapt, keep it until the end. Now, please start breathing in a simple way without making any movement (*see Exercise 1*).This cool breath is very healing. *Sitali pranayam*, with the power of the navel. Those ladies who are pregnant, when they go to deliver, they practice this breath mostly incorrectly. I have gone to those classes, and I have seen. You are doing it very correctly, but you are not doing it very powerfully. Everybody is pregnant here, so please participate strongly. Breathe strongly, not wrongly—strongly.

Are you going to give up? Don't. Keep up! Remember when you were in the womb of the mother, the labor pain—you will experience that. You can yawn and sneeze, and you can even stop, but then continue. Keep going. You are not causing the labor pains. Come on, please. Let us all go through it. Breathe properly—strongly, but not wrongly.

There are two words you have to learn in life. One is grateful, the other is ungrateful. Those who remember grateful will be full of great things. Those who are ungrateful shall always have a void of great things. That is all. You want to know prosperity, you want richness, you want happiness, be grateful. Your aura is set, your energy is set—you can all do it. The arcline is blue, blue and bright. The energy in the arcline is very powerful. You are absolutely vibrating with me in a very beautiful tone. The God-given power that He gave me took away from me the dream, so all this fanciful living and dreams, this pain, anxiety, and fear, this is the time to get rid of that.

See, I am keeping up with you, and you should be keeping up with me. When I know I can't keep up, I have to let you change. So it will be for you today to do as much as you can because this is the best way to do it. That is how it should always be done. Go through the flush of my energy. Tomorrow bring your eighty-year-old grandmother and your nine-year-old daughter, or a sister or a relative.

People lie, but the aura doesn't. Please, let it go through you. Save your body's energy and just go through it.

If you are ever in pain and you do not know what to do, play this music, this *Rakhe Rakhan Har*. It doesn't matter what the pain is. We are not making any claim, but by

There are two words you have to learn in life. One is grateful, the other is ungrateful. Those who remember grateful will be full of great things. Those who are ungrateful shall always have a void of great things. That is all.

People do yoga, people do therapy and counseling and all that. But aren't you aware that if you do not breathe, you are dead? And that breath, which can keep you alive—why can it not take care of your little mental disorientations?

the time this song comes to its third round, you cannot feel the pain. Try it. It is not an open challenge. It is not a miracle, nor is it not a miracle. You put this on anytime, especially when you are hurting, and first round, I don't promise you; second round, maybe. But when it repeats the third time, you will not have pain. It is a guarantee. It is a fact.

If you don't have the music with you and you are in a position where the restroom is available, please go and sit on the seat and deeply inhale and powerfully pump your navel point. In three breaths of life, the pain will disappear.

Mental pain is much more serious than physical pain. It is an attack. When it comes, your body cannot stand it. It damages your body. I have realized that there is a certain way of life here such that when I deal with people, they hurt. I let it go, and it hurts deeper. It causes physical problems. You do not have to suffer. You are not born to suffer. You are alive; it's a fact of life. Hold the Breath of Fire in yourself, the Breath of Life, and pump the navel. The navel has the pure energy. You can live without the Breath of Life through the navel in the womb of the mother. Remember that.

Tomorrow we are going to get rid of these stupid imaginary personality conflicts that we create and that cause us to suffer and lose everything and become absolutely exploited idiots in spite of our wisdom. That we will do tomorrow. What I am trying to explain to all of you here is that you might have great problems and not think much of yourself; but you could develop your arcline through the Breath of Life, which is an open breath. If very experienced yogis are made to sit, they can create that atmosphere. I am convinced of that.

You know, people do yoga, people do therapy and counseling and all that. But aren't you aware that if you do not breathe, you are dead? And that breath, which can keep you alive—why can it not take care of your little mental disorientations?

Do you know how we made this tune, this shabad, *Rakhe Rakhan Har*? It was so necessary. Somebody came to meet me at the airport, and they were in so much pain. But what could I do at the airport? I couldn't find a room. I couldn't counsel. We were all packed. So I took a paper cup, and I started creating the eight beats. These words are eight beats. We created the sound and then put the words of the shabad to it, put music to it, all fine.

This is a song of victory. Your defeated life can turn into victory. These words have that power hidden in them. It is open and honest and you will find that I do this shabad in prayer, around the house, I repeat it all the time, because I don't believe in suffering. Knowledge only means that when you can avoid suffering, do. If you can't avoid suffering, knowledge, religion, then God won't mean anything to you. It is totally bogus nonsense to go and suffer. What for? There is enough suffering normally, and then you go and suffer. It is ridiculous, you know? But some people do not know anything. They are desperate. They play the martyr.

This is 1989. I am often asked why I am teaching now. Because 1989 is a year of prosperity, and in prosperity, people freak out fast. In years of adversity, you keep yourself together. You pitch in, and you fight. But in prosperity, you fall apart. It is very funny. In adversity, a husband and wife will stick like glue. It doesn't matter that he is sleeping with 10 women and she is bullshitting the whole world, who cares? But the moment they become a little rich, things start happening: Where are you going? What are you doing? There are fights. Prosperity is very difficult to handle. You can handle God if He comes in your house. But prosperity you can't handle, because it is an energy. It is a free energy. If you want to make somebody sick, give him ten thousand dollars cash, and let him go and run around. First of all, the police will pick him up, if not that, then somebody else. To handle energy, you need gloves. You need discipline.

Man was not prepared to do yoga. Hatha Yoga? My God! Just stretch like this for two hours and one hour like this. I have done that, and it is too much for me. I can't handle sweating like that. You can run three miles and sweat like a water tank, no big deal. But mental energy has to be controlled, and it has to be controlled by the breath, air—*pavan*.

Pavan is the power. The Breath of Life is the power, and shabad is the word. Word is the air, and word represents air, which is why you see me chanting this shabad. This shabad eats up pain as a hungry traveler eats up breakfast. It is very powerful. It has eight beats. Play this anytime but when you are hurting, I promise that by the third repetition, you will not have pain. It is a guarantee. It is a fact.

"In the beginning there was a Word, Word was God, Word was with God, Word was God." And Nanak says, "*Akhree naam, akhree saalaah, akhree giaan geet gun gaah, akhree likhan bolan baan, akhraa sir sanjog vikaan.*" The whole lengthy thing explains what the word can do; and these words have permutations and combinations. The moment they start and you begin to hear them, your eardrum, your neurons have no power; the *Agia* Chakra, the pituitary, the Third Eye, will start totally tranquilizing the brain. Try it sometime, when you are deadly hurting—put it on.

If you are afraid, then there are certain things I want to share with you. Everyone gets afraid; it is normal. There is nothing wrong with being in the trap of fear, because you should be afraid. When you are afraid of God, you are the best; but if you are afraid of other things, too, that's OK. Afraid is afraid. (Whether you are afraid of God or you are afraid of other things—even this is a religious thing.) The fact is that being afraid is afraid. Here are a few words that have a certain beat: *Chattr Chakkr Varti.* I am not asking you to chant it or repeat it or even listen to it. Just sleep with it. The next morning you will have no fear at all.

There was a student of mine who used to have those terrible dreams. I am not joking. What is she doing? Celestial Communication. If you bring a chronic patient who has nightmares, there is no medicine in the world that can heal that person. But if that person goes through this Celestial Communication for a couple of hours, there will be absolutely,

You can sometimes hear but don't act; and you can sometimes speak but don't mean it. You call that effective? No. You make no impact in life. If all the words you speak are impactful, there is nothing, as a human being, you cannot create. It's a promise—not mine. It is a promise of God.

absolutely nothing. That's how fast the healing effect of certain things works. This subliminal body communication is extremely penetrating. Pride has a fall, and we don't say it out of pride; we say it as a point of service.

Sometimes you are very poor. Things tumble down right before your eyes, and you don't have a nickel to call me with—and collect call I won't accept. Let me put it this way: If you have in your collection this music and you have this exact movement of the body, just see what miracle you can produce to put yourself together. There must be some people sitting here whose life has come to zero, a dead end. I am accepting the challenge. It is between you and me. Come on. Practice *Dhan Dhan Ram Das Gur* with Celestial Communication.[1]

When you do body language like this Celestial Communication, do you know who it is meant for? It is for the deaf. They can't hear, so they create sign language. You think you are not, but mostly you are deaf and dumb. Am I wrong? You can sometimes hear but don't act; and you can sometimes speak but don't mean it. You call that effective? No. You make no impact in life. If all the words you speak are impactful, there is nothing, as a human being, you cannot create. It's a promise—not mine. It is a promise of God. I have been a witness to it. I saw with these two eyes, which can see little earthly things, and I heard it with my ears.

Once a very saintly man came to somebody's house, and he drank a glass of water. There was some water left in the glass, and a young man of the house took that water and drank it. There was an elderly person in the house who said, "Idiot, why are you drinking his water? It is not hygienic." Scientifically, it is right. That person was very mad, and this young man was very shaken, because that family was very rich, and they were always supposed to be right—proper protocol and manners, and so on. I couldn't tolerate it. I said, "That infected water of a saint will free him of the disease for which in three days he is going to be diagnosed." I am never exact. I am very evasive by nature. But you know sometimes, too much is too much.

That lady said to me, "Which disease?" I said, "Six months and nine days from now, this son of yours will be dead but for this water that he drank; it will take care of it." Now, you know, when in a family conversation, horns get locked? She told her husband, "I am going to take the boy myself. I am going to check it out. I want to know." And the fact is, he was discovered with a fatal disease. But another fact is that he has to live, and that saint had enough prana in that one ounce of water to give him about sixty years of life. So add sixty years to that number of months and days, and exactly that will be the day he dies. It is not the medicine; it is the *pranic shakti* that makes the body live. Don't you understand?

Jesus Christ was born in a manger. Every year, we create that manger; it has become holy. But he is dead on a cross, and everybody hangs that cross around their neck. Don't you understand? He was a body, he was a man, he was born immaculately or out of nine

[1] To learn a traditional Celestial Communication to *Dhan Dhan Ram Das Gur* and *Rakhe Rakhan Har*, See www.kundaliniresearchinstitute.org

intercourses, why discuss that? That doesn't make any sense. The fact is, there are about two billion people on this Earth who believe that he was the son of God. That son of God didn't get shelter, no inn accepted them. Can you believe it? He was born to be with donkeys and ducks and all that stuff. Don't be blind. He was hung on a cross over a thief. They let a thief go and hung him. They could free one person, either Jesus or that thief, and they let the thief go and hung him. The cross has become a religious symbol, and the manger has become a divine instrument of memory. Why? What did he do? He forgave those who put him on the cross. His forgiveness, his kindness, his compassion were more than God. When a man's kindness gets confirmed, his compassion becomes infinite, and, actually, he becomes more than a God. Because God started obeying that man, such a man becomes a memory.

The power of prana is the power of life. It cannot be decided. When you are in love, do you brush your teeth each time you kiss? When you kiss, what do you do? Nothing, you go over and under and left and right; that is all fair, that creates no infection. Why doesn't it create infection? Because love itself kills disease. Love itself heals. Love is the giver of life. Love is not kissing and hugging and all that; that is not love. You are just dumb. Love is not that physical, biological kissing business. Love is the exchange of pranic values for life, for which we long to live.

The purpose of life is not to have thirty-five- or sixty-room houses and nine servants to clean them all the time. Do you understand? I have a friend who has twenty seven rooms, and he was telling me that everything is fantastic. Money is all perfect. But now he takes three pills to sleep, because he can't sleep. You may have the comfortable king-sized bed with silk on it and around it, the canopy, the whole thing, but you may not get sleep. You cannot buy sleep. You cannot buy happiness. You cannot buy health. You cannot buy forgiveness.

We are trying to teach you tonight to let the past go. Tomorrow, we are going to get rid of what they call the daydreaming concept. We are going to hit the root of it, because that is the cause of it all. Daydreaming makes your ego big, but in practice, it gives you nothing.

I just wanted to share this night with you with the idea that you can go home now, relaxed and normal. You are relaxed; you are normal. We put you through the trance, and we took you out. You are okay; there is no problem.

Now keep playing that song.

◆ ◆ ◆

May the long time sun shine upon you,
all love surround you, and the pure light within you, guide your way on.

Sat Nam

Home, home, guide your way home and go and relax. There is an expected situation that you may get tonight. Certain dreams that you might not have touched or totally completely gotten rid of. Your subconscious has worked through it. It is normal, so don't feel it is anything. Tomorrow we expect you to come on time. I will try to rest tomorrow as much as I can and meet you halfway, okay? Thank you.

UNLOADING THE PAST OF HARSH MEMORIES I—THE KRIYA

January 10, 1989

There are no breaks between the exercises. Move immediately from one exercise to the next.

1. Find a posture where you can sit comfortably and you are firm. Whatever posture you choose, you have to keep it until the end. If you cannot sit, lie down. Whatever you do, be firm. If you are sitting, then keep the spine straight. If you are lying down, relax and take care of yourself. Make a circle of the lips and suck the breath in very fast, sharp and deep. Exhale powerfully out through the mouth, using the navel and the ribcage. There is a very slight, subtle pause between the inhale and the exhale. (When done correctly the sound of the inhale will be a continuous, fast sucking sound; slight pause; and the exhale will be shorter, punctuated sound, almost like a "ha.") **7½ minutes**.

This is a cooling breath; it is very healing. Power the breath from the navel. Birthing mothers practice this breath. The ribcage has to move, because your Breath of Life is imprisoned in the ribcage. Move the spine, take the force of the shoulders, and shake the ribcage with your breath. We are going to deliver a baby. You are going through the womb and the labor pain of your mother. It is not going to be very pleasant, but keep going. If you do the breath right, it will set your aura for the next step. You can't do the next step correctly if you do not stimulate the energy.

2. Immediately put the hands on the Heart Center. Inhale and exhale deeply a few times. Close the eyes and look at the tip of the nose through closed eyes. With a long, deep breath, begin the guided meditation. **16 minutes**.

Guided Meditation

Please, now, concentrate. Go deep, go deep, deep into your memory. Pain is insane. Pain is insane. Let us pick it up and pull it out. Go through the memory of every pain you can remember from day one. Pull it out. Pop it as you do your pimples. You can do it. Take your pain and understand that pain is insane, and the insanity has to get out.

The best way to get it out is, when the energy is right, remember it and repeat it and say "bye" to it. Go. Remember the pain precisely, like a surgeon remembers precisely the area to cut out the gangrene—exactly, precisely. Leave nothing to the imagination. Remember the painful moments precisely. Your parents, your relatives, your brother, sister, mother—whatever the case may be; each year, all the insult, degradation, reaction, betrayals, treacheries; all the lies you have to live with; the love, the rejection. Everything can be repaired in this world but a broken heart—everything—honest. This is a moment of honesty. This is one time for total cleansing. This is your God-given chance.

Remember every pain. Pain is insane. Remember it precisely, precisely, in detail, and it will burn out. Those who have their yesterday alive with them will never have tomorrow—it is a law that you and I can't change. Pull it up, burn it up. But you are required to remember it precisely and then let it go.

The greatest kindness is when you are kind to your own self and don't ruin your future. Whatever wrong you have done, you have already done. It cannot be redone. Face it; confront it. Precisely react to it, and then let it go. Your best makeup is your Radiant Body, which attracts everything. Go through all the undesirable experiences, because you cannot keep them, live with them, and be miserable the rest of your life. Burn them.

It would take about twenty sessions with a psychiatrist to just go through the introduction of the pain of a rape. You can totally dramatize it right now and then forgive it. You will be free. You don't have to go through a lot of sessions. Your love affairs that never came through, your separation; don't try to pretend that you only remember good things and that they didn't come through. Remember even the worst thing from your fantasies—unbelievable fantasies, dreams. Recollect them. Gather them together and burn them. This is the time to get rid of that. Flow with me and precisely pick up these pimples and pop them. Clean yourself out.

Guided Meditation continued next page.

In simple Western English, we call it the self-hypnosis of getting rid of your pain. You don't have to be hypnotized by somebody. You can totally hypnotize yourself and experience that far-out energy in the moment. Burst out! You are the perfect actors. Replay those dramas and go through it precisely. We are going through the wet dream of pain. We are going through the conscious acting, not the subconscious acting, of it. We will not be in a position to carry this energy for a long time, because we have created it. So before it starts becoming weak, you have a chance to react to it: relocate your pain, react to it, and then get rid of it.

Precisely go through the dream; perfect your own performance. You are the actor, you are the director, you are the producer, you are the stagehand, and you are the stage. Reproduce your own drama tonight and just go through it. The easiest way to remove from your memory the painful injurious memory is to go through the cycle of the creative self-hypnosis and just cut it out. You can cry, you can laugh, you can smile—you are going through it. It is not just acting. It is going through it. Pain is personal, but everybody goes through it. Some express it physically, some try to express it mentally, some try to express and deny it, some accept it. Please let it go through you. Go through it. There is no harm. You have the right to live healthy with clean memories.

There are two words you have to learn in life. One is grateful, and the other is ungrateful. Those who remember grateful will be full of great things. Those who are ungrateful shall always have a void of great things. That is all. You want to know prosperity, you want richness, you want happiness? Then be grateful.

3. Begin inhaling and exhaling very deeply at a moderate pace of 8 breaths every 15 seconds. Continue for **30–60 seconds**. Continue powerfully breathing and begin the gong meditation. "The universe was created with the sound of the gong. Fly with it. Spread your wings and go away." Continue for **4½ minutes total**.

We have to regenerate our energy when returning from our self-hypnosis. We want to wake up, and we want to do it through the Breath of Life. Deep breathing is very good, very healthy.

4. Chant with the mantra *Rakhe Rakhan Har* by Singh Kaur. Gong meditation continues with the chanting for **1½ minutes**. Chant for **5 minutes total**.

Copy the sound; it will take away your pain forever. Anytime you are in pain, listen to this mantra. The sound of the words has a tranquilizing effect on the brain.

5. Celestial Communication with *Rakhe Rakhan Har* sung by Singh Kaur for **2 minutes**. Celestial Communication is the creative expression of the soul. As a teacher or practitioner, you can learn one of the original Celestial Communication sequences that go with this mantra, or you can make up your own.

6. Clap your hands to the beat of *Rakhe Rakhan Har* sung by Singh Kaur. It has a heartbeat in it; an eight-beat. Clap in rhythm for **2 minutes**.

TO END: Inhale deep, suspend the breath, and begin pumping the Navel Point heavily. Move the spine and shoulders fast and heavy. Repeat 3 times. First time, suspend the breath for **40 seconds**; then **20 seconds**; then **11 seconds**.

This shabad, Rakhe Rakhan Har—these sounds, these words—contains eight beats. This is a song of victory. Your defeated life can turn into victory. These words have that power hidden in them. It is open and honest. I do this shabad in prayer around the house. I repeat it all the time because I don't believe in suffering.

◆

Rakhay rakhanhaar aap ubaarian
Gur kee pairee paa-eh kaaj savaarian
Hoaa aap dayaal manho na visaarian
Saadh janaa kai sang bhavjal taarian
Saakat nindak dusht khin maa-eh bidaarian
Tis saahib kee tayk naanak manai maa-eh
Jis simrat sukh ho-eh saglay dookh jaa-eh

God Himself is looking out for me,
Gives me the light, and takes care of my affairs.
God is merciful, and never forgets me.
God guides me, giving me good people to help me.
God does not allow any harm to come to me.
I take comfort in the thought of God.
When I remember God, I feel peaceful and happy
  and all my pain departs.

" Tonight I am going to take you through what your mother took you through—it's called rebirthing. In the spiritual world, rebirthing is a process in which an individual, his psyche, and his pranic psyche are reunited at the time when the breath of life became the supporter of life, the original pure psyche from the Navel Point. So basically you are alive because of the Third Chakra. "

– Yogi Bhajan

UNLOADING THE PAST OF HARSH MEMORIES II

January 11, 1989

ODAY WE ARE GOING TO GET RID OF A LOT OF GARBAGE. Yesterday a lot of people who normally come to thank me after class never showed up, because they were so spaced out. So I felt very lonely.

Well, here in the United States, these two classes I am teaching and the third class I am teaching in San Diego would normally cost six thousand dollars plus a six-month commitment and all that; they call them rebirthing seminars. I personally feel that there are two most idiotic things in America; I won't name them, but understand that they both cost a lot of money. I am very competitive, but I have a very different approach. I believe that knowledge should be given, not sold. I used to teach five-day Tantric courses and charged only thirty five dollars. I could have charged two thousand dollars a day; people were willing to pay that. But I was not willing to do that.

I believe there is a basic honesty, and it has an orbit that one should not cross, even though he is trusted, he is loved, and he is a teacher. All three things are a given, granted. But if I tell people to jump, some may, some may not—but why tell? If you give a tall order to somebody who cannot take it, then as a teacher, you are cruel. If you give a small order to somebody who can do more, then you hurt his ego. So if you are not an intelligent human being to begin with, why should you become a teacher at all?

Being a teacher is a very responsible job. But those who call themselves teacher, in any way, shape, or form, but then betray their students—I can tell them to look at the cockroach, because that's their next incarnation. It's true, honest to God! This is in every scripture. A teacher who betrays, lies, or undermines a student in spiritual teaching and he calls himself a spiritual teacher, then he ends up a cockroach. The punishment is established; it cannot be repeated, reverted, or denied.

One-third of your time goes to depression. You love each other, but after a while, you find out you can't talk to that same person. It is not the people who talk, it is not the degree in communication that talks, and it is not the religion that talks. I will tell you what talks—the understanding, that's what talks. The conflict of egos will create tragedy; the union of egos will create heavens. As long as your subconscious is overloaded with all the dirt of the world, you can't make it here—that is my fifty-nine years of experience living here in the world. I have been very rich, you

The conflict of egos will create tragedy; the union of egos will create heavens. As long as your subconscious is overloaded with all the dirt of the world, you can't make it here.

Between conscious and unconscious, there is the subconscious, and whenever the subconscious gets loaded and doesn't discharge itself through dreams and daydreams, life becomes almost blocked, like a blocked artery.

can't even imagine; and I was very poor, you can't imagine it either. In between those two extremes, I have found that one thing is sure: You can always start over, and you can always make it happen, provided your ego doesn't conflict.

There are twenty two religions, and I have studied them all. I would never have been a religious man, but I wanted to know what the reality of a man is. So I had to study the religions. Every religion takes you to a promise, honest to God. I started at the Sacred Heart Catholic convent, and I am basically very Catholic. You might see me sometimes going for confession; habits don't change very fast. It's basically a very Catholic thing to confess guilt. If not, you make it up so that you can do some Hail Mary's. But my concept of the Christian religion is very simple: I love Jesus not because he was a son of God or a great Christian, or because God sent him. I love Jesus for one thing only: He taught practically what he believed; he was an honest teacher. He always believed he was the son of God, and he lived up to it. They let a thief go, not him; they hung him, and he didn't care. My problem is not between Moses and Jesus and Guru Nanak and Buddha and all that. I don't worship men; I worship teachings. I have never kissed a postman, but I do read letters, and I have kissed a lot of letters. There's a difference between you and me. When the postman comes to the door and brings a big bundle and puts it down, I never say, "Hello, come in and have a cup of tea." I never care who he is. He's doing what he's paid for. But the letters he brings to me from my love are very precious to me.

Life is an experience. And let me tell you something more—a Yogi Bhajanism. Somebody told me, "You are teaching Yogi Bhajanism." So I thought, "All right, let me teach a Yogi Bhajanism today." Yogi Bhajanism is that if you, under any circumstances, waste your time on wrong taxes and wrong depression, then you are wasting the preciousness of your life. Life is much more precious than you and I think. Therefore, when you meet a girl and take her on a date, tell her about the pits during the date, rather than putting a green garden around her and bringing flowers and casting a spell around her and being on your best behavior, when three days later she is going to find out you are the biggest liar, worst debauchee, and absolute thief in the world. Don't tell her you love her when you have already beaten your last girlfriend to death, you know? Try to be honest. Don't take her to the best restaurant when you already have thirty thousand dollars worth of bad checks swinging around your way.

I live in Los Angeles, and I am very grateful to God that I lived in West Hollywood to start with. My career started there, so there is nothing that America will produce in two hundred years that I do not know by heart and by experience. I have seen the good days, with these actors and actresses and their Hollywood business, that whole thing, the whole charade. I went through that; there is nothing more for me except to see that you don't get hurt anymore.

Tonight I am going to take you through what your mother took you through—it's called rebirthing. Rebirthing is a process. Let me explain it because a lot of you have spent a lot of money on rebirthing. Let me tell you the science of it, and then you can go through it.

In the spiritual world, rebirthing is a process in which an individual, his psyche, and his pranic psyche are reunited at the time when the breath of life became the supporter of life, the original pure psyche from the Navel Point. So basically you are alive because of the Third Chakra. You are alive not because "I have a terrible flu, and a cough; you know where I hurt—tell me." I am explaining something that you have to understand: In your life, when you were in the womb of the mother, nine months and four days, give or take a week, you are alive, your heart beats, you talk, you learn—that's a real meditation. After the one hundred and twentieth day, when the soul comes in, you learn everything about your mother, your father, and your environments; they have what is called a perpetual mental impact. Your mind grows and learns and goes with it. When you have that little meat hanging, then you become a boy; if not, then you are a girl. But when you become a man, you lose the right side of your brain; it becomes the supplementary brain. With a woman, she has both sides of her brain—left and right. She is more confused and complicated because she doesn't know which one to use when; that's her problem. Man has to compete and bully everything to affect himself, because he has only one initial thing—win, win, win, that's all! That's all that makes him a male—ridiculous, but anyway.

God is very merciful. He made you in His own image but kept the teapot in His own house—that's what I have realized by being a great holy man in the world. God made humans in His own image, gave them the domain of the Earth and the Heavens and the Infinity and everything, but He kept the tea cup and tea kettle. That He pours, and you drink. I don't call Him stupid, because then He will slap me, and I am a little individual. I don't say He is great, because I know He created me, How can I say He is not great? Because only the great can create a person like me, you and us. But I am still worried. What did He mean when He gave us a stomach but didn't provide anything for it and made us so insecure and so stupid that sometimes we live only ten years and collect for two hundred years? One thing I am asking God, which I want you to ask also, is this: "Almighty, what kind of neurotic are you that one day people love each other and the next day they hate each other—such a fast switch?" There is no answer; none of you in this room has the answer. I have the answer. Let me tell you the answer, let me tell you the answer once and for all, so that at least in the United States you may say that you had a real yogi and he knows much.

Between the conscious and unconscious there is a subconscious. Unconscious means intuition, remember that. Unconscious means intuition; conscious means

whatever you see and do with all these five senses. Between conscious and unconscious, there is the subconscious, and whenever the subconscious gets loaded and doesn't discharge itself through dreams and daydreams, life becomes almost blocked, like a blocked artery. They call it arteriosclerosis or something like that, and your heart starts going berserk. Or it starts when you do not absorb enough oxygen—your breath is not deep enough, and you get an iron lung; now there is a disease for which there's hardly any cure. The problem is that each day you do not breathe deeply enough to meet the blood, which is in the lower chambers of the lungs. When the oxygen doesn't go and touch it, the blood goes back not as red as it should be. The quality of that blood starts killing the lungs and also starts killing you. I have found that in spite of the deepest breathing, which is my habit, my natural pranayama, Los Angeles, doesn't have oxygen. I never knew. There must be some, but if there were some, then why should I have gotten that sick. So, I mean, there is an air problem here.

Between you and me, when the subconscious gets overloaded, signals start going berserk, and that is when you fight and quarrel, you know what I mean? The art of communication, the art of love, all the arts start falling apart. You have two things in your nature: One is phobia, or fear, and one is phenomenon. If you have a mother or father phenomenon, there is no treatment known today by either man or science. Phobia, yes; fear, yes; but if you have a father phenomenon, you have a perpetual, subtle authority problem. If you have a mother phenomenon, then you have a perpetual identity problem. When you have both the authority problem and the identity problem, you are cooked; you are no use to yourself, forget about me!

I am very demanding. So what we are going to do is this: We will tackle that other part, what you call the father phenomenon. Fear of authority, fear of tomorrow, fear of the unknown—all this is branded in one phrase, father phenomenon. God is a father; it's old English; I didn't make it up. That's the way it is, and you have difficulties with it. When you have mother phenomenon, you have personality problems; you don't trust your own identity, nor your mother's, forget about the Mother.

Your life moves in an electromagnetic field on an axle and within an orbit. Do you understand what I am saying? If there is no perpetual harmony and absolute balance between those two movements, be ready for a lot of trouble in life. Trouble is not that you don't have money, trouble is not that you don't have health. If you are not healthy and you have no character or you have no body, you can still survive happily if you have a balanced, contained self. A contained self is not easy. You forget that the other human is a reflection of you. Have you ever understood that when you behave, talk, or deal with anybody, the other human sees your reflection. You can only see your face in the mirror; but in spite of all the makeup, the other person sees your face

all the time. You can lie, but the eyes never lie. Your eyes tell the whole world those stories that you want to hide. You think you have a secret? Your only secret is that there is no secret. You are more open than a book! Your face tells where your mind is, and the mind tells you where you are.

If somehow your subconscious can be cleaned, one way or the other, then there is only one outcome: Your soul will shine through the mind; it will shine through your own face. Then you won't need that cream and powder and mascara and all that. If your nails have a lot of blood going through them, you don't need all that false nonsense that you pay fifty dollars for. And you would never need lipstick if you had beautiful, red lips. But you don't. Your lips are dry and messed up. So, what do you do? You put that poison over them.

The problem is you don't have good lips, and you will never have them. There are certain things that show your personality faster than you can. Eyes, lips, and your reflection between the Third Eye, the angle from there to the tip of the nose—they show everything. If anybody knows how to read hands or faces, they can read more about you than even you know about yourself; it's very easy. One thing more that nobody born of the Earth knows how to tackle is his hair; it's very difficult, which is why we Sikhs cover it. We don't want to go into the phenomenon. So what do we do in the morning? We tie it up; we put a turban around our hair. At night we braid it; we never bother with it. We have one style, all of the time, three hundred sixty five days a year, because we know the two solar centers on the head are going to make or mar our tomorrow. We know the whole science of it. This is very well-described.

It was funny—I went to visit a Jewish family, and this lady, who is married to this Jewish friend of mine, said, "One thing we have in common—you people don't show your hair, and you will never see the hair of those who are good." I said, "Yeah, they are very good." You see, in the morning, she goes and puts on her wig; she has the best hair in the world. I said to her, "If I had seen under this wig, I would have been a little flirty with you; but I avoided it because I could see there was dead hair on your head." She said, "No, that's my wig; that's not my hair." Her ego got to her, and she took it off—and there I got her. You can get anybody on ego, you know? It's very easy, just play a little role and get going.

I will tell you a story: There was a great physician, a man of medicine, who had the power to create and clone as much life as he wanted to. God sent the message of death and asked him to come back. But he didn't want to die. Aflatoon was his name, and he created five hundred clones like him. So the messenger of death came looking for which one to kill; he had one warrant, one arrow. The Angel of Death went to Almighty God, and he lay down flat. And God said, "God of Death, what's wrong with you?"

You don't have any relationship with your soul. You have absolutely no relationship with your mind, because, you must understand, God has given you the spirit. But like a diamond, like a stone, it needs to be cut, mended, sharpened. Life is not strong without angles.

He said, "Master, punish me as you want."

"What did you do? Should I give you a couple of Hail Mary's?"

"No, my Father. It's not true. I have sinned. I went with your warrant, and I saw that there were five hundred of those people, and I didn't know who to kill. I have come back."

"You brought the death warrant back?"

"Yes."

"You didn't use it? Well, you are wise. Now go, and just start laughing and say, 'Whosoever created all of you now, in just form, is perfect; there is no defect except one.' And that one will say, 'What?' Then hit him."

You must understand: You can hide everything in your life but your ego. You can hide everything but your face, and your face tells your story, much, much in advance of anything you can tell with all the vocabulary at your command. If you go to lunch with somebody, and you are going to suffer at four o'clock, you will start feeling unwell six hours in advance; that's how our clock works. Our body clock is in relation to our mental clock, because soul, mind, and body have a living relationship. You don't have any relationship with your soul. You have absolutely no relationship with your mind, because, you must understand, God has given you the spirit. But like a diamond, like a stone, it needs to be cut, mended, sharpened. Life is not strong without angles.

When I was lying down in bed, they asked me, "Are you teaching the class today?"

I said, "Yes."

"What has come over you?"

"Nothing. Commitment."

"Can you teach it?"

"Yeah, very good, I will be very good but a little late; but I will be good."

You must understand that you don't live by your body; you don't work by your mind. You live and work through your spirit. It is called soul, it is called spirit. It's the greatest living organism on this planet through which every life lives. It's called *pavan*, the vehicle of the prana. *Akasha*, the ether, is space, and if you go up beyond twelve hundred miles, the *pranas* are not there, and you will start suffocating. You can land on the moon with your own oxygen and your own air; but you can't land there just by yourself, you will flip.

Pavan guru pani pita.

   - Guru Nanak, Siri Guru Granth Sahib, page 8 (from *Japji*)

"Water is the nurturer of life, and air is the father." In the United States, everything comes out of a fountain of greed; nothing here is simple. Even bananas here

taste different. Nothing is organic. Listen, we are organic human beings, but we don't have anything organic. Our relationships aren't organic; nothing is natural. But what can you do? People are people, and people have their own lives; but tonight we have our own life to tackle. If you cooperate, it will be easy on me; we can do a good job, and it will be good for you. If you don't cooperate, we will push you anyway. It doesn't matter. So, ready?

◆ ◆ ◆

All right, sit on your heels and put your hands on the ground as if you are going to deliver a baby in a very cave-man method. (*See Exercise 1.*) Cave-man method was to deliver babies and have intercourse always from the back, remember this. That's how society came to be; it's our original method of intercourse. Two things we used to do as humans: First was to deliver a baby like this. We thought we will push it out; we never thought we could deliver a baby lying down—that's a very modern thought. And second was that we never had intercourse facing each other. So today you are not doing anything other than that.

So let's do it. We are working with the pineal for the first time in the United States; you have never done this before. So please be very careful and be systematic, all right? Use both hands and put the weight from the shoulders down over them. Whether you sit on your heels or you rise up, it doesn't matter; you just have to have that posture. All right?

Now, if your neck has somehow gone wrong or you do not sleep with a hard round pillow or you have had an accident, cover that faculty by putting your chin up, but not too much. You have to maintain a posture, but be convenient with it, all right? Now start doing the baby breathing. Hammer it! It will change your personality for the good, because your intuition comes when your motherly faculty starts working. Some people are afraid because they do not know what they have to reveal, so they are trying to hide. Come on, breathe. Everybody has to become a big mother. Come on, I want to hear it!

All right. Sit down like yogis, with crossed legs and your hands around your neck. (*See Exercise 2.*) Where that apple is, is called the thyroid area; yes, she made us eat our own apple. Now kick, and kick again, kick again, otherwise it will not be very free. All right, good, got it?

Now close your eyes and meditate. As the gong sounds, start going up. When the gong takes the plateau, listen—there will be a very few minutes in that whole energy. You can't hold on to more than that. When the first gong hits, it will be a very heavy hit, and with that go away. Then, when it comes down and the energy becomes normal, pick up all your pains and repossess your self. Get bewitched! We have only 15 to 20 minutes, the energy cannot hold further than that, okay?

You must understand once and for all that the sound of the gong is the sound of creativity by the hand of God. Your mind has only one thing which it cannot resist, one thing it must obey and that is the sound of the gong.

You must understand once and for all that the sound of the gong is the sound of creativity by the hand of God. Your mind has only one thing which it cannot resist, one thing it must obey and that is the sound of the gong. I was not there when God created it; He should have consulted me. We would have done a better job, but He did it all by Himself. That's why He is so lonely.

Dr. Khalsa will take care of your physical problem; that's not my problem. Mental problems are my problems. I am not a psychologist or a psychiatrist, although I have done my Ph.D. But as a spiritual minister, I feel that people are not supposed to suffer; we are not born to suffer. So, could you please have mercy on me and fill up this gap? Because if you leave the gaps, you are going to be filled up with other nonsense. An empty house is always visited by vagabonds.

Come on. Move your navel; it's a very right thing to do. You might be thinking I never keep my eyes open; I haven't done anything. But we are not willing to accept your noncooperation. The sound of the gong does it all anyway; you are just a tool. So come on and get going.

All right now, put both hands on the Navel Point and press it hard! (*See Exercise 4.*) Deep. Do it for your own best of tomorrow, if you believe in tomorrow. It's the beat of the heart. Don't worry whether you know or not; just meditate.

Now, please repeat the words of the mantra. (*See Exercise 5.*) Follow the line with a hard tongue. I am not asking you to do it religiously. I am asking you to do it scientifically. You have to do it with the tip of the tongue—strong tongue, use it!

Please open your eyes and follow the Celestial Communication. (*See Exercise 6.*) It is a body language, a perfect prayer. Go through this by your own virtue; inhale and hold the breath and make the body absolutely dense. Let it go. It's a simple science; the law of contraction and expansion.

◆ ◆ ◆

It was a good class, and you were very cooperative. If you start showing this kind of cooperation, life will be much better for all of you. It may not be very good for me, because then I have to teach. And that's the problem; I will not be available to you for a long time period, because I will be gone with my grandchildren. I want to be with them in the deep winter of New Mexico. It's very cold there, so don't come. But it's a very beautiful country, and if you love to ski and do those kinds of things, New Mexico is the place. God lives everywhere, but His postal address is Española, New Mexico. You know why? One hour from there is a desert, it's a high desert, and one hour from there is a ski place, one hour from there is the most beautiful town in the world, and one hour from there you can go into the living hell if you want to. So New Mexico is all four things: heaven, hell, desert, and lush green mountains.

In winter it is very pure; it's all white. Planet Earth purifies itself by putting the pure water in it. This is how the cycle of life works. We get to earth, dirt earth; from the earth grows the plant, which gives us food; we eat the food and that turns to blood, blood turns into semen in a female or a male, and they create life—that's the start of our life. Life grows, and in the end it leaves behind what it created, which goes back dust to dust, as far as our body is concerned.

The mind has eighty-one facets. You have three, solid, equal minds: negative, neutral, and positive. God gave you the negative mind to be negative, to see the danger for you. He gave you the positive mind so that you can become an achiever—successful and understanding. You should understand what is positive for you. Negative tells you negative, positive tells you positive and the neutral tells you what to do. Now, the greatest mystery and misfortune is that when the negative tells you what is negative, the positive tells you the past; the positive mind starts digging around in your subconscious past. "Oh, second of May, this happened to you. This guy is a cheat;" it will put all the garbage you know before you. You don't deal with it only with the negative mind; you also use your positive mind. When you use the negative and positive mind, you have no time left for the neutral mind.

You can make as much money as you want. You can have as many relationships as you want. You can do anything you want. But you will not be happy, I can bet on that. Happiness comes when you see your soul through your own mind, and you realize this girl called soul and date her. It's a very personal, private relationship. You always find relationships with the outside world. Well, that's a good idea. Man is a social animal, and you have the right to be social yourself. But you all have one basic habit, because your one chakra is overactive compared with the others—it's a law of nature. So your entire circle of friendship and desires and achievements will be based on that chakra.

Somebody once complained to me, "This woman has sixteen hundred cats; she feeds them!"

I said, "What's wrong with that?"

"She is a lunatic, spoiled. Look at how she's wasting her money."

"No, there is no problem with that; I don't think there can be any problem."

As a girl, she had been left in the street like a stray cat herself. She grew up, became rich, and she picked up the idea that there should be nothing stray in the world. So she found every cat and stray dog that had been thrown out, especially around the holidays. So every August, she picks up every stray dog, and dogs are a very good business; but cats nobody wants, so she ends up keeping all those cats. She feeds them, grooms them, nurtures them, cares for them, and that way she feels that she is paying off the karma of being abandoned in the street. She was found in

You have to learn to have a relationship with your own mind and with your own soul—that's the sole purpose of this life.

a garbage can as a child. Now she is a multimillionaire. She is very rich, and that's what she does.

What I am trying to explain is that our one karma, one thought, becomes the master thought, and it runs us around, which is why we go around it. But it is your life! The circle of life is dust to dust, which will be completed by all one way or the other. So the question is not whether you go to God or not—I am not interested in that. Whether you are divine or not is not my problem. Whether you are rich or not is not my concern, either. Whether you are happy or not, I don't care. Whether you are healthy or not, forget it. There are a lot of medical doctors available for that. But when God wants to take care of you, He will, one way or the other. Chances come, opportunities come. You are healthy, happy, and holy; you have nine holes and whoever has nine holes is holy; that's no big deal.

Then what is the problem in life? One simple thing: Either life is fulfilled, and you're content, confident, and caring for yourself, or not. You can care for the whole world, I don't mind, but if you don't care for yourself, you are sick. You have to learn to have a relationship with your own mind and with your own soul—that's the sole purpose of this life.

Well, after eight point four million lifetimes, we will go to God one day or the other. Forget about it. In the end, if there is no chance, He will say come on in, all are free. You know when you go to a show and there are no tickets available? They open the doors and say, "Come on, everybody." So, too, one day, God, out of His mercy, will do the same. There's a couplet that I would like to share with you.

Khuda puchega jannat mein pak baazoon se
Gunaah kyoun nahi kiye kya hum raheem they
　　—Traditional Punjabi saying
God shall ask the people in the heavens.
Why didn't you commit the sin? Didn't you trust that I am forgiving?

What I mean to say is, God has many ways to reach you—positive, negative, and neutral. But this is all the game of God. If you want to play His chess, He is a big player. But I tell you the simple ways of life, and the simple ways of life are, you want to be happy, you want to be healthy, you want to be holy, you want to be respected, you want to be noble, you want to be prosperous. All that you want can only be done one way—if you know your soul and know your mind and thus know your Self. And that's difficult, because neither your mother nor your father ever told you to do that. American society doesn't tell you that. It's very funny: One girl told me, "I am spiritual. I am divine."

And as she was telling me, I said, "Far out. Why don't you tell me how you got all that?" I won't tell you what she meant by those words.

We have two ways to lie, either we boast or we deny. We never, ever speak the truth—never. Because, unfortunately, God has given me the eyes through which I can't see all the faces of the people, but I do see the auras. And even though people can lie, their aura doesn't. Sitting right in my presence, they lie to my face. I have the training to say, "Yeah, well, we can make something good out of it." Actually the best in you is not only good! This God you are talking about, you have the right to tell God to appear before you and do your things, and you don't have to have a long prayer and go to Hail Mary's and all that. You can do only one thing: If you connect with your own soul, then that is the peeping hole, the key to the chamber in the very heart of God. God cannot abandon you; He can't abandon His parts. He is stuck with you.

People say, "God is free." I say it's a lie. God is not free. He sends you five breaths per minute, on average, and gives you the breath of life despite the fact that you abuse Him, you use Him, and you cheat Him and lie and do everything. Whether or not you go to church, you still get the breath of life. Whether or not you are religious—who cares? As long as you get fifteen breaths per minute, you are considered alive. Isn't that true? And that life is free to you, that life comes to you because God loves you. So, all of you who are out there finding God are wasting time. You have to find your own soul, not a soul mate and sexy games. If you want to have intercourse, do your soul in; if you want a friend, make your soul a friend. The soul has a little voice; sometimes it starts speaking to you.

It said to me one time, "Yogiji, don't eat this rich food. It's not good for your body." I said, "Could you shut up, you stinker in my head?"

You know what I mean? You know that communication? You remember?

The soul says, "This person has an ulterior motive." And I say, "Stop it! You are just a good-for-nothing, sitting in my head like a rat making holes. Get out of me!"

And it says, "I tell you, don't do it."

Then it slowly tells you: "This girl is a psychic shark, watch out for the teeth."

I say, "I love to swim in the deep ocean. Get out of me."

She, my soul, says, "No way, honey, I am right here."

"I shall not listen to you, my little voice."

"Yeah, that I know. Do what you want to do, but you know better."

"Don't cater to my ego! I have decided as a human being not to listen to the voice of my soul."

Today my soul said to me, "Why not?"

"If I start listening to you, I will be so right that these people will run out, they will freak out. I have to be at their level. Don't you understand?"

There are eighty one layers of the mind. They are storehouses filled with your past, and your present life can just point out that fear. And, God, it is just like an avalanche. A lot of these avalanches are responsible for messing up our lives, do you hear me?

"Yeah, I understand, but I thought you were different."

"No, we are all the same. We are called human."

So, for the time being, when you have this kind of communication, which I have explained to you, understand this: Within you lives the prettiest girl or boy, opposite to your sex. If you are gay, there is a gay there; if you are neurotic, there is a neurotic there. There is a perfect girlfriend and a perfect boyfriend—whatever you call it. You have one friend, the sound of your soul, that is the word, that is the mantra—and you must learn to hear it. You have to hear it if you want to enjoy your life. Even if you have some other interior motive, that voice is still the best thing you have.

So please, relish your days of living and enjoying, and if you care to come to San Diego, I will be there Saturday, in the afternoon. I am going to run away for a while. Although California is very beautiful, and I have nothing against it, I have never called this place my home, and I never will. I live here, but I vote in New Mexico; I am a resident of New Mexico.

Guru Ram Das has given me the best blessing, the best piece of land at the ranch and everything. Come sometime, it's pretty. The water is natural, organic; the air is clean; the sky is very clear. That's one place where I actually see the stars. The natural showbiz is there. The showbiz here is the kind of showbiz that's plastic. We have there what is called the Divine Studios, and we have the super Paramount and whatever you want to call it—the best of Columbia and everything. After that, if I return still breathing, and subject to the availability of the number of breaths, we will go to a special course here in Los Angeles. It is called inverted and converted inner personality. I have never taught it before, but I think you are now developed enough to go through it. It takes away the layers of fear that we are born with.

Do you know what the most serious accident of life is? When you are born with a ton of fear in your mental layer. There are eighty-one layers of the mind, storehouses filled with your past, and your present life can just point out that fear. And, God, it is just like an avalanche. A lot of these avalanches are responsible for messing up our lives, do you hear me? Do you even understand? Do you speak English?

So we will set our self up and get rid of what I always called "unwanted loan." In our spiritual language they call it *samskara*. A *samskara* is a debt that has to be paid; it sits there and waits. It's like that rattlesnake. When a rattlesnake wants to attack, it moves its tail. It jingles and then attacks you—and that's what the mind does. First the mind directs you, and once the mind finds out that you've started listening to it, it starts the avalanche. The mind is very clever; it's like a horse—if the bridle is not rightly maintained, it can go anywhere it wants. Actually, the mind was given to you by God out of love, in friendship, so that you can connect with infinity all the time.

I would not have become Sikh, as a religion, ever. But when I found out that I was promised everything but that nobody would tell me what Infinity—from which I came—is, well, that's when I started looking into my own books and meeting my own holy men and asking questions. That's when I started discovering for myself. I found out whether it is true that we are all equal in the light of God and whether we love each other and if not, why not? I had certain questions. My first question in life was: God created us all, so why don't we love each other? I found out we don't. Just now, before I came here, I had a big fight in my own living room. Somebody told me, "If you want to have this thing, you can have this thing. But I don't want anybody else to know about it." What is this? I feel differently. These days, sometimes I go to lunch and nobody wants to go with me. Do you know why? Because they cannot go if I have to take my security, and I have to take some other people, and we become a party of five, six, ten, twenty people. Americans do not feel that more than two or four max is human. It's not personal. I took a vow and I came to the United States, but I shall never eat the way people eat here.

I was invited to dinner by a beautiful friend and student of mine—he is three things for me, and he has adoration I can't believe. I went to his house, which sat on a couple of acres. I sat down and for the first time ate an artichoke. You know, it's very difficult to eat artichoke if you don't know how. We sat at that table, which was a redwood tree—a full, perfect, grown-up redwood tree chopped right in the center. I suggested to him that he should have a telephone so I could talk to him. Do you understand there was sixty feet of table between me and my host? How would you like to eat artichoke when you do not know how to do it? That's was my unique individual experience of an American perfect dinner.

Another experience that I always recall is when we went to a very rich house in New York, a house you would love just to see, forget about living in it. They have all these people who serve and cook the best food, the whole thing—you can't believe it. There were about twenty dishes. Then a fight broke out over who will sit on my left side and who will sit on my right side. You know what happened? We ended up eating standing in the kitchen; nobody ever sat. It's a great country with funny habits.

You know why I am not blaming you? You are all immigrants, and you want to be somebody now. That's what you want to be—somebody. There is no royalty in America, there is no big deal, no status, nothing. So people have created false notions of status. But that's not America. America's real status is that all are equal under one Sun, under one God, as one country, which is why Guru Nanak said:

Ek ong kar sat nam

—Siri Guru Granth Sahib, page 1 (from *Japji*)

There is one God and everything is His creation.

If we don't know who we are, if we don't see our reflection in each other's eyes, then that's where the problem is. This problem will continue until humanity comes to an understanding: They need peace, and peace will only come from a deep love of each other.

Aval allah noor upaa-i-aa kudrat ke sabh bande.
Ek noor te sabh jag oopaji-aa kon bhale kon mande.

- Kabir, Siri Guru Granth Sahib, page 1349-50

From one God's light everybody is born.
Who is good and who is bad? Who am I to judge?

So basically, as long as we have a spirit and a soul, we all know who we are. If we don't know who we are, if we don't see our reflection in each other's eyes, then that's where the problem is. This problem will continue until humanity comes to an understanding: They need peace, and peace will only come from a deep love of each other.

You know who you love? Who wears the best clothes? Cleanliness is Godliness, beauty is God's given gift. And yet you love status; you do not love light. You know what I am saying? You love status. And I tell you as a spiritual man that spiritual status and ego are so big that ordinary people are way, way better off with that.

One day I went to see another holy man, and everybody started telling me, "Oh, Yogiji, you are great. You look great." But I was sick. And I asked myself, "What great are they talking about?" They are supposed to say good things to me because every spiritual man is afraid. But I have a very powerful tongue, and I lick my fears.

You know why you lie? You are afraid. You are afraid of the status of another man. You are afraid of the position of another man. You are afraid of your own insecurity. There are eight facets that force a man to speak out straight and clear. Communication is the biggest problem of the male and the female. People do not talk straight. Have you been married to somebody and you both had to assure each other for thirty years that you love each other? Once a constitution is written, it's written; it's signed, it's sealed, it's passed, it's done. I love you, you love me, matter over. But I have to tell you every day, "I love you, I love you, I love you." And you have to say, "I love you too, I love you, too . . . But where are my flowers?"

Once somebody asked me, "Do you love me?"

I said, "I love you."

"You didn't send me a present."

"My God, that's such a stupid idea. I'm your spiritual teacher; you're supposed to send me a present! I'm not supposed to send you a present."

"Oh, I'm sorry. Should I bring a present to you?"

"No, now I have the right to ask for a present."

"All right, Yogiji. Tell me what you want, and I'll bring it to you."

"Tell me—on your birthday at six a.m., what prayer was I asking for you?"

"I don't know."

"You know."

"No, I swear. I do not know."

"You are lying. You were sitting down on the chair, and you were dreaming, right? Repeat your dream."

Now he was in a state in which he couldn't lie, because I didn't want him to lie in my presence.

He said, "Yes, I thought you and I were sailing in a boat and you picked me up, and you put me into the river head first three times. Isn't that true?"

I said, "Then you got it. But you said I didn't give you a message?"

"I thought I was dreaming."

"Dreaming with me? It was your birthday; I was telling you to go across the river of life. Though you have a boat, you can be put in the same deep water if you're not careful. Take care, my 'sun'."

And then I spelled it. When I call people my son, they think I call them s-o-n; no, I call him s-u-n. They never ask me to spell that word.

Please take care of yourself. Go back home and have a good sleep, and whatever I do with you tonight, it is my night. Have a nice night. God bless. Thank you.

◆ ◆ ◆

May the long time sun shine upon you,
all love surround you, and the pure light within you, guide your way on.

Sat Nam

May God give you the strength to go through the spirit of prosperity,
because it is in adversity that man keeps everything together. It is in prosperity
that we lose sight of everything. May your unseen eye and your deep sight come to
you as a guardian angel, and may your Third Eye see your dangers
and keep you safe and serene.

Thank you.

UNLOADING THE PAST OF HARSH MEMORIES II—THE KRIYA

January 11, 1989

There are no breaks between the exercises. Move immediately from one exercise to the next.

1. Sit on the heels with the hands flat on the ground, equal weight on each side, fingers spread. Chin is up. Begin a short powerful inhalation and exhalation through the mouth. Pace: one breath per second. **5 minutes**.

This exercise works on the pineal gland. Move the spine, move the shoulders, keep the balance. Deliver the baby of its neurosis and all this neurotic compensation. Let's get rid of the old dirt, but let us prepare ourselves. Move, move! It's a real intercourse with the Self, with your Breath of Life.
Come on, breathe. Everybody has to become a big mother. Your intuition comes when your motherly faculty starts working. Come on, I want to hear it!

2. Sit in Easy Pose. Bring the hands to the throat, as in a choke hold—left hand over right. Look at the tip of the nose through closed eyes. Meditate. Inhale deep and exhale. Take several more quick breaths and begin long, deep breathing. Begin the guided meditation along with the gong. **14½ minutes**.

Guided Meditation

Breathe deep and constant, deep and constant, deep and constant, deep and constant. Let's get out of the body so that we may not be disturbed. Let us get into the space. Now, any pain that you remember in your life, any injustice done—just start dealing with that. Get into the space. Recollect your pains and drop them. Repeat them and dramatize them; they will all burn out. They will never bother you again; you will never have any kind of awful dream or daydream. With that it will be out of your life. Anything you want to get rid of in your life, any nonsense, this is the time. Fly free in the space, redramatize your painful memories and drop them. Keep up; this is the time to unload your garbage into the space.

Remember, remember, remember, recollect your garbage and drop it. At the time of reentry, it will all be gone—just remember and collect it! Now drop it! We are going back to the reentry. Recollect now! This is your last chance; we have two and a half minutes before landing. We are taking the height again. Take the height, recollect, and drop it.

You must understand once and for all that the sound of the gong is the sound of creativity by the hand of God. Your mind has only one thing, which it cannot resist, which it has to obey, and that is the sound of the gong.

3. Stay in the same posture as exercise 2, and immediately begin Breath of Fire. Continue for **2 minutes**.

Your Breath of Fire should be done from the Navel Point. Pump your belly powerfully, because your mental health is proportionate to how powerfully you pump the navel today. If you can breathe fast now, from the Navel Point, as strong as you can, then you will have a lot of energy tomorrow and you will feel happy. The vacuum you have created through what you have dropped will be filled with positive energy.

4. Sit with a straight spine. Sit majestically, as if you are the only yogi on the planet. Put both hands on the Navel Point and press hard. Listen to *Rakhe Rakhan Har* by Singh Kaur as you meditate on the Navel Point. Keep the Navel Point pressed and your spine straight throughout the **4 minutes**.

Press the point of the navel and straighten the spine like steel. Think, "I will sit as majestically as if I were the best and only yogi on the planet." Try it my way— fake it and you will make it. Believe me. Tomorrow's karmas, which are going to cause you pain and suffering, have to be burned today.

5. Keeping the posture, close the eyes and begin to chant with the mantra, *Rakhe Rakhan Har* by Singh Kaur. Chant with a hard, stiff tongue for **2 minutes**.

6. Open the eyes and begin Celestial Communication with *Rakhe Rakhan Har* by Singh Kaur. As teachers and practitioners, you can practice the original sequence or make up your own. Continue for **3½ minutes**.

Celestial Communication is a body language, a perfect prayer. As a teacher or practitioner, you can learn one of the original Celestial Communication sequences that go with this mantra, or you can make up your own.

TO END: Inhale and suspend the breath for **30 seconds,** making your entire body like stainless steel, so the entire energy can go to every fiber of the body and equalize. Exhale. Take two quick deep breaths, then inhale deeply again, and suspend **30 seconds**. Exhale. Inhale deeply, suspend the breath **30 seconds**. Exhale. Take six quick deep breaths. Exhale. For the last time, inhale deep and suspend the breath for **30 seconds**. Hold this pranic energy, let it go through every fiber of the body, by your own force, pressurize every cell in the body. Make it tough, hard and stiff. It's a simple science: the law of contraction and expansion. Exhale and relax. ◆

"As a human being, your foundation is not developed. You don't think you are a light of God. I presume that you're just like a candle, which is not lit. So when you exchange candles with each other, give your light to somebody and tell him to feel happy. A candle is supposed to give light. "

– Yogi Bhajan

DROPPING YOUR PERSONAL PAIN

January 14, 1989

*T*HE IDEA IN TEACHING THIS COURSE IS THAT A LOT OF PEOPLE ARE IN PAIN. It's not that I'm not in pain. I've got a fever, I've got influenza, name anything you want to name, I've got all of those right now. Not that I have to go back and get sick, but this sickness is physical, it will go away. One can endure physical sickness, but when the mind is sick, one cannot endure it. People think that to become religious and spiritual is a gimmick; it's not, it's a very serious subject. You have been given a rock called diamond. If you do not cut it, if you do not facet it and you do not coin it, it's of no use to you. You are Western people, you don't care, but you do suffer. Your suffering is much deeper than can be said or done.

This is how you start diverting your life. Each day, in a different way, diversion starts taking place. People who love, they get together. Love combines us, love unites us. Our love is very commotional, and there's no reason for us to believe that anybody even understands it. You have two powers, you have a mind, three of them, so that you can work out your intelligence and consciousness, and you can pull through life. But because your mind and your feelings and your emotions and your commotions, it doesn't matter who you belong to or who your teacher is, my experience in the Western world is, you only want a teacher when it suits you. Lots of teachers have come, lots have gone. Lots will come, lots will go. I never came here to go. I came here to stay.

My idea is, I'm a spiritual teacher, not a geometry teacher, not an algebra teacher, not a mathematics teacher. If somebody even says he is my student, he's not, because I never initiate anybody. So none can authentically say he is my student, ever. I've never done that. When I initiate somebody, somebody will be worthy of it. But even those who call themselves my students, they don't expect me to get into it with them and tell them, "What were you doing at four o'clock this morning?" They don't want to answer to anybody. So they have nobody.

A spiritual teacher is somebody who can get into your spirit and ask you, "What are you doing? Where are you going? What is right and what is wrong for you?" Here, these days, they even tell us not to counsel people because that can affect their life. My response to that is, "If we are not to affect their life, what is the use? I should open an ice-cream shop and start selling ice-cream.! Why should I pretend as a spiritual teacher and try to be nice? So that I will have lots of students?" What difference does it make if I've no students? As long as my own student is my own

When you are truthful, you're light, bright, beautiful, and there is nothing handicapped. When you are not, you have six hundred theories and nine hundred theorems and different angles.

student, and as long as I initiate myself as me, and as long as I know that my journey is toward God, and as long as I know I've to complete it, that's all that matters.

So, today, all the doctors and everybody told me not to come here, and practically, it's not possible to come here. But you know, it is shocking to me that there is no book on it. You've one mind which has three equal parts: positive, negative and neutral. Each part has nine aspects, which in turn have three parts, so there are eighty one parts of the mind—nobody understands it. You can bisect the body. Yoga scriptures say that there are seventy-two meridians, or arteries, seventy-two thousand relevant nadis, and their functions. Yoga also says that you have seven chakras, the eighth is the aura. You have ten bodies, and your presence should work, not you; but you've never developed. As a human being, your foundation is not developed. You don't think you are a light of God. I presume that you're just like a candle, which is not lit. So when you exchange candles with each other, give your light to somebody and tell him to feel happy. A candle is supposed to give light. Am I right? When you give somebody a candle, it doesn't mean that he is dark, just that you are giving light, a candle is a symbol of light. We go to church, we pray, we light a candle. We go to a religious place, we light a candle, which means light. Truth is light. When you are truthful, you're light, bright, beautiful, and there is nothing handicapped. When you are not, you have six hundred theories and nine hundred theorems and different angles.

It's a very funny story, I was coming in on an airplane and this guy said, "Hi Yogiji, how are you?"

"Oh, my God, how are you? I'm fine."

"I met you in 1970-something."

"Yeah, I must have met you, too. I meet people all the time."

"Now I'm studying with a different teacher."

"Good, wonderful, very fantastic. God bless you. What are you learning?"

"Oh, it's all very mystical and secret."

When these people do these kinds of dramas, if you make a list of spiritual groups, that many groups are there, and that many spirits are not there. This is a very funny world. Everybody wants to do something, but they do not want to do everything, which is where you get the English word, debauch. You are debauched, and you live in debauchery.

You are sincerely insincere. You have no relationship with your soul. You've never found a friendship with it. You don't talk to it. You don't tell it what you want, it doesn't tell you what you should do. So, we have twenty girlfriends and thirty boyfriends and all that jazz going on. It is ridiculous, isn't it? I told my soul today, "Darling, body is very sick. Mind is very pressured. How are you?"

She said, "Your intuition told you not to accept to teach in San Diego, you be-

came emotional because someone laid a number on you and you agreed. Remember? Even if you have to die, you're a spiritual teacher, you promised. You can't break it. If you break it, who will keep it? It's a simple thing. If you break what you said, what you promised, who will keep it? Therefore, get up, tighten your belt, get in the car, and get going baby boy. Go and do the job."

All right. The job I'm going to do used to cost about six thousand dollars and required a six month commitment; it's called rebirthing. I've to do it within an hour or so—and that's all it takes. I've to do rebirthing within the time we have here because it is essential once in a while. Not that you have to become a baby boy and be born and all that. But because you stock up a lot of fears, a lot of tears, a lot of doubts and many times you go inside and weep and you cannot even shout, that's the way you live, and we call it civilization. We are all victims of civilization. I came to San Diego and I couldn't recognize it. This used to be all land. With my own eyes I've seen it. Now, my God, it's a whole city.

So, between the conscious and the unconscious, there is a subconscious. Unconscious is intuition—don't misunderstand the word. Unconscious means intuition; those little voices which are the guiding voices are the voices of the soul. The subconscious has many, many facets. "My father has many mansions and my mansion has many rooms." It has a memory, perpetual memory, inferior memory, projective memory, camera memory. You read scriptures and you meditate, you do everything; everybody is doing something. But when it comes to cleaning house, you call the maid: "Clean my house, I'll pay you ten dollars an hour; see that it is cleaned." So, whenever all this subconscious stuff comes up, you call Yogi Bhajan: "Come on, baby boy, come and clean us."

All right, you have invited, so let you suffer, why should I bother? It is your problem, but don't have a loss; and if you have to cry through it, go through it and let it take you the way it has to take you. Whatever your experience, let it be yours and feel free. But please, let it go. I shall feel very good if you just cooperate and behave so that I don't have to repeat or yell and scream and tell you to keep up and all that. All I need is your courtesy today. The rest I'll take care of.

I'm very ready, if you are very ready. But when you leave this place, you will not be the same as you are right now—that's definite and that is what I believe in. It's called the touch of the teacher. I'm not a teacher to you and nobody is my student. But I have the touch of the teacher. I had a teacher and I have it now. When I touch my teacher, I touch the universe. So, are we ready?

What is the latest time you have a baby-sitter at home and you have to get up and all that stuff? Or boyfriend is waiting on the corner? Are you free to be with me? I can go otherwise. Up to five o'clock? Ok, are you all okay? You know, I have come

The subconscious has many facets. It has a memory, perpetual memory, inferior memory, projective memory, camera memory. You read scriptures and meditate, and do everything. But when it comes to cleaning house, you call the maid: "Clean my house, I'll pay you ten dollars an hour." So, whenever this subconscious stuff comes up, you call Yogi Bhajan: "Come on, come and clean us."

all these miles, I'd like to do something. I'm also very commercial you know, I have to come again. And if I have to come again, then I have to do a good job, otherwise who will call me next time?

I always do my own public relations. All right. We are going to bundle up certain things. It's not going to be straight because what we are going to do is address the *samskaras*, the previous incarnation and the path of this previous incarnation, the karma which you have to pay. A *samskara* is a debt which you took on and that *samskara* is the debt for which you wrote, "I owe you." You can't get out of that. Doesn't matter whether you are American, German or French, that is your "I owe you." Sometimes when you promised, you didn't care; and when you wrote those papers, you never cared. All that recorded karma is called *samskaras*, which stand on your head. It's a toll you have to pay. The second karma is karma which you don't create, actions and reactions which are beyond you, that's the touch of the spiritual teacher. Spiritual teacher cannot do more than this; don't misunderstand. A Padre, a holy man—really a man of God, not a pretentious person who thinks, 'I'm a man of God,' but really a man of God—can only take your karma and divert it into dharma, so you may not suffer. From many facets of life, it can give you one facet of life, that's all.

This whole thing is a gimmick, a lie: "I went light and I went this." Nobody does anything. It's all imagination and story writing and Hollywood showbiz. So just understand, there are three simple things: one is *samskara*, one is karma and one is dharma. How does karma affect you? *Samskara* is "I owe you." You've got to pay it. There is no reason to disbelieve it. The theory of the *samskara* I can make you understand: The tenth Guru, who became Guru Gobind Singh from Gobind Rai, was very kind-hearted, very brave, and a very courageous warrior and spiritual person. There was a very humble vegetarian who was his *bhakta*, his devotee, for a very long time, and he came to see him. Guru Gobind Singh was sitting on his throne and he was pulling the meat of a pigeon with his hand and feeding his falcon. The devotee came, and he brought lots of gold pieces and lots of beautiful alms and everything and he bowed; but when he got up and looked, he almost had a heart attack. He thought, "What? Such a cruel Guru? What is he doing?" He didn't say anything, you know, you don't say anything to your teacher but thank you. So he said, "Thank you," and he slipped out. Guru Gobind Singh understood and said, "Bring him back in."

The devotee returned and Guru Gobind Singh asked him, "Bhai, you came with a lot of love to pay me respect. Is that true?"

"Yes, master."

"You saw me doing a *karam*, an act and you got mad or angry or confused."

(There are three words in the whole world: *param, karam, dharam. Param* means doubt, which makes you go berserk; *karam* mean action and reaction; *dharam* means that which has no action or reaction, the path is straight.)

Guru Gobind Singh said, "You are a great person. Why do you feel so upset?"

"I don't know." *(Yogi Bhajan said, "He was American," to which the students replied with laughter.)*

"What can I tell you? It has taken me ten, twelve years to come and this is what I saw."

"No, no. That's all right. You did see me doing what I'm still doing. But don't go with a doubt. Ask this pigeon and this falcon yourself. That's why I called you back, not that I want to explain anything myself."

So the devotee stood and said, "Oh, pigeon, oh falcon, remove my doubt."

Guru Gobind Singh said, "Close your eyes and they will talk to you both."

When he closed his eyes, he saw that the pigeon and the falcon were both Sikhs of the Guru, who had promised each other, in the name of Guru, five hundred gold pieces. One followed through and the other never gave. Both died. One became a pigeon, the other became a falcon. The falcon went after the pigeon, and the pigeon ran to the Guru. The Guru asked the pigeon, "Why?" He said, "You are the guarantor. In your name, it was done. So, please, with your own hand, finish this death of mine so that I can be liberated and be free."

Sometimes, your life is just short, for a little while. I'm a great teacher, international blah, blah, blah; but in my previous life I never taught anybody. Whosoever came had to prove to me, "I owe you," perhaps I was like the show-me-state Missouri, that's the kind of teacher I was. Now you see, I'm so compassionate, I don't even care. I don't initiate. This is how people change, and that is *samskara*.

Second stage is *karam*, action and reaction. *Karam* is not physical action and reaction. *Karam* is all mental. You've no power to think. As a human being, you've no thinking power, that power is with the animals, not with you. You think that you think. The intellect, the *sahasrara*, gives you a thousand thoughts per wink of the eye; and those thoughts become feelings and then emotions and then you become desirous, and you pursue them. These are all thoughts; but all those people who think that they think, they are the biggest mess on Earth. Somebody asked me, "Yogiji, I want to open my Third Eye." I said, "For God's sake, close it. It's open with everybody." Opening the Third Eye is not a requirement, closing it is. It needs to be closed so that you may not have night dreams, wet dreams, day dreams and terrible dreams. Do you know how much time you waste in dreaming? In twenty four hours, if he keeps awake ten hours, six hours he is in dream stage. What you call thinking, planning and all that stuff, that's not true; it is your reaction.

We are beast, we are human and we are angelic. The angel part comes in dharma. Dharma is not a religion, it's a science of reality. Dharma means that with

Fifteen times per minute the breath of life comes and touches us, that's the gift of God—and we say we do not know God. Without the breath of life you cannot live.

intuition you can see everything. It's known to you. If something is not known to you, you have to search it out. But if it is known to you, you don't have to search it out. Therefore, please know that God made you, don't search for God. He made you. He is your God. Some people love God, but they don't trust God. Some people believe in God, but they don't trust God. I've yet to meet a human being who straight away says, "I trust God." Talk to any human being about God and they start messing around, "Oh, no, how can we? How can we be this?" What a big lie! We lie all the time. Fifteen times per minute the breath of life comes and touches us, that's the gift of God—and we say we do not know God. Without the breath of life you cannot live. So whether we are atheist or we are very spiritual, we are almost the same, because the first faculty of a man is to trust. If you don't trust, you are a bust. No big deal.

In your life many things will come and go. You will be miserable one way or the other. I look at my life everyday as a human being, practically. You must understand, my soul is a prisoner of the rib cage, and in that rib cage God sends me the message, a visitor, fifteen times a minute to tell me, "I'm with you, I'm with you, I'm with you." And in return, I say, "Ha, yeah, Thou, yes." In return I say, "*Wahe Guru.*" It means, "Thou art with me. Your wonder is that You are with me." That word, "*Wahe Guru*" only means "*Sat Nam;*" it means "really." It doesn't mean more than that. Some people just make up big stories, but *Sat Nam* only means, "Really? Are you sure?" Because there are five tattvas, five tattvas and seven chakras are tying in a knot—and that's called human personality. Human personality must have an impact. Human personality must not have public relations. If your presence doesn't work, your powder and your makeup won't work. You know what the main problem is? We all wear makeup. We cover up everything, we look pretty, we use the computer now, we do everything to what? We do everything to do what? To attract. My dear folks, whatever you're going to attract, you are going to have to live with it. Are you ready to live with that weight? No, you are not. You cannot handle it, and then you start crying. I got a telephone call the other day.

"I just met this girl on the subway."

"Then what happened?"

"Oh, we became friends. I taught her a lot about Kundalini Yoga. I told her about you, I did this, this, and that. Now she is changing me and my wife is upset and she calls me here and . . ."

"Wait a minute, thief. What are you trying to tell me? From the subway you didn't go home direct?"

"How do you know?"

"That's the problem: I know. Because you are blaming that girl doesn't mean that you are so simple and honest, crystal clear and saintly."

No, saint and Satan both are in us. Truth and lies are always in us. Reality and non-reality are always in us. Good luck and bad luck are always with us. Fortune and misfortune, everything that has an action and a reaction, it's Newton's Third Law. Action has a reaction, equal and opposite, that's called karma. In English, I can simply say, "So shall you sow, so shall you reap, if you do not sow good, you shall weep." Understand that? We harvest every day. Every day we wake up and we start sowing; and every night, we harvest it. It is that deadly night which you do not know. You call yourself sleepy. A lot of people say that one should sleep eight hours. I say, "Give me one person in the universe who sleeps eight hours." You cannot sleep above that. You lie down, you curl around, you balance, you do the whole thing, and once in a while there comes a sleep where you do not know you are male or female, religious or non-religious, here or anywhere—that thirty-one minutes is all you have to recuperate for the next day. Those who have that recuperation, those who have more than thirty-one minutes to sixty-two minutes a day, are entitled to change the misfortune of others; that's all it is. It is a thirty-one minute game, total.

I'm going to put you in a self-hypnosis and trance. I'm going to change your capacity. I would not have done this, first of all, I would have done it procedurally correct. Go through it slowly. But because I'm not well, I'm going to cut through, I'm going to cut a lot of garbage. I'm not going to lie to you. I'm going to cut right through. In counseling, the majority of psychologists just go through a kind of mental, chit-chat, boyfriend or girlfriend. These people want to talk; but they know fundamentally what wrong is. That's it. We all know what wrong is. Wrong is when we are overloaded subconsciously. We are unable to release through nightmares and we are afraid. We take a lot of pills and here we are. But today neither your trauma is going to work nor your drama is going to work. You are not paying six thousand dollars. I asked somebody last time, "Why do you charge so much money for this science, this is a simple yoga."

They replied, "Oh, if you don't charge people so much and take them through it, they don't act."

Well, let us see whether you act or not. Come on, let's do the business now, okay? Enough is enough.

◆ ◆ ◆

These hands have a very psychic communication if you just work with them. We'll not interpret the communication of that. Close your eyes and look at the tip of your nose. That's the fix. The eye focus, this fix, is sometimes so powerful that there's not a single drug which can take you through. It's so powerful. It's very good. It stimulates your renal, your heart, your lungs. We are all mothers. We all create

Karma. If you want to get rid of the garbage then do it right, otherwise, you will be stuck with it. I can guarantee you.

Invite the psyche from the universe to become pure. I'm no miracle or gimmick; I'm doing something, but remember, I'm just a teacher. Dance your spine and give your breath a power. Look, I'll tell you, after being sick for two years myself because the Golden Temple was attacked in 1984. The problem became bad, I became involved. I knew that after that what follows is the death of thousands of people. Sikhs are very devoted, and the temple is well-respected. It was not going to be easy. So I tried to restore peace even though I couldn't breathe myself. I left a lot of things behind.

It's just a simple science. People say, "I want to have personal self-esteem." Right? "I want personal success." Right? "I want to be rich." Right? Everything is okay. But do you know that if your prana in the breath does not touch the blood stream you can become sick. You can be handicapped. Your body's power will not radiate. If it can happen to a yogi like me, internationally respected and known, recognized, how do you stand a chance? Now I'm doing my own pranayam and all that, like a kid, I get up in the morning, I do the whole thing myself. I wish I had been doing it all along because even I, in that pain, in that agony, forgot that I'm also subject to karma. So, I regret that. I cannot serve my students, I cannot go and teach myself, I cannot talk much. I'm a wise man. I can counsel right, but I'm not available all the time. So, there are a lot of handicaps. You do feel for people. When you feel for people, you feel their problems, you feel their pain. One day somebody wrote me a letter and I laughed. I said, "Oh, my God. This is nothing, this is a simple thing. But it's all there is for him." Then I laid down and put a quilt on my face and went to sleep. When I woke up, somebody asked me, "What's wrong?" I said, "I just felt bad that people cannot handle these little things."

I'm not competent to serve everybody and help everybody. I never came to America to do what I'm doing. I came here to be happy-go-lucky with people and tell them that everybody has God within them self—don't search it out. You are the creation of one God and your duty is to be beautiful. Beauty is in your radiant body, not in the powders and creams and all that. I'm slowly, slowly, holding you and talking to you in between in order to give you a gap, so I can cook you well. You understand what I mean? Slowly and gradually, now you are in a thoughtful form, that's called first stage. First stage is when a person gets into the thoughts. Now you are not what you were. First you were people, personality, identity; now you are thoughtful identity. Not that simple, dead, drive identity, that pure ego. Now, the ego is bright in all of you. And how many minutes have we taken? Fifteen, that's all. Fifteen minutes—believe me or not.

You can even feel it yourself. You are not the same; and fifteen minutes, that's sometimes all it takes. One minute. One minute can change the life. One minute. You are driven by fear. But I will tell you another way. I do not believe in poverty. I believe that poverty is a drama to attract the attention of rich people. I believe you can all be rich, provided you direct your psyche. I'm a scientist. Energy can be changed into material and material can be changed into energy. You saw that there were certain gifts given to me today? Right? Now, they will go tonight on the altar and I have to pray. It is hiring, it is not giving. The guy has a wish and the person has a gift, whatever it is, it will sit on the altar and there the servant of these people will pray to God and beg and ask for their will to be granted. Sometimes things are both negative and positive and if you ask me, I would say, "No, it is not possible." Then I say, "Wait a minute." And that is how sometimes weeks go by until things are taken away from the altar. Because an altar has no alternative, and a person who has no altar is no person. If your personality, your reality, your words, your everything has an alternative and you do not mean what you mean to say, you are the meanest man living in good clothes. You are the bad guy.

It doesn't matter which religion you belong to. No religion is bad. It's the people. No mother is bad. It's the nervous system. No husband and wife have to have a divorce if they can hold it. Every day, in a different way, different things we say, we walk away from our loved ones, every day. I'll complete this poem when I go back to Los Angeles and make a song out of it. Why do we do that? We need a nervous system. The armpit—that's where three nervous systems meet. Nobody wants to do the exercise and so what they do is block up the armpit. They say, "it's blocked forever, so the insanity can be forever." Now, ask any medical doctor, and they aren't used to it themselves. It's a junction station of three nervous systems? You may not smell, that is, you may not physically smell, but you may mentally stink. It's the most live center of the whole human. I went to a health club in Miami to get what they call a "wrap, an herbal wrap." I'm an herbalist, so I wanted to go and see. I have always believed that God cures, doctors diagnose and herbs heal—and herbs heal in a way that you don't have a side effect. Other medicines have side effects; there's no doubt about it. So, I went to have an herbal wrap, and what did they do? They took two big hot sheets underneath, put a towel over, and asked me to lie down. Then, two more sheets, two towels over that and wrapped me up.

"That's it?"

"What do you expect for twenty dollars?"

"What are these herbs?"

"Must be some damn mint."

And this was the guy who was giving me the treatment!

Saint and Satan both are in us. Truth and lies are always in us. Reality and non-reality are always in us. Good luck and bad luck are always with us. Fortune and misfortune, everything that has an action and a reaction, it's Newton's Third Law. Action has a reaction, equal and opposite, that's called karma.

I came here to be happy-go-lucky with people and tell them that everybody has God within them self—don't search it out. You are the creation of one God and your duty is to be beautiful.

He said, "I do it every day. You want it? You just stay here."

Thank God I got sick, really. If I had not gotten sick, I would not have created all these herbal supplements. I would have just been enjoying the money and comfort of the United States. God did me a very good thing. Now, I know how life is. And that same day I sat down and I said, "This is not this; all this pill popping is no good. Let's put these twenty herbs in a proportion and make them as real as though three thousand years from now, a yogi could have done it. Let's do it." And folks, we did it. It was real. I asked someone to make a pie from them because people like to eat sweets. And last night, when we had tried every medicine, I went into the kitchen myself, put ten main things together. No big deal, no big secret. Put those ten things and two apples and cooked it up and ate it. Here I am today. Otherwise, I would have come in an ambulance.

But this is how our life changes. Life is nothing my dear folks. I honestly tell you that there is no such thing as love, there is no such thing as hatred. When you can't reach somebody, you hate. You hate not to reach. When you reach, you are in love. Or you want to reach, that's all. But it requires energy, it requires spirit. It requires strength. We need strength. It's not untrue that your biorhythm changes all the time. Every two and a half hours, your nostril changes. Every two and a half hours, your nostril changes and your whole energy changes.

When you were in the womb of the mother, everybody has a little meat like the clitoris; and after the acid bath, the clitoris becomes a penis or remains a clitoris, from clitoris to penis and clitoris to clitoris. There is an acid bath in which men lose their right side of the brain. So the problem is that no male has a right side to his brain. He has to learn to activate it. It's a medical theory. Don't ask me. Ask those who found it. We found it six thousand years ago. Kundalini Yoga is very old science. Kundalini Yoga was founded so that the male can compete; he has to win, he has to get it, he must have it. A woman has a left side and a right side and she is confused about which side to use.

I enjoy teaching. That's why I teach. I don't teach because I need money. No, I've never taught for money, from day one. You cannot buy me, you cannot sell me. I teach out of fun. I have always done it that way. In my poverty, I have done the same thing. In my richness I have done the same thing. I don't care. I'm just a free person. And I'm going to enjoy this. But you're going to do something.

No, it's entertainment, isn't it? To see your auras going through changes and then I can see precisely how your creative projection has to change now to adjust because you are a bad liar. Your aura speaks. The men's faculty is that he didn't have a good day yesterday and his creativity was zero; he's trying to be creative and effective right now. I enjoy all that. That's what I actually enjoy.

Keep up the rhythm. Keep up the rhythm. Index finger has to be straight. This is your index finger, your wisdom, your Jupiter. It's not a small finger. When you raise this finger (the middle finger), it means, "God, you _____," this finger you know what it means. Raise both fingers and it means victory. That's what it is: God and Earth. It is a science; it is not some yoga lesson so that you can sit for hours and hours. It's something real. So, value it that way.

Have you paid? Should I walk away? What do you think I've come here for? To teach for money? I just made a professional commitment to meet with you and be with you, so I can do it and you can do it and your life can be better tomorrow and I can vouch for it. I'm very sincere in my life. This is big business. You've got to do it right. We want to pull on the third meridian and cross, so that our lungs can stimulate and our brain can understand. If there is any faculty or any disease that you are going to face tomorrow, let us get rid of it today, and that's what I'm doing. And you complain. What is this? Is it a joke? Don't do this. You are not sincere to yourself.

Okay, folks. This was what the class was, okay? That's what you paid for. All right.

◆ ◆ ◆

May the long time sun shine upon you,
all love surround you, and the pure light within you, guide your way on.

Sat Nam

Note: In this class, Yogi Bhajan also taught a special meditation for prosperity. Find this Ashtang Mantra for Prosperity in the Appendix on page 433.

DROPPING YOUR PERSONAL PAIN
—THE KRIYA

January 14, 1989

There are no breaks between the exercises, unless indicated. Move immediately from one exercise to the next.

PART ONE

1. Close the eyes and look at the tip of the nose through closed eyes. With the hands palm up in front of the body, the elbows relaxed and fingers pointing forward, move the forearms up to a 45-degree angle and then down again, alternate left and right. The forearm never goes below parallel.
After **30 seconds** breathe powerfully through the mouth. **3 minutes total**. Inhale. Exhale and relax.

The hands have a very psychic communication if you just work with them.

Break: Open the eyes, move the head and neck, and relax. **30 seconds**.

2. Maintain the eye focus from Exercise 1. Bring the arms up to parallel, with the elbows slightly bent and the palms facing the body. Continue the powerful breath from Exercise 1 but increase the pace. Alternate the hands, left and right, as they move toward the face. Allow the rib cage to twist gently with this movement. Pace becomes like a Breath of Fire, but through the mouth; exhale as the hand comes toward the face. **1 ½ minutes**.

3. Open the eyes and laugh loudly. **30-60 seconds**.

PART TWO

1. Close the eyes and look at the tip of the nose through the closed eyes. Bring the hands in front of the shoulders. Extend your Jupiter (index) finger and keep it straight throughout the movement. Snap the Saturn (middle) finger against the thumb as the arms extend parallel to the ground creating a 60-degree angle, a large V in front of the body. Then return to original position and repeat. Exhale as the arms extend out and the fingers snap. Continue the breath through the mouth.
Pace: One breath per second. **1 ½ minutes**.
Increase Pace: Two breaths per second. **1 minute**.

2. Continue to keep the eyes closed and look at the tip of the nose. Put the thumbs on the Mercury Mound at the base of the pinkie finger. The hands are held at shoulder level at a 60 degree angle out from the body, palms facing each other. Bring the mudra toward the Heart Center, alternate, left and right hands. Don't touch the chest. Continue the breath through the mouth in rhythm with the movement. Exhale as the hands come toward the chest. Increase the pace toward the end of the exercise, like a Breath of Fire. **4 minutes**.

Remember the Greek God, Mercury? Let us communicate with God ourself. Employ the God, Mercury. Come on! Get out of you and on to God.

3. Inhale and place both hands on the Heart Center, right over, left under. Exhale. Take two more quick breaths and then begin the gong meditation and visualization. The gong begins to increase in intensity for the last **1 ½ minutes**.
14 minutes total.

Guided Meditation

Pick up your pain and your memories, which you do not want to get rid of, right now, and come with me. Go into your memory and pick up all that hurts you. Pick up your pain and it will be burned out. In the space there is a re-entry and everything will be dropped; please collect them all so you may not be left with any dirt.

Let us float through the space and collect your garbage. We are going to drop it at the re-entry. Now come with me to the height to drop the garbage! Come on, let us go. You can float with me now. Come with me, come, come, come. Open your heart.

4. Continue the gong and begin chanting with *Ardas Bhaee* by Nirinjan Kaur. Just copy the sound, copy it perfectly. Chant loudly, from the heart. Use your tongue, stimulate the *Shushmana*, the central channel. Use the tongue to speak the words; it will have a different meaning. Kiss the words. After **3 ½ minutes**, silence the gong but continue chanting for **3 ½ more minutes**.
7 minutes total.

TO END: Inhale, suspend the breath **30 seconds** and stiffen all the muscles of the body, even in the inner organs. Let the energy be equally distributed. Exhale. Repeat twice more.

◆

Ardaas bhaee amar daas guroo
Amar daas guroo ardaas bhaee
Raam daas guroo raam daas guroo
Raam daas guroo sachee sahee

The prayer has been offered Oh Guru Amar Das!
Oh Guru Amar Das, the prayer has been offered!
Ram Das the Guru, Ram Das the Guru,
Ram Das the Guru, it is sealed in Truth.

" We all want things in one way; we all have the will and we have free will, but that's not enough. Free will is given to you to find out God's will—and that's intuition. "

– Yogi Bhajan

UNLOADING THE PAIN OF PERPETUAL MEMORIES I

February 14, 1989

THERE ARE A LOT OF THEORIES IN LIFE AND A LOT OF RELIGIOUS ASPECTS—many religions, many people, and many teachers. I am not saying that's going to stop; that will continue as it is. But there are certain fundamental things that are real. Man has been continuously trying to search for God and has been frustrated. Now two-thirds of the world feels there is no God. Some Buddhists believe in truth, but if you talk about God, they get mad at you. The communists came out with a theory that there is no God. Well, if there is no God, why are we searching for one? The question is, if there is a God, where is It?

If you do not have the vastness of your life, then you have only the wastefulness of your life. Life is very vast, as vast as God is. Denying it or accepting it won't work. You are not living for wealth; a lot of wealthy people are unhappy. You are not living for power; a lot of powerful people are very unhappy. You are actually looking for something that will get you to a place where you can find happiness—eternal happiness, forever. Everybody wants that. But when you come to this Earth, you have something in you called memory. Now, what is this memory? Memory is something that always affects you. You may not remember what you ate the day before yesterday, but there are certain accidents and incidents in your life that you never forget. How many things can you remember? Lots! How many things can you repeat? Lots!

Life is a gift. But if you are not alert, then that very life, which is a gift to you, becomes unenjoyable because you have created a rift in your own life between you and yourself. That rift is called desire—a rift between what you want and what you are and what you have. How many times in your life do you hate yourself because you want something and it is not there? Your quick answer to the problem is, "I am miserable; life is miserable." It's not that somebody else has to hate you. So many times you put yourself down, so many times you are upset, so many times you are negative, so many times you are depressed because you do not get what you want. There is a fight between you and within you. There is a fight between you and what's around you. "He got that, and I didn't get it;" so there is a fight there. There are many fights in your life, and sometimes you lose and sometimes you win. When you lose or something doesn't happen the way you want it, then you are scratched, and those scratches are very deep memories.

Life is a gift. But if you are not alert, then that very life, which is a gift to you, becomes unenjoyable because you have created a rift in your own life between you and yourself.

You want to be rich with wealth? Take the whole planet Earth; it doesn't mean anything. Rich is that man who has infinity on his side; poor is that man who is defined, limited.

So, it happened—your hand got burned. The matter ended, and you healed; the skin got grafted, and you are okay. But those memories are oozing all the time, and you carry that pain extensively. Unfortunately, the mind carries painful memories more than it carries happy moments. Is there a rational answer for why man does this? The fact is, every man wants to be happy, forever, but you can never be happy forever if you think you are clever. You are intelligent, but you don't use your intelligence to satisfy yourself; you use your intelligence to be dissatisfied all the time. You use all your positive faculty for negative results. I think that we are in a position to get rid of some of those faculties, because this is what I have come to conclude: If a person is not happy, that person shall destroy everything he really longs for, that person will destroy something that is very precious to him. Love will turn into hatred, positive will turn into negative, good health will become diseased.

Look at me—I didn't want to rest. I wanted to create what I have come to create. Big deal. But within two years, I was grounded. Now, I could say, "I am a Yogi; therefore it should not happen to me," or I could say, "I am Siri Singh Sahib; it should not happen to me." But the law is the law: So shall you sow, so shall you reap. You overwork, you become neurotic—even if it's for the achievement of a very noble thing—somewhere you have to pay.

Los Angeles has about five or six million people. Let's say it's seven million people; six point nine million of those are unhappy. If you talk to them, they will tell you every complaint in the world. Those who are not unhappy will look to you like loonies. They do not know what happiness is at all.

I met one funny guy, and I asked him, "Why do you even want to work?"

"For the joy of the competition."

Can you believe that in Manhattan, a man has an office where he has three hundred employees who do nothing but his international accounting? Three hundred men working on his business accounting; everybody surrounds their semi-cubical kind of thing with computers that have so much capacity you can't believe. This man took me to New Jersey to a kind of warehouse. In that huge building, there was nothing except some security guards, some highly paid engineers, and just a few offices. I said, "What is this? Do you import things?"

"No, this is my master computer headquarters."

Well, we talked, and I thought the friendship was very good. He was a rich man, we would go for a good dinner, and then I would say goodbye and go to the ashram and stay there. I would get rid of him, and he would get rid of me. But it didn't work out that way. He told me he wanted some private time with me. So we went to one of his rooms in the office, and within one second, this guy started crying. When he finished all that, I asked him, "What are you crying for?"

"I am very unhappy; very, very unhappy."

Just imagine—this man is unhappy. Not only unhappy, but "very, very" unhappy. He said he was being haunted by a memory. He made a promise to his dying father that he would become the richest man on the Earth, and he is not. Can you believe this? He has to fulfill his desire.

You want to be rich with wealth? Take the whole planet Earth; it doesn't mean anything. Rich is that man who has infinity on his side; poor is that man who is defined. If you have a horizon, it doesn't matter how big it is; if you have a dream, it doesn't matter how wonderful it is; if you are a yogi, it doesn't mean how pure you are; if you limit yourself, you are limited. Limited edition is a limited edition.

We do limit ourselves. I don't want to say it short-circuits us, but we do limit our self. We say, "If this happens, then I will be very happy." Now if that happens, you should be happy, and then forget about it. But instead, we say, "And then if this happens, I should be very happy." The reality is that you do not know what should happen to you. I don't blame you, because you have one thousand thoughts coming from your *sahasrara* per wink of the eye. Calculate that—each thought has twenty-five pounds of atmospheric pressure on the brain.

If you could just understand the capacity of your brain; it is known to have the computer capacity of thirty trillion message units, that's how good a chip it is—thirty trillion. That means your brain can take thirty trillion messages per impulse—that's what your brain is, and that's known. Your body is ten trillion cells, and your brain controls each cell, each molecule—electron, proton, neutron; it controls their change every seventy-two hours. Therefore, every movement of every cell is being controlled, which means thirty trillion impulse messages; it's simple mathematics, no big deal. If you want to make a computer equal to your brain's capacity, you could have an eighty-mile by eighty-mile square and an eighty-mile high building filled with chips that can process thirteen trillion messages per impulse—and still, that would be only five percent of your brain. That's how vast this little thing in the skull is.

The brain cannot see God because it doesn't have eyes; it cannot feel God because it has no senses. But your brain can give you a total concept of God, of how infinite God is. Your brain is so competent it can give you an experience of multiple infinity. If you go to the higher mathematics, you will stop at one thing, called infinity. Now, cross infinity to multiple infinity, over to extended infinity, infinity into infinity, infinity into the multipliable infinity, infinity into all multiple facets of infinity. If I start talking infinity, I will just finish the class and will not use any other word but infinity.

If you have one house, you feel good about it. But there are people who have a hundred houses, and they are very miserable. So there is no concept that can give

you God. Knowledge has no concept of God, a yogi has no concept, a swami has no concept, a saint has no concept. Every concept you build by your experience, it can tell you no more than that. So what is the idea of doing *japa, tapa,* and service? You could give everybody everything and still be miserable. It's a question of happiness; it's not a question of God. We are not here to find God; that is the gimmick that religion sells, and I hate it. There is no such thing as God. God is everywhere. And wherever you say God is, still God is a little further than that. Who wants to find God? It's like some common weed; it's everywhere. Why go after that? We are not after God; but we know that if we can find God, we can be happy, that's all.

We are after sex, but what for? Everybody knows it's a simple action that lasts five minutes, twenty minutes, half an hour. Extend it, put drugs into it, and all that, and maybe you can do it for an hour or two. Is that what you are looking for in sex? No. You are looking for happiness. You drink; you become an alcoholic. Are you after wine or alcohol? No, you want something extra; you want to get lost, to space out. You want to see infinity. Why? Because it is in you. You are hounded by a dreadful reality that one day you have to merge in that infinity. You cannot stop it. You may be evil or you may be divine, but that push cannot be stopped.

Think of Guru Nanak. Was he a multimillionaire? Was he a king of a state? Was he an emperor? No, but when you remember him, do you have reverence? Look at the Hindu. He takes a little stone—a stone is a stone, everybody knows it is stone—and he carves it and makes some shape; he makes some God out of it. Sometimes he makes a very funny God, with an elephant head and a human body, and all that stuff. But as long as that stone was just a stone, you could take it and throw it, and he won't mind. And if I asked him, he would give it you. But once his stone becomes something of reverence to him, if you touch that stone, he will cut your hand. So what happened to that stone? A stone is a stone; a stone cannot be God.

When the Mohammedans came to attack India, they killed everybody and won. They destroyed every temple and every statue in it because they said, "Worship one God. Don't worship many Gods; don't have statues." I don't know what they call them—heathens or something. But you know, in Mecca, there is one big black stone, the Kabbah. It, too, is just a stone, but every Muslim feels that he is one with God if he kisses that stone. Now what is the difference? To a Muslim, Allah put that stone there. To a Hindu, when a stone has an elephant head and a human body, it becomes the God of Happiness, prosperity; it becomes Ganesha. To a Christian, if you give him a cross on which Jesus was crucified, he will kiss the cross; it is a symbol of respect. But for another person, they don't understand.

Your life is your life. You can share it, you can love it, you can be everything. All you want in your life is a glimpse of happiness—not too much, just a few memo-

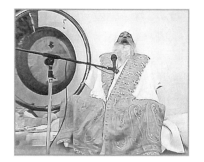

ries. But because your life is loaded with garbage—the memories of sadness, pain, and ridiculous, the memories of nothing, the memories of darkness, passion, and clouded with insanity—you do not know how to figure it out. When you go to the top story of the house, you don't know whether you will meet a cobweb or something else, but you know there is something precious there. Something your great grandfather has left, so you want to find it. You don't care that you get all the dust, all the cobwebs, and all that. Sometimes you end up cleaning the whole house to find something you want to find.

Tonight we are meeting here to get rid of those painful memories. You don't have to do anything; they'll be gone. Not all of them, but as much time as we have we'll try to put you through it. You must understand that the sound of the gong is the creative sound of the universe; you have no defense against it. You don't have to hypnotize yourself to go deeper into yourself. In exactly three seconds, the first stroke of the gong hypnotizes you, whether you like it or not. You can resist for maybe one minute or two and not go with the vibrations of it, but then it will carry you anyway. Then you are floating with the vibratory sound of that impact, which is like a hydrolic press, nothing can stop it. It squeezes the cloth into a little cubical bundle.

We are not asking you to do anything tonight except let it be. We are asking you, because as much as you will resist, that much time you will lose in letting it go. But if you just say to yourself, "I want to let it go," then we'll see you let it go. All right? Let's make a deal? So be it.

◆ ◆ ◆

I think we have a proposition before us that we must either go for peace or we must perish. In World War II, the total number of people killed was thirty to sixty million lives. Russia lost eleven million soldiers and seven million civilians, eighteen million total; Poland about six million; Germany about four million. If you look at the whole world, sixty million people died, and then we came to the negotiation table and created the United Nations. Similarly, in the First World War, we killed and killed and then we created a League of Nations. After a Third World War, there will be nothing to build; it'll be over with. But from where comes the strength for peace? It comes from within you.

Vengeance, vendetta, attachment, greed, love, hatred, any faculty of life that you have today, whatever specific thing you have, will limit you. Whatever you have, go one step above it. Find out what it is. For example, if you are very, very, very, very, very depressed, just go, just press the button, and just go one point beyond it. I have to repeat this story to you:

Once I got an emergency call and I was told that I must come back to the ashram. So I came as fast as I could.

A woman had come from Portugal and her visa was only for twelve hours (Portugal and India didn't have a relationship at the time.) So she got the visa for twelve hours, and she walked in and said to Swamiji, "Show me God. Quick, right now! Otherwise I am going to commit suicide."

He didn't know what to do, so he called me: "This is a crazy woman. She wants to see God. I must show Him, otherwise she is going to kill herself."

"Did you tell her what is in the scripture?"

"Yeah, but this is a Western world, she doesn't understand."

So I talked to her about sophisticated things; but she said, "God now or nothing!" She didn't speak good English either.

So I changed my clothes, and I made her change clothes, and I asked her, "Sit down. I will show you God."

We sat down opposite each other, and I said, "Look, make me one promise. You shall not open your mouth, no matter what, until you see God. And if you have to open your mouth and you have realized and felt God, then you utter the word, "God," otherwise don't lie."

She said, "Okay."

So she closed her mouth, and I jumped up, put my hand behind her neck and covered both her nostrils and clogged it up. I was so quick and fast, she didn't know what to do. Finally that struggle came, the struggle for life, and she remembered that if she opened her mouth, she had to say God. Now, how long can you hold the breath?

Finally, she said "God," and I let my hand go.

She said, "What was it?"

I said, "When you did not have the breath of life, what were you trying for?"

She said, "I wanted the breath of life. I just wanted it."

I said, "You put all that energy into getting just one breath of life. So far you have probably already breathed one million times, but you never valued it. You never understood it. Because you can collect anything you want, but if you cannot get the breath of life, it's nothing to you."

Something on which our entire universe is based, and we never bother about it. We never breathe consciously. But when it is not there, then we realize what we have lost. Fifteen times per minute God comes in, and fifteen times per minute you go back to God—that's the direct relationship, the breath of life, and still you are trying to find God? People feel that if they can find God, they will conquer the whole universe. It's not true. When you find God, you will conquer yourself. Once this self

is conquered, you are the king of kings, you are the holier of the holy, you are the saint of the saint, you are the happier of the happiness—once your self is conquered.

Come along with me. I like to work with you. I am the garbage cleaner; that's what you said to me twenty years ago. I will end up cleaning your garbage. If a house is remodeled and cleaned, then good people come, and they will pay more rent; but if you are a slum, nobody comes, nobody even wants to live there. Our minds are so clogged up, there is so much garbage, so much fear, so much insecurity, so much anger—about nothing! The beauty of it is, even you do not know why you are angry, why you are depressed, why you are afraid.

Jab dant na deeyo to doodh deey-o. Jab daant dee-e to aann na deyaa?
—Traditional Punjabi saying
When you never had teeth, God gave you milk, when
He has given you teeth, now He won't give you food?

The question is, you love God, I agree. I am not saying you don't love God. But you don't trust God. You love God, you want to read God, you want to study God, you want to worship God, you want to do everything God, but you don't want to trust God. You mislead yourself by not trusting. When you don't trust, you rust. Trust is the highest power. Do you know what the power of trust is? When you trust and you have faith, then there is nothing fake for you.

There is a great story about a king; he didn't have a son, so naturally his daughter was to become the queen. The king was very worried. He said, "Who will marry this daughter of mine? She is so beautiful, she is such a good warrior, she is so independent."

The grand vizier said, "Don't worry, your daughter meets the God Vishnu every night. He comes on a Garud, a big flying bird, and visits her. The whole night they enjoy themselves."

"Why didn't you tell me?"

"It's between God and His creation. Why should I bother you? I thought you knew."

What happened was, there was a young carpenter boy who had fallen in love with the princess. So he made up a wooden Garud, and every night he would sit in it and jump to her window, make love to her, and tell her all about God. And in the morning, before the sun rose, he would go home. People in the palace saw a huge bird flying. In those days, there was no airplane or helicopter, but there was a story that Vishnu traveled on a Garud.

Unfortunately for this young king, the neighbors got together their army on the border, and they were out to attack. So the king said to the girl, "My dear, you are

Fifteen times per minute God comes in, and fifteen times per minute you go back to God—that's the direct relationship, the breath of life, and still you are trying to find God?

going to be the next queen. So why don't you tell your lover, this Vishnu God, so that we may avoid this war and the matter may be settled."

She said, "Fine, I will tell. No, no regret."

So the next night he came, and she said, "My Lord, you have made enough love; the question is now of war. This is how the enemies are going to attack us. Can't you just take care of it?"

He said, "It's fine, don't worry about it. It's nothing, I will destroy the enemy."

The next morning instead of going down, he just wound up his Garud and flew toward the enemy. He knew that his love game was over anyway if the enemy attacked and the army walked in. Nobody was going to believe him.

The real Vishnu, sitting in his Heavens, told the real Garud, "Go and get in the wooden Garud."

"Lord, what about you?"

"Don't waste time, that wooden thing will fall, and along with it my entire goodwill will fall, nobody will worship Vishnu. It's not what this kid is doing, this façade he has done is in my name. It's my identity that is in trouble."

Naturally, the real Vishnu and the real Garud came into this wooden Garud, and that same moment the armies of the enemies saw a huge bird coming out, just as they had read in the scriptures. So they ran. There was no war. There was nothing. To cut the story short, faith works. Faith moves everything; otherwise man cannot even move stones.

What is faith? Perpetual trust in Infinity. Faith is not God, faith is not religion. You all just mess up everything. It's nothing but a perpetual trust in Infinity. In Sikh Dharma, faith is described by one line:

Ang Sang Wahe Guru.
With every limb of me God is.

You are going to believe it; you can only believe it, but you can't doubt it. But if this is faith, where is there no doubt, no duality? In divinity. The divine is where there is no division. The divine is where there is no duality. If there is a duality, it is not divine.

Faith is nothing but perpetual trust. You always think one thing: It is between you and me. But, no, that's not true. Father, Son, and Holy Ghost—it is always in three, it's never in two. Me, you, and the Unknown, because the owner of this planet is still Unknown. Your shortcoming is very, very simple. You always calculate things between you and your knowledge, between you and your data. Have you ever had a date with the Unknown? Do you think we are crazy because we get up in the morning and meditate? No; we knowingly go in the morning on a date with the Un-

known. And then during the twilight zone, when it's not day, and it's not night—the changing of the guards—why do we meditate then?

Somebody was telling me the other day, "Since I have become spiritual, I have become miserable."

I said, "Same as me."

"What is your story, sir?"

"When I was not that spiritual, which I am now, I was absolutely very happy. I thought I was the king of the universe."

"Now how do you feel?"

"I feel that even if I am a part of the dust, I am miserable, because I have not yet achieved nothingness, *shuniya*. Only nothing can merge into infinity, and I have to go home. Identity is only for here."

We have all the knowledge, we just never apply it, which is why we become desperate for the Unknown, for infinity, for the entry. When we are desperate enough, we calculate our psyche. Once we calculate and make a beam out of it, everything opens to us. Nothing can stop it. But you have to be loyal to your own consciousness. They talk about whether a husband is loyal to his wife or not? I say, who cares? A wife is loyal, children loyal? I say it is all useless. Each person has to be loyal to his own consciousness, and then intelligence will work the way out. You have intelligence equal to God, but you have consciousness to yourself. Once you relate to your consciousness with a mutual trust, everything will open up to you.

We all want things in one way; we all have the will and we have free will, but that's not enough. Free will is given to you to find out God's will—and that's intuition. The moment you trust your consciousness, your intuition will become handy, opportunities will come to you, and you will be out of bounds—boundless, where there is no bondage.

I never knew that you did not know that you have eighty-one parts—subparts—of your brain. My apologies. I thought it was known. But what do I know? I thought everybody knew. But we are writing it now, and we will give it to you with a little Western explanation.[1]

We got rid of the transient memories today. Isn't that the person who walks around the city? What do they call him? A transient. Transient fears. If you could have seen what left you, you would be very ashamed. These are not your fears; these are just what you get in relationship to nothing. These are just floating phobias and fears. They have nothing to do with you. You will feel light; your load will be less.

We will meet again tomorrow. Come and bring your friends, your enemies. You must! Because if your enemy does not have a phobia, he will let you live.

[1] Referring to The Mind: It's Projections and Multiple Facets by Yogi Bhajan, with Gurucharan Singh Khalsa. Available from www.kundaliniresearchinstitute.org.

I remember once, I asked my grandfather, "With those people, we have had animosity for centuries. But the tragedy is that you are the head of the estate, and you send them everything—gift this, gift that."

He said, "Gift is the only way to remove the rift, but one should be swift."

"Swift, gift, rift."

"If the enemies are well fed and happy, together and contained, they won't have time to bother me."

Make love as a gift, don't just make love; make love as a gift to remove the rift of your own life within you. Try to understand that there is no problem outside of you; outside is all okay. Earth rotates by itself; you don't have a handle to keep it going, you know? It's automatic.

◆ ◆ ◆

May the long time sun shine upon you,
all love surround you, and the pure light within you, guide your way on.

I am healthy, I am healing well, and it's going to be fine. Tomorrow we will meet at the same time, and I should be very grateful, if tomorrow you take a lot of liquid. This meditation you are doing, you will be very thirsty, and it will continue. It won't cause hunger, but it will cause terrible thirst because the equilibrium of impure water has to release out of your tissues to make space. You have to have courage: *Pani Pita,* fatherly courage. Fatherly courage and a brave man's courage have two differences: Fatherly courage has compassion, kindness, and wisdom, while a brave man's courage has wisdom and strength. If a brave man's courage can win the body, Fatherly courage can win the heart. Life is in winning the hearts, not chopping the heads.

Sat Nam

UNLOADING THE PAIN OF PERPETUAL MEMORIES I—THE KRIYA

February 14, 1989

There are no breaks between the exercises. Move immediately from one exercise to the next.

1. From Easy Sitting Pose, lean back onto the hands, keeping the spine and neck straight. The torso is at a 60-degree angle. Open the mouth wide, extend the tongue, and focus the eyes at the tip of the nose, half open. Long, deep breathing through the mouth. **3 minutes**.

The lungs need to be cleansed at the deepest level. Breathe effectively.

2. In the same posture, begin Breath of Fire. **2 minutes**.

3. Sit straight, like a yogi, and inhale deeply and exhale deeply a few times. Close the eyes, concentrate on the tip of the nose, and let it go. Meditate on letting go. The gong is necessary for this meditation; please use a recording if an instrument is unavailable. After a few minutes, while the gong continues, begin the guided meditation:

Guided Meditation

You are entering a reign of forgiveness. Practice forgiveness of the self. Sit alert, practice forgiveness, float steady. Forgive yourself; don't fight, don't fight; you are resisting. You are in the region of forgiveness. This is the hemisphere of forgiveness for the self; redeem yourself. There is nobody above you, nobody under you, nobody around you; it is only you, and this is the hemisphere where you can forgive yourself. This is a very rare opportunity. Don't ask forgiveness of God; God shall guarantee your own forgiveness. Whatever you will forgive, God shall forgive, guaranteed. Go for it! Don't fight! Forgiveness eats up the misfortune.

After **20 minutes**, begin playing *Har Nar Wahe Guru* by Nirinjan Kaur. The gong continues over the mantra. Listen to the mantra for **4 minutes** and then begin chanting. **33 minutes total**.

TO END: Inhale deep and hold for **30 seconds**. Exhale; inhale deep again, hold for **15 seconds**; let it go. Inhale deep again and hold for **45 seconds**. Exhale, inhale deep again, and just chant and merge in the sound as it comes. Begin chanting again for **30 seconds.**

Let the sound purify, rectify, amend, and mend. Keep on holding and understanding this. If somebody accepts you, you are noble, you are trustworthy, divine, radiant, wonderful, pure at heart, glowing, radiant, good for everything. You don't have to hassle at all. That's the way to get acceptance—not to manipulate, manipulate, manipulate.

We have a proposition before us that we must either go for peace or we must perish. But from where comes the strength of peace? It comes from within you. Vengeance, vendetta, attachment, greed, love, hatred: Any faculty of life you have that is specific will limit you. Whatever you have, just go one step above it. ◆

" Holy means that against all provocation, against all temptation, against all negativity, you shall remain positive—that's holy. When everything in you fails but your tolerance—that's holy. When everything is adverse and you can sustain a hand of friendship—that's holy. "

— Yogi Bhajan

UNLOADING THE PAIN OF PERPETUAL MEMORIES II

February 15, 1989

THE PURPOSE OF THESE CLASSES IS TO UNLOAD THE GARBAGE OF THE MIND. Twenty years I have been in America, and I do not see anything wrong with you, although I am not very enchanted with your blue eyes and your blonde hair and all that. To me a human is just a human, and unfortunately God took away from me the ability to see you as you are—that is, as you see yourself in a mirror. I don't see you that way, and I am very grateful for that perpetual blindness. If I could see how beautiful you look sometimes—and you are very beautiful—but then see your ugliest, dirtiest action, I would be a very sad man. So, I think God did a great justice and prepared me to be a great teacher by taking away my personal touch with any human being. I was joking the other day that if I could not see the Arcline at the breast of a woman, then I would think that all of you are men and that there are hardly any women. But when I do tune in to my optical nerve, I see you as you are.

You must understand that although your eyes can see, they cannot see if there is nothing in them to see. Your ears can hear, but they will not hear if there is nothing in them to hear. Your brain can think for you and plan for you, but it will not think if it is not working right. There are five *indras*—eyes, ears, nose, mouth, and touch. Your mouth is to talk; sometimes you talk and have no control over what you are saying, absolutely no control. You see, but you have no control over what you are seeing. The fact is that it's not your fault. You know who you are. You know what you have to do. You know what is right for you. But you don't have your mind.

People sometimes say so-and-so is brainwashing somebody. I say, "Good. I think you all should wash your brains." Yesterday I came to teach a class to get rid of your old pain and memories, and I found that you have so much transitory fear that even that didn't leave yesterday—it was shocking. You do not want to be a specialist, you don't want to be committed, you don't want to give a perpetual standard of yourself to something. You shift from man to man, woman to woman, person to person, job to job, place to place. You have become a nation of window shoppers. To be very honest, even if you are very beautiful looking, and you are well dressed, and you think you have the best designer clothes and the best car, and you have a big house, and you have a ton of money, and whatever you call it, that's nothing. That's all worldly nonsense.

If you say tomorrow that "The Himalayas belong to me," what could you get out of it without a mind of your own? Don't you understand that you are overloading

You do not want to be a specialist, you don't want to be committed, you don't want to give a perpetual standard of yourself to something. You shift from man to man, woman to woman, person to person, job to job, place to place. You have become a nation of window shoppers.

We are human beings, and we have our mind to compute things for us, but we have become a bunch of emotional creatures—that's all.

and cluttering your mind with so much variation of thought and dreaming, planning and desiring, that your mind can't even handle it—and that you haven't developed your mind to handle it? That's not America's problem. I am just mad that God gave you something so beautiful—a vast land of three thousand miles to each side—and you have exploited it. I was joking this morning that India is one-third the size of the United States, but the population is about ten times more than the United States. Per capita income in India is way, way less than you think it is. If they riot and fight and blow the whistle and then jump into the ocean, they have reason to. What about you?

You have not yet started. But the rate of interest is eleven percent, and the stock market is ultimately going to tumble. Things are going to come out and become real, because this camouflage cannot go on. The fact is, you cannot handle more than three trillion dollars as a national debt. You pay two thousand seven hundred dollars in interest per capita, whether you are born or not. This cannot go on. And neither can your emotions go on.

You have become a plastic nation; you go to buy something, and you give that plastic card at twenty percent rate of interest. Can you afford it? I have got plastic cards, but I have never used them in my life. Once in a while I use them to keep them current—maybe I buy something—but I pay it off within thirty days.

It's not that I have not been poor. I came into this country with thirty-five bucks in my pocket. I didn't bring a bag full of money. Maybe I don't understand you, but that's why I am a teacher. But how much can I teach? I can teach yesterday, I can teach today. But yesterday I was sad—I thought I was doing something good, but what I saw coming out of you was ridiculous and not very satisfying. Just understand one thing: If you keep on at the rate you desire, at the rate you think, and at the rate you desire to think—not even a carburetor can distribute gas and air at that rate, you understand what I am saying?

The faculty, the RPMS–revolutions per minute—at which your piston of a mind can draw in thoughts is absolutely insane. Somebody was thanking me the other day: "You have a great meditation class." I said, "I don't know what kind of meditation it is—it's rare I put myself into it—but there should be a response to that meditation." We are human beings, and we have our mind to compute things for us, but we have become a bunch of emotional creatures—that's all.

I was talking to a girl today and she said, "I don't want to cover my head; I don't want to do this."

I said, "I didn't ask you to do anything."

"But is it not a part of your religion?"

"No, it's not a part of religion; it's a part of being human. What's wrong with asking you ladies not to be out to sell yourselves? Or to show by body language or dress language that you are for sale?"

"In every store there is a sale."

"Only those stores that cannot sell offer things for sale. The moment a woman is out of the veil, she is out to sell. She bears not the real price." It's the law; I didn't make it. This is the law of nature. The male doesn't have the right side of the brain, so he has the capacity to hunt, the capacity to kill, the capacity to conquer. The female doesn't have that capacity; but when a female puts herself on sale, the hunters come through. The relationship between you is of a hunter and the hunted; there is no love relationship—it can't be. We just talk and talk and talk, and you may not understand what I am saying, but I do not understand what you are doing either!

Man, by nature, is a hunter and a conqueror and an attacker; he must win. He lost his right side of the brain in the womb of the mother through the acid bath. That is why your clitoris remained a clitoris and his clitoris became a penis; that's a psychological effect. I am not talking me and the heavens and seeing something that I know and you do not know. This is a medical phenomenon—it's true. It's medically, scientifically true. Any female who is asking for love, who is rude in her language, and who in negotiation doesn't know how to cover herself, any woman who doesn't have any shyness around herself, doesn't create a mystique, and doesn't have any creative aura is out to be hunted.

Now, I can change the rules, and you can follow the dictates, but I can't tell the moon to shine like a sun, and I can't tell the sun to become a moon. I don't have that power. A woman who comes out with a face that does not represent her victory—just listen to me—she is out for trouble. Because this male, this man, he smells, he sees, he hears, he watches, he does everything. Now, even if a man conquers a woman with love (it is 1989, and you call it "love"), there is nothing in it. It's a relationship of the hunter and the hunted.

I am not worried about who is married and who is divorced. The only thing I am worried about are those children who will not have parents and how angry they will be. Because I have seen parents who have parents and children who have parents, and I have seen how angry they are, you know what I mean? Yes, even when parents are there and children are there—how angry those children are! Now think of a child who doesn't have parents. Or children who have half parents and play between this parent and that parent. What shall be their fate?

They say that nationally, as a nation, eighty percent of you transgress, plus nationally twenty percent of you are gay, plus nationally six million women are required to be prostitutes in order to keep the industry going, plus nationally you require four divorces in your lifetime to keep industry growing, plus nationally you entertain all the tourists of the world, plus nationally you have all the five major sins of the drugs. Still, under one God, we have now one nation, and we should thank God.

If you want to know what you really are, it's what your enemies tell you. Because they tell you a very bitter, horrible truth that they know about you, which is something to learn, something to change, something to face, and something to understand.

The Chinese empire went down the tubes and blew itself up because they started smoking opium. The Indian civilization went berserk and became a slave and lost everything because of marijuana. The Egyptian civilization lost itself totally and became bankrupt because of desert peyote. Rome lost itself under alcohol. You have all of them—have I counted wrong? And something more! You have "PSP, ESP, TPC, CPC"—that's all extra.

All right, every woman wants to wear a bikini and walk on the boulevard. But just understand, a woman has to do nothing but through her body language say she is for sale, and she will be captured. What price will you pay for her? Now, I am talking of the neurons of the brain. The moment the pattern of the neurons of the brain and the initial self of the male say, "It is mine; it is available, and I can have it," that is when the conquering mind will come through. Man is there to conquer a woman. He will never respect her; therefore, he cannot love her, because what you love you must respect. What you don't respect, you don't love. Therefore, your relationship can never be one of love; it will never be, and it cannot be, because the basic initiation is in invoking the man and then creating the relationship. Which is why, in Kundalini Yoga, we don't initiate—doesn't matter who one is. We are forbidden by law—that moral, ethical law of Kundalini Yoga—that if a human is not worthy to initiate himself into the teachings of Kundalini Yoga, he should never be initiated by any teacher.

Once I was offered an entire estate, a sole corporation, and all its facilities, and all that person wanted was for me to put my hand out and say I accept you as my student. I said, "I can't do it;" I let it all go. There are certain things that we are bound by, certain scriptures, certain morals, certain ethics that say as teachers we are not out to exploit. We are here to bring goodness, happiness, and better lives to the people who come to us in trust. You come to listen to me in trust.

If love does not have the fiber of trust, it is not love—it is bait. It's a very painful process. Love is used as bait, and underneath is a harpoon of commotions and neuroses that you pierce through each other's hearts and kill each other forever. The pain is everlasting.

I wrote that poem *Everyday (see appendix)*; it came right through me, even though I didn't actually want to write that poem. I even put that poem to music so that the copies could be given to parents to understand the feelings of a child. Somebody may say, "My history is different, my chemistry is different, my this is different, my that is different; I couldn't understand it, and he couldn't understand me." But do you know that the poor child doesn't understand anything of it? He doesn't understand why those "who are responsible for bringing me here could not be here for me"—that's his question. And do you understand the anger that comes out of that betrayal and where it takes him? Here I am, trying to clean your mind and get rid of your pain, even though medically they tell me not to teach. But I see you drifting and rifting into a deep pain. How can you be confident about yourself when you do not know what you are?

So the only relationship we can have is this: I keep on doing what I am doing, you keep on doing what you are doing, and perhaps some good will come out of it. There is a central, certain, fundamental basis on which there cannot be any compromise: No woman can be a man, and no man can be a woman; but in spite of this fact, there was a woman who lived as a man. She was with a woman for twenty years, and they had three children; his wife didn't know he is she, and nobody in society knew he is she. It was that singer; what was his name? Oh yes, Billy Tipton. He acted for all these years as a perfect father and a perfect man and a perfect artist and a perfect singer and very rich; a good father to his adopted sons. Before marriage, he told his wife that he could never have sex because he had been in a car accident; and she thought that he was so beautiful and so darling, and she loved him all his life. Only when he died, at some old age, did the paramedics find that he is she. They asked his older son, in whose lap he died, "Do you know that your father has gone through some sex change or some operation." The son said, "No." And then they found out the secret. Maybe you have a secret, too? Your problem is you only look in the mirror and see what the mirror tells you.

If you really want to know who you are, listen to what your enemy is saying about you. Enemies are very important. What your friends tell you may just be encouragement once in a while, as dessert is after food; but in reality, if you want to know what you really are, it's what your enemies tell you. Because they tell you a very bitter, horrible truth that they know about you, which is something to learn, something to change, something to face, and something to understand. We are going to let it go. We have to work hard tonight because I didn't feel satisfied about the class yesterday; it didn't work out the way I wanted it to work out. You are too clogged up. That "liquid plumber" last night, it didn't work. You only let your mental outburst go. I wanted the original fears from your mind to go, your original pain to go, so that you can be relieved of that pain. But you are sticking to the whole thing so badly. We produce so much by desiring so much that our memory is overloaded with pain. Whatever you desire, when not transformed in the subconscious, becomes a living soul, and living souls are fine—but bleeding ulcers are not.

◆ ◆ ◆

I just want to feel good. Otherwise next week, I will cancel the class. I don't have to go through all this. The idea is not to get a bunch of people and collect ten bucks; we don't need that. The idea is not to give you a six hundred dollar seminar on the weekend and all that. The idea is to just make you better people so that in your own

life, you can enjoy and will feel more comfortable—that's the idea. It's a very, very different attitude, which you don't have any concept of. I used to teach a whole five-day Tantric course for thirty five dollars, and we used to pay for everything, including food, because the idea at that time was not to make money; the idea was to really give those people some relief in life so that they could be anything.

It's not very relaxing for me to put you through pain, but understand that we have three purposes—to be healthy, happy, and holy—and health is very important. If you are in the right posture, at the right angle, and your elbows are as good as mine—if you can ever get to that real posture—you will never ask again what ecstasy means. *(See Exercise 4.)* In this way you can give a better you to yourself. We want you to work with us because it works.

We would like you to understand something. It's not that meditating with the gong is the only way to become God, to become Divine, but it's a very easy way to have a normal, happy life. The human brain is one of the most excellent things God could ever create.

Sometimes you are very hurt, and you can't call it a stretch because there is pain in the elbow. But slowly, in that situation, with that high frequency of the gong, if you stretch yourself, you will be surprised. I have seen people in the worst arthritic condition stretching. The body can produce poison, the body can make you sick, the body can make you totally zero; but the body can also make you the most powerful, most intelligent, and most ever-loved man or woman on Earth.

This entire experiment is only in the body; that's why you sell your looks. But if a mind is corrupt, your good looks won't sell a thing. You can sell love by the pound or by the ton, but if you are not trusted, you are fooling yourself, because trust is the fiber of love. You put the sale sign up, but there is no sale in it—I mean, where is it going to go? They say love is blind, but do you know what that means? When you love somebody, you don't look into any detail; you trust right away. Once in a while, you are betrayed—once, twice, three times—and you become conscious. You think, "Hey, wait a minute, what's going on?" I don't believe there is anything called a "lie"; there is nobody who lies to anybody. Some people just can't face the circumstances, so they say something to gain time and get some space. So you get temporary space and time, but what you lose—love and trust—that's the cost of lying. You can lie as much you want. I don't think anybody should be punished; I don't think there should be any punishment whatsoever for lying. People punish themselves enough; why should we have all this other punishment? Even the stupidest person knows when he has been taken advantage of, when he has been lied to.

I am teaching these classes to give you a chance to develop your neural patterns. All the pain and the garbage you are carrying in the subconscious, which will take

years and years of different treatments and seminars to get rid of—we just want to be rid of them as fast as possible, so you can go on your way and make something of yourself. Yes, the classes are hard; I don't disagree with that. What is one hour, and you can't even stretch eleven minutes out of that? You can't stretch your hands? I want to see whether this meditation is good or not. Stretch your hands, stretch them the right way—just test it. See and stretch; just test it. If your body really can stretch right, aren't you sorry you didn't do it right the first time?

Your brain has the power to create flexibility, it has the power to control the motor, the muscle, and in so doing it sometimes gets rid of the disease that's in the way; that's the process of a kriya. It's quick, on-the-spot relief. Once, I got injured, and I couldn't sit in Lotus Pose. There was nothing anybody could do; I simply couldn't do it, even though I used to sit in a perfect Lotus Pose. But I had found that after I had recuperated (from another injury), I couldn't do it anymore. Nobody told me to do it, because everybody knew I couldn't. But one day, we decided to play frog in Lotus Pose. Everybody started doing it in Lotus Pose, and without even realizing that I couldn't do it, I put myself into Lotus Pose and started doing it, too. When I finished I looked at myself and said, "Not bad. I can't do it but I have already done it!" I didn't do anything wrong, it just happened. I was back again; I was right, and that's what I mean.

Your body has an extempore capacity to correct itself. Your brain has the capacity to produce whatever it needs to produce in timelessness, provided you know how to reach it for help. We are giving you release from your mental pain, we are asking you to project out—plus we are asking you to be healthy, plus we are trying to get you to be happy, plus trying to be holy. Holy doesn't mean that you are spiritual; just that you are holy. You can be as spiritual as you are and you can be as graceful as you are, but to me, you are not worth a penny if you do not have the ultimate grit to adjust.

Holy means that against all provocation, against all temptation, against all negativity, you shall remain positive—that's holy. When everything in you fails but your tolerance—that's holy. When everything is adverse and you can sustain a hand of friendship—that's holy. Holy is not whether you put on good robes, and you look good, and you know a few scriptures, and you talk nicely, and you can convince people, and everybody trusts you and believes you, and you are fantastic, and you are a religious leader, and six thousand people bow to you in the morning and six million at night, and you call yourself holy, forget it! You are holy to yourself, you are healthy to yourself, you are happy to yourself—that's the first step of divinity.

A glass that is full of water can quench anybody's thirst with just a few drops, but an empty glass can't do a thing. You can act professionally holy, but then you are a just a holy actor—there is a holy spirit, but you are not holy. You think that holy is

I am teaching these classes to give you a chance to develop your neural patterns. All the pain and the garbage you are carrying in the subconscious, which will take years and years of different treatments and seminars to get rid of— we just want to be rid of them as fast as possible, so you can go on your way and make something of yourself.

The idea is to set you toward the goal of happiness. My attitude is to leave behind people who have conquered their own sorrows, their own pain.

the person who can take something from your hands and produce diamonds from it, that he can make you virtuous, make you rich, show you anything you want to see, and all that stuff; that's what you call holy. But that gimmick everybody can do, or a few can; but this is all drama of the Earth. The drama within you is the real drama; outside the drama will continue happening whether you are part of it or not. Inside you, if there is a smiling man, a compassionate man, a kind man, a loving man, then that will show up in your face, in your eyes, in your whole self—that's what God loves; that's holy.

I will meet you next Tuesday, and I'd like to be with you. I want you to come and come prepared; don't come to take a yoga class, as that's a bad mental attitude. Come with an attitude of, "I am going to go, and I am going to do it and see whether I can get an experience." When you are sick, you get medication, and when you are mentally clogged up and mentally sick, you do meditation; it is the same thing. The idea is to set you toward the goal of happiness. My attitude is to leave behind people who have conquered their own sorrows, their own pain.

Knowing where pain comes from is no big deal. Knowing that you have five hundred previous lives and their karmas is no big deal. Knowing where you will be tomorrow is no big deal. But being, today, and shining like a Sun, with a fragrance of all the flowers of the world, and a smile that no one cannot appreciate, and with the warmth in your words that can totally nurture every drowning heart, while still, above everything, having the cutting truth that can let a person know that you are a living truth, that's a human, basic and fundamental—real and beautiful.

Beauty is not in your makeup. If you have to do makeup, make up with your God, that's the real makeup. Don't look in the mirror and feel how beautiful you are; look in your consciousness and see how beautiful you are. We are asking for a change in your life so that you can not only be a saint yourself but you can also uplift others and give them a chance to be themselves. Life is full of vendetta, anger, misery, and pain because we get it all together and store it in our subconscious. We have to change it! We need to live happily. I pray that if God has given me life—for whatever reason—then it is His problem.

Before I go to my real home, I would like to share something with you that I have shared within myself. I am misunderstood most of the time. I am told I don't know how to love, I don't know how to say no, I don't know how to draw a line, I am this, I am that. Believe me, all that is true. And I don't believe I am true. But I do believe that the experience given to me out of God's grace is very true: It's not what you have, it is what you have within you, with your God, that matters. It's not how long you have traveled or how much you can do psychically or how powerful you are that matters. Real power is when you want to be together, how much time does it take:

one second, two seconds, three seconds? In your whole life, all you have is nine seconds to answer everything right, to do everything correctly. Nine seconds, that's all you have. You have to work at the speed of light—one hundred and eighty-six thousand miles per second.

Your brain's neurons have a per unit capacity of thirty trillion units, and your mind can understand the ray of the Sun striking and you can see its reflection by the naked eye. Therefore, you have the capacity to see that speed—one hundred eighty-six thousand miles per second, right? You have twenty aspects or facets of your life: five things that give you experience—the tattvas—and five things that give you feeling—the senses, and you have ten bodies, which is twenty. But you will have to be twenty plus one—and what is that one? Do you know what that one is?

When you are negative, negative is always like a straight line; you have to be positive. Do you know physics? Do you know that the electron works as a point and dash at the same time? From there they call it the mathematics of the equation. The equation is that it cannot work as either—it should work as either a dot or a dash—but when man found out the parts of the atom, he found out that electrons work on a dash and a dot at the same time. They were very surprised by this; they built up a whole theory of equation. But ultimately God is male and female in one, big deal—dot and dash no big deal; it was no surprise to the spiritual world.

For the scientist, though, it's a big deal. And yet the Chinese have been talking for five thousand years about yin and yang—this is the same thing. In Morse code—dit dit, dot dot—it's called dot and dash. The base of everything in the world is dot and dash. In other words, the base of everything is disease and health, life and death, day and night, right and wrong. But the question for you is how you look at it. If you look at everything positive, feel everything positive, be with everything positive, you will become super positive, and you will be happy thereafter forever—that law shall never change. And that's what we are trying to do—work our neurons in our brain to come to that understanding.

I believe that we have stimulated our brain through drugs and chemicals, through preservatives, to the extent that we have preserved it forever. And now we need something to stimulate it. That's why I am asking you to come to class. And I expect that you won't have too much in the stomach, because we need whatever energy you have to stimulate yourself.

May the long time sun shine upon you,
all love surround you, and the pure light within you, guide your way on.

Sat Nam

It is a state of mind that can make you laugh at the treachery and the weakness of another person rather than feeling miserable yourself.

◆ ◆ ◆

Next time we meet we are going to do the series of the Mental Triple Trance.

God knows how many days I have to live. But all of this will be taped and recorded so you can enjoy the testimony of those beautiful experiences, which I believe man deserves. My faculty to teach the Mental Triple Trance is only because somebody was kind to me and taught it me. So I share a state of mind with you, but it is mine; it's not yours. It is personal—it is a state of mind in which your grit can explore the world without hurting it. It is a state of mind that is sophisticated enough for you to deal with adversity with an most sophisticated smile. It is a state of mind that can make you laugh at the treachery and the weakness of another person rather than feeling miserable yourself.

This state of mind makes you go and pray deeply about the betrayal you feel when somebody couldn't be with you, rather than feeling the loneliness and feeling left out and all that stuff. It's personal; it cannot be stolen, it cannot be taken away. It is forever, it's perpetual. We will go through the Triple X Trance—past, present, and future. We are not going to read past lives, though sometimes that happens. You can go through those lives, but there are lots of avenues and streets we will walk through just to see the city—the ordained city, the kingdom of God, within our heads. These are very heavy, deep meditations with personal experiences. Even you cannot share and say where I was. You will try to share, but words cannot describe them. They are personal. They may make you feel good, and you can express the good feelings and that may be a start; that may be what we need.

So these meditations we will do, and we want to do them intimately—not as a teacher and a student but as people to people in the possibility of our own self and the God within us. We also want to explore that strength. We want to know—actually I want you to know—whether God exists or not. It is a question, or it is an answer—you can find out through your experience.

I don't believe that you are rich. I don't believe you are poor. I don't believe you are great. I don't believe you are small, because small contains all in it, and all is in small. Spell it—S-M-A-L-L. I believe the beauty of man is that in adversity, he can create prosperity; in anger, he can create a smile; in vengeance, he can create forgiveness; and in hatred, he can create love. They are the two sides to a coin. Whatever side the world presents, man can present the other side; he can balance it out—that's what yin and yang mean. It's not that you have one black thing going upward and one white thing coming down, and you say this is yin-yang. That's not it. There is no yin-yang like that, and there is no divinity, and there is no religion. It's all bogus. What you have been taught so far in the religious world—you have been cheated. I went to synagogue, I went to church, I went to gurdwara, I went to temples. I went

everywhere, and they all told me to uplift myself, to become holy, become great. But for what? To hang myself! That's not what religion offers.

Religion offers this: When adversity comes, you offer prosperity. If a hungry man comes, feed him; he will be your friend, not an enemy. If a hungry man comes, he says, "I am hungry." If you say, "Get out," he will say, "Okay, I will get you out of the Earth." And he will kill you; he will become angrier. When hunger and anger get together, it's a revolution.

I remember the story of a woman who knew her man was cheating on her, but she was very happy that he was cheating. She asked him, "Do you know that you laugh all the time?"

He said, "No, no, no, no! I love you, I love you. You are beautiful, you are wonderful, and you are fine. Do you doubt me? Am I going somewhere?"

"No, no, no! That's perfect, perfect, perfect. You go wherever you want. You are lord of my world."

She gave him so much appreciation. One day, he came very, very late and snuck into the bed. After a minute, she turned on the light and said, "My dear, you are very badly hurt. Let me take care of you." He had had a fight with that woman. She had scratched him so bad and cut him, and he didn't know what to do. While putting on the balm and cleaning his wounds and putting on the bandages and comforting him and washing him, she said, "You love her so much, but she is so cruel. I'll pray for you. Don't worry, you will be healed by tomorrow."

First he felt little, second he felt shy, third he felt guilty, fourth he felt this, fifth he felt that. But he finally fell asleep, and to his surprise, when he got up in the morning and took all the bandages off, his body was as new as it could be. He was shocked.

He said, "You are a goddess! Did you know all about this?"

"No, I knew nothing."

"Did you know I would be injured?"

"No. I was just sleeping, waiting for you. I felt like I was getting injuries, and I knew you were being injured. We are tuned to each other."

Now, how many husbands and wives in this room have that kind of tuning? Love is an infinity. It makes you tune in at exactly the same frequency. The bifurcative vocal messages, as well as the transmission message through space, of the feelings and of the bodies and the tissues and the dance of atoms of one lover and another lover all dance at the same frequency. It's called the rhythm of life. You don't know anything about it? Well, go get some books and read them to learn. The rhythm of the lover's molecule is itself a dance of Shiva and Parvathi—creator and the creation. It is all within you. Let's not be romantic and horny tonight, but just understand that every intercourse is between a God and a God Itself.

I believe the beauty of man is that in adversity, he can create prosperity; in anger, he can create a smile; in vengeance, he can create forgiveness; and in hatred, he can create love.

They are the two sides to a coin. Whatever side the world presents, man can present the other side; he can balance it out—that's what yin and yang mean.

God is He, God is She, and God is It. That's why when I used to teach at UCLA, I used to call Him, Heshit. You can't use the word God in a university, but you have to teach all about it. So I made up a word—Heshit. What could they do to me? So God is He, She, and It. But whatever God is, it's all within you. Those of you who find yourself in love, see if your molecules and somebody's molecules play the same rhythm, play the same notes. Do you speak the same language, body language, physical language, language in feelings, language in emotions, language in desire? Do you have the same capacity of projection? Do you reject negativity at the same frequency and strength? Do you open the window of your heart and close it at the same time when you both want to be?

Do you understand there's one God and one universe and you are one part of it—related, connected, and absolutely one with the entire self? Do you know the end is endless? You have to know all that. You have to feel it. You have to know it, and you have to live it. We'll try to curtail the circumstances of time and space next time. We'll go through those meditative triple trances. We have to. And after that we'll find some time somewhere to work it out and clean it out. Because we, the people, have the right of collecting garbage; we, the people, have the right to synch it out. That's what I believe. Otherwise, too much is very much. So if you have any appointment, still come, because this is an appointment with you for you. I'm just an instrument. Have I done a good commercial? Is it acceptable?

We want to do a series next week to just clean it out—clean out the karma and spread the dharma. Dharma is not doing things in certain determined times, and doing all that stuff. Dharma is to be the infinite, to be forever. You all have the right to do it. If one drop of yogurt can make a ton of milk into more yogurt, then one thought of a man can make a man into God. I honestly believe in this. It's not what people tell you; it's what you tell inside yourself. Do you understand me? Because who fails? You don't fail. Inside you, you fail. Outside, there are so many things that can keep you happy and get you going. But ultimately, they don't get you going because inside you fall apart.

I remember a story of a person. I was told to pick him up. He was my friend, my officer, my colleague—whatever you want to call it—and we were very much in love.

He said, "Bhajan, please, can you do me one thing? We are going to this event."

I said, "Yeah?"

"Will you pick me up?"

"What's wrong with your car and driver? You have a better car, so you should come pick me up. It'll add to my ego."

"No, no, no! Pick me up in your jeep."

"Look, we are rugged officers, we are field people. We wear clothes and a uniform so that we can stand the weather. You should go enjoy the limo."

"No, no, no! It's a chance to see you, to travel with you. Come pick me up."

"Okay, whatever you say, but what's wrong with you?"

"I have a headache, and I've taken already six aspirin."

He said the pain was horrible. The type of pain you can't stand. It numbs you and makes you go crazy. Anything that hurts you is unwanted and unrequired. You're not meant to be hurt, and yet you allow yourself to be hurt by your own pain.

I said, "This is why you wanted me to pick you up? You're not even in a position to go."

"I want to go, I'm dressed to go. Pick me up. Take me dead or alive."

"If you really want to go, let me get rid of the headache."

So I put a certain pressure on the temples—just rubbed the pituitary a little bit and then went back to the neck and changed the entire flow of the serum.

He said, "I am fine; I can go."

We got to the event, and he was constantly looking at his watch. He was waiting for the moment when that horrible pain would return. And I know he's not going to get this pain back again, but he's not sure. So after two hours I asked if he wanted to go back home. When we got home, he asked me stay to with him.

I asked, "What for?"

"Will it come back again?"

"It won't come back. Just get into bed and relax."

"Can I call you if it comes back?"

"Yes, I'm just a finger away. Call me on the telephone. What difference does it make? I'll come, but you won't be hurt. Believe me!"

The next day we met and smiled. I asked if it had come back. He said it hadn't.

I said, "You know I did nothing to you; it's simply that you trust me. You feel I'm a God's man."

He said, "But it's true, you are, and it worked."

"No, there was nothing. You desired to be hurt. You wanted to be in pain. You thought it was going to come back. But your mind had already decided within you that you are healed."

You all can heal yourself. You all can be happy. You all can be prosperous. Nothing can stop you, because God is in you. And if God could have created anything better than you, He would have and He should have and He couldn't. So you are His ultimate product. Let us deal with what we have. Okay?

Thank you and good night and God bless.

UNLOADING THE PAIN OF PERPETUAL MEMORIES II—THE KRIYA

February 15, 1989

There are no breaks between the exercises. Move immediately from one exercise to the next.

1. Take Surya Mudra in the hands: the tips of the Sun (ring) finger and the thumb are together. With the hands lifted in front of the face and palms outward, alternately circle the hands. As one rotates out, the other rotates in; the right hand moves in counterclockwise circles, and the left hand moves in clockwise circles. The entire forearm moves from the elbow, not just the hand on the wrist. Open the eyes and look straight ahead, beyond the movement of the hands. Move faster and faster! The movement will force a quick breath, but don't manufacture it. Allow the movement to change the breath, authentically. Continue for **5 minutes**.

2. Keep moving the hands and begin moving the neck, the base of the spine, and the buttocks. Move everything, go crazy! **5 minutes**.

Go crazy—it doesn't matter. You will laugh; it is fine with me. The pelvic bone has to be moved in relationship to the skull so that the structural improprieties can be worked out. The ribs and the ribcage, the spine, and the spinal column, and all the wiring that goes through it, called nerves, are in a lot more trouble. Through the years, you got shorter in height. The padding goes away, and you begin to have trouble. It starts first with a headache, which means the spine is out of gear. Let it go; it will take away some of the load of the anger—not all, but some. It will give you a little release, or it might make you dizzy, but still do it. It's better to be dizzy in this way than to remain dizzy otherwise. This way at least you look dizzy; the other way, you look perfect outside but inside you are dizzy anyway.

3. Bring your arms out to the sides, with the elbows bent, upper arms parallel to the ground, and forearms at a 90-degree angle, palms facing forward. Cross the hands in front of the face, alternating left in front and then right in front. Move forcefully on the inward movement only. Release the arms back out and then move in again with force. Continue for **1 minute**.

Then bring the hands into Surya Mudra again and continue the movement for **1 more minute**.

4. Place the hands in Gyan Mudra. Extend the right arm up 60 degrees and to the right 60 degrees; extend the left arm down 60 degrees and to the left 60 degrees. The right palm faces down and the left palm faces up. Stretch the arms away from each other in a straight line. Do not let the elbows bend! Meditate with the eyes closed. As the gong plays, just flow with it for **6½ minutes.** Reverse the position of the arms, extending the left arm up and the right arm back. Continue meditating to the gong for another **1½ minutes**.

Close your eyes completely and get into it. Move out of your body, just as if you were flying out like birds, but with a conscious mind. Keep the elbow solid, straight. If it hurts, it's okay. If it hurts, it means there is a pain in the body that will be taken out. Stretch out in the right way and let us go into the space. Stretch out, stretch out. This is your projection of power. If you straighten it out, balance it out, then the body will be forced to develop the immune system and the tattvas. It's a simple theory known to man: These days you need your immune system, more than ever before. It is powerful; it will guard you against your future disease. Keep up and you will be kept up. I didn't say it wouldn't hurt. Did I say that? It will hurt terribly, but still keep the elbows stretched. This will protect your body from disease. If your body is out of balance, it will hurt. But it just means the body is out of alignment, the tattvas are out of alignment. Stretch it harder so that you can quickly get into a painless state. As the sound carries you, project out, project out; let the mind heal itself, let the body heal itself; project out.

5. Put both hands in the center of the lap and meditate as the gong continues. Project yourself out with the sound of the gong for **6 minutes**.

Let the mind heal itself; let the body heal itself. Project out.

6. Continue meditating as you listen to *Everyday* by Wahe Guru Kaur for **5 minutes**.

The neurons of the brain have no defense, no way to patronize or to synchronize their own message when the sound of the gong hits the ear. Therefore, the gong creates a very shattering philosophy among the neurons. But the human brain is one of the most excellent things God ever created. When you let yourself and the wave of the gong go, the neuron patterns in the brain have to reassemble—and that's where you get the strength: thinking right, thinking correct, going to the point. It rejuvenates you without all those vitamins, because there is no better strength than the strength that the neuron patterns of your brain can form.

This gives us what you call the manual strength to deal with the toxins of life: the pain, the displeasure, the fear, the threat. There are so many forces that work on you, just realize in forty five minutes what you can produce. The bang, the sound of the gong. If it is placed in the space and you let yourself go out, you cannot be there alone, without oxygen. But your mind has the capacity to survive you; and that way, you give relief to your physical body.

◆

" Tonight, we are going to deal with this mind of ours and unload our unfulfilled dreams so we can have a little space to live. It is called jerking out the jerk in us. You know? In simple American slang English, we say, It is too much; we can take in no more! "

– Yogi Bhajan

CLEANING THE CLUTTER OF THE MIND 1

February 21, 1989

Whatever comes from your soul shall stay. Whatever comes from your mind has to be worked out.

AM NOT DOING A COMMERCIAL, BUT I AM IN A GOOD MOOD. I am going to be sixty years old this year. This is my life history: I became a Master of Kundalini Yoga when I was sixteen and a half years old. It is the youngest age at which anybody has achieved this status. If status is a lie, it is fine; if it is a truth, who cares? There is nothing to gain or lose by it. It is between a Master and a Master. After doing Kundalini Yoga and becoming a Master, I went crazy and wanted to do these occult powers. I really wanted to know how the five tattvas affect a man and how they do this and that. So I practiced all that. It is not that I didn't learn it either. I learned it, I practiced it, and it works. It is a truth. You can make a donkey out of anybody and make an elephant out of anybody. It is the most vicious side of the power, energy, and divinity that I ever experienced.

I also found out that most people are not right. One says this, one says that; it is a bizarre thing. Then I found out that spirituality and religion are the most corrupt things on the planet. And after I had that experience, they made me the head of the religion! Do you understand this huge dichotomy? I couldn't say to them, "No, I don't want it. I don't believe in it." On the other hand, I definitely knew that they used spirituality as nothing but a salesman's shop to promise people God. Neither the man who is promising nor the man has been promised knows what God is. Everything lives on a hope, and it goes on. You pay me thirty dollars, I pay you twenty dollars—money is exchanged. So religion has come down to the grassroots, to the individual. It is that bucket that goes around the church to collect the money to sustain the church that is the compromise.

And I tell you for a fact that in science and in art, when it comes to compromise, it is totally not real, period. When you are real, you are real; there is no compromise with yourself or God. I was fortunate that I got sick. I couldn't even teach if I had wanted to. But then I started looking into why I had gotten sick. And I realized: How can a man of my caliber and with my kind of sadhana get sick? Why? That was the question. And I found that just as the doors to the Golden Temple had been locked up and the blood started going, the same had happened to my heart. Man is a prototype—a copy—of his belief. This experience with sickness only proved it to me. Otherwise, if anybody would have told me this—and I tell you, I would not even hurt an ant, but I might have slapped that person's face—I would have said, "Liar, shut

I can never believe this idea that somebody's brain doesn't work. The brain is such a highly sophisticated computer that God gave us. If it worked out even a part of what it could work out, it would be more than anything we have ever produced or we know how to produce.

up. You are just laying a number on me." But the fact is that when I was into my illness and I experienced it, that's when it happened.

Then I started looking around at you guys. You are American? Very good. You have good sex every night. You do everything in the world. You dance. You pretend you are this, pretend you are that. But really you are just the most beastful, commotionally, and emotionally satisfying people on the planet. You can afford it. Not everybody can afford it, but you can. Your leftovers could feed one-third of the world. That is how wasteful and irrational you are. But I feel God has given you a vast land, less population, and a lot of money, and you can afford to do it. It must be the karma that you get to enjoy for a while.

I understand where the pain and the problems are in life: They are not anywhere. It is a simple theory. Let us put two and two together: The soul is deep and dormant. The mind is shallow and yellow. And when I say yellow, I mean cheap. Yellow journalism is a term that you all understand. When we color over things and cheaply try to attract other people and lay a number on them—that is how that yellow journalism came about. Now, should we blame people for their shallow, yellow minds? No, because the subconscious records daydreams, night dreams, thoughts, desires, wishes, and emotions. It records your own dreams plus those of all the people you know who project them onto you. What you do not understand is that everyone is a signal station. If a million stations send signals to you, then you shall receive them, even without knowing. That is the unconscious state that the mind has. And then what happens? You get bloated. Overloaded is called bloated. And then your own life starts falling apart.

Whatever comes from your soul shall stay. Whatever comes from your mind has to be worked out. Whatever comes from your mind will be faster than you can understand and so shallow that you can walk into it. That is what the mind does. The mind is quick. It is actually a contact between you and God. Without you even knowing it, it can make you feel you are nothing. It can make you feel you are everything.

Now, within that philosophy, when the subconscious gets overloaded, it starts blowing the circuits, and you reach a state of numbness in your physical action. It can be mental impotency; it can be physical impotency; or it can be sensitivity into impotency, which is when we say, "I don't have the spirit," or "I don't feel like it." In medical science, in psychiatry, they say, "He is psychotic; he is neurotic." They have a whole science about it. Then they say, "His brain doesn't work." You know one very funny thing? I can never believe this idea that somebody's brain doesn't work. The brain is such a highly sophisticated computer that God gave to a person; if it worked out even a part of what it could work out, it would be more than anything we have ever produced or we know how to produce.

Look at the situation of the mind. You have ten trillion cells. Your body has ten trillion cells. These cells change every seventy-two hours. Old age is when those cells start changing from every seventy-two hours to every eighty hours and to every eighty-five hours or more. That is all. No big deal. You know the doctor is right: We die of old age when our cells start taking longer to change. You start becoming senile, old, and, capacity-wise, a little wrong. Now, ten trillion cells you have, and each cell has three parts: electron, neutron, and proton. That means each cell has three things to take care of it. That means thirty trillion units live in you. So you are a living combination—a living, organic combination of thirty trillion units. Per the impulse or beat of the heart, your mind receives, controls, administers, and keeps the change going. This means your mind has the capacity, per impulse, to receive, control, and administer thirty trillion messages. I mean it is simple, layman mathematics. That is how the mind is.

Tonight, we are going to deal with this mind of ours and unload our unfulfilled dreams so we can have a little space to live. It is called jerking out the jerk in us. You know? In simple American slang English, we say, "It is too much; we can take in no more!"

One day I was very funny and said to somebody, "Believe in God!"

He said, "No, no, no. No belief in God. Nothing outside."

I said, "God is inside."

The person said, "If God is inside, then I have absolutely no belief. I know what is in my inside."

So I said, "Breathe." The person breathed.

I said, "How much of your left lung and right lung at this time has been filled with oxygen, and how much is the difference between the blood underneath and your air? And how much is the diaphragm pulling into you at the right capacity rate to bring the air down so the blood can be oxygenated?"

And the person said, "What? What are you asking?"

I said, "Each breath means it must go deeper to fill the lungs and oxygenate the blood to make it healthy and then come out with the unwanted wastes, and that is how breathing is."

I said, "My dear person, you only breathe, but remaining there is, if I estimate right, a four-inch distance between the air you breathe and where your blood is ready to be oxygenated. Your diaphragm puts the pressure, and that pressure touches it. It means you are only breathing twenty five percent out of this. Five percent oxygen potential is oxygenating the blood, and then we take vitamin E, Geritol, vitamin D, vitamin this, good food, etc.; but the very oxygen in your breath does not touch your whole blood. We have the shallowest breathing habits."

Mindwise, whatever we think in messages, receive in messages, and take care of regarding the messages—whether those messages are done, fulfilled, understood, analyzed, processed, progressed, rejected, or accepted—is all stored in the subconscious. Finally those messages start overflowing. They overflow in three ways: One is through daydreaming, which is the worst. Night dreaming and nightmares and that kind of stuff are reasonable if they are not to the extent that they tax the nervous system. I don't mind if a person sleeps the whole night; but most people are not actually sleeping. They are working through a dream that is equal to sixteen hours of hard work. Image a person digs a six foot by six foot by four foot trench during the day—that is what one nightmare is equal to. Plus the aftershock of the nightmare, like an earthquake, can go on for about a week to ten days. And if it is unfortunate enough to fall within the half of the moon, meaning you are in the seventh or eighth or ninth day of the moon and you reach the eleventh day of the moon, then it becomes a permanent scar. If it is your thirteenth, fourteenth, or fifteenth day onward, you are safe. That is how the body works.

The body is a very, very highly sophisticated system. So I thought I would just share with you a certain series in which I am going to get rid of this subconscious stuff. It is easy, and you should know the art of it and science of it and the experience of it, so that you can live light. These days, lots of people are selling enlightenment and meditation and lots of other things. But basically you must understand you have but one power—mental power. You cannot avoid the interlock between you and the sound of the gong, because you are the byproduct of the wave and the strength of the wave that is called light and sound. Playing the gong is an art. It took me about four to five years to perfect it. I can create an effective rhythm with it; I can play it; I can interlock it. I can see your aura, and I can push you through; I don't need you for that. I mean, I don't mind if you do not meditate on me; I am going to just push you through anyway. It is just like pulling a tooth out of a man's mouth. When the forceps are in and the dentist has the strength and the Novocain has already worked, all there is left is to pull it out. And for that we need only one-tenth of a second. If in the whole meditation today you can coordinate yourself for one-tenth of a second, that is all we need. After all, to burn a big heap of good, dry firewood, you need one little matchstick. So, if in this whole series, little by little, you just give us one-tenth of a second, the rest will all work out with you. That is all we need. Once that sound sinks in—where you are not hearing it and you are getting it—it will do the work. And that is what the science is about.

I am not going to make you Christian. I am not going to make you Buddhist. I am not going to make you divine. I am not making you Allah Azraheem. I do not know what *Wahe Guru* says. I am just trying to clean out your garbage. That is all this night is about: cleaning your mental garbage. I could say other words, but because I am a holy man, I can't. I love that word that you Americans have taught me. But unfortunately I am Siri Singh Sahib, and I am not supposed to say a lot of uncouth things. I am also bound down by unwanted discipline. But I think in my religious world, they knew I was a rebel, and they just tied me in to fix me.

Mind. Mind. Mind. The right side of the mind is not with men. The left side of the mind is devastating because it is with the female; it makes her confused about what is right, what is not right—"I am too much, I am too little." You know, it is a Libra balance. Have you seen the real picture of a Libra? Those two pans of the balance are always upside down, as if a high wind has hit it. So it is not the quality of the woman that matters; it is the balance of the woman. Unisonness of the mind is what woman has to use, and the unit of the mind is what man has to use if they both want to be happy and successful in life. You can be successful—not happy. That is the criteria you have to understand.

I don't mean the spiritual experience—I know God, God knows me . . . then what? God knows everybody. If I know God knows me, so what? Big deal. The question is, how much mental garbage do I have? The bulb is on whether or not the glass is clean, whether or not the light comes out. It takes that light to be able to go to others and not cheat them, not hurt them, not reject them. All the negative things we do to others, we also do to ourselves. You do not hurt anyone; neither can you. Nor do you have the power to do it. You first hurt yourself, and then that hurt reaches the other person, and he returns the hurt through a curse, which multiplies your hurt many, many times. That is actually what happens. You might be thinking you are hurting somebody: "Oh, you son of so and so; oh you dog." You abuse a person and make him look inferior and make him feel absolutely good for nothing and bring tears to his eyes. You did a wonderful job of it. And that person will say nothing to you. Instead he will say, "God, make him impotent, make him blind, make him dumb." You know? Only God knows how many curses his mind is going to send on you. You, idiot human, living nicely, knowing kindness and compassion have created a machine of abuse—and you think you have hurt somebody? You have dug your own grave, because whatever comes in pain and in reaction has the force.

I saw one time a very funny thing, and it is true what I am saying to you. We were sitting on a bus, and we were going toward Tampa. Somebody bought our tickets, and we sat down. A person I know and respect wouldn't sit on the one empty seat, even though the secretary told her that she had to sit. But she wouldn't, because the person sitting on the next seat was black. Now watch this American humanity; this is something I saw and experienced myself. This woman would not sit on the seat because the next person sitting was a black person. Finally the bus driver stopped the bus. He said, "Lady, either you sit down, or you get off the bus."

You cannot avoid the interlock between you and the sound of the gong, because you are the byproduct of the wave and the strength of the wave that is called light and sound. Playing the gong is an art.

So I said, "Could you? I'll sit there, and you can sit in my place." I provided a seat to her. Now that person who I'm referring to was our student. Four years later, she developed a disease. Half of her face became so black that even she couldn't believe it. And it was not just black only, as that could have been tolerable. It was that disease—what do they call it? Acne or something like that. She had those little blackheads all over her face, and there was nothing she could do. She tried creams and this and that and the other, and I said, "Well, it is a day and night. You should enjoy it."

She replied, "I don't like it. My liver is bad, or my kidneys are bad. I don't know what is bad, but there is something wrong."

I said, "Definitely. I am the only one you don't believe. Everybody else you believe; but look which side you sat on and look which side that person was sitting." I think the man on the bus realized what happened, and in his heart he got hurt. He thought, "God, you have made me black, and this woman hates me just because you made me black." And he was just overtanned, and she was totally undertanned. That is all it is.

You know, our minds do play games. Our minds automatically hate things. We are brainwashed. We have been brainwashed by religion, by society, by our social structure, by our own parents, by our own you-name-it. We do not even see the other human as a human if, in that microscope of ours, he or she does not fit our number. If a rich person comes, we go and open the door. If a poor man comes, we kick him out. It is all mental games. Mental games are very heavy, and we play them consciously and unconsciously. Today we are trying to explain to you how your mind is loaded and how you feel it. Right? All right.

◆ ◆ ◆

Let's work it out. This meditation is to jerk the jerk out of you. Have you ever done a Paranoia Breath? When you are hit by a definite attack of phobic paranoia within yourself, you breathe this way because you need oxygen. You need the pranic body. When you breathe this way, it is a natural process. All of these are natural processes, so don't feel ugly about them. If you do this breath before the paranoia hits you, if you charge it with the breath, it will give you oxygen. And we need that red blood. Within three minutes of doing this breath, your aura should totally change.

I know why people do not practice Kundalini Yoga. It's because it does not seem so sophisticated. It doesn't suit you. Who wants to sound like a duck? But that is what you do when you are in those paranoid situations. God bless you—I hope that situation may never arise, but if it does, it can take so much energy away from you that you cannot even relate to it. But if right now you force the diaphragm deeper and let the air come deeper, it is good practice.

The next exercise is very light, and the balance is very difficult. Just keep it and do it faster than you think possible. We are sending a message to the brain—but the brain doesn't know what. A mudra is a physical connection that forces the neurons to move or not to move in the brain, to create patterns; the mudra activates them to think, "What is going on?" We will repeat this exercise in a little bit, because it is not good to create energy and not then circulate it into the body.

Do you know what my problem is? If I do not give you a good class, then you are not going to come again. You know what I mean? And if you don't come again, and if I do not do a good job, then a week later, you are going to hit the wall. But that doesn't have to happen. Just get rid of the junk, stay clean, get going, enjoy your life.

Now, I do not know what I have done, and you do not know what you have done; but just go in your mind about thirty, forty minutes back in time before you did this and just feel yourself then and find out how you feel now. Make no concession to me. That's how much it takes to clean your garbage. It is an initiation to get into the house and clean it. Tomorrow we will see, what the garbage collectors will come and get.

◆ ◆ ◆

We have initiated this kriya only with the idea that you will go through it for a day. When you come tomorrow, do me a favor: Do not have anything in your stomach except liquids. I also ask you this: I don't know how regular you are, but you may need to go on some kind of mild laxative so that you may be reassured that you are clean. We are going through this series on a relationship of faith. You trust me. I trust you. You come here to learn from me, and God has given me the privilege to serve you. I don't play that game of, "I have got you, and you have got me." You don't get me; I don't get you. It is just a simple privilege to serve you; and it is a privilege and honor that somebody touched me and I learned it and I enjoyed it and I still recall and relish those experiences.

The capacity of man is not that he can catch God by a tail. The capacity of man is not that he can create miracles. The capacity of man is not that he is the most successful, the most beautiful, a multimillionaire. It is not that he is president of the whole world and the world bows to him. No, the capacity of a man depends on two things. Even when it seems impossible, according to that person, his heart is kind

The capacity of a man depends on two things. Even when it seems impossible, according to that person, his heart is kind and his head is compassionate. There is nothing beyond that. The heart is kind. Kindness and compassion are the two things that guarantee your strength.

Yoga is the union between man and God, within the God and within the man, and there are no two opinions about it. But the test of it is when time hits you and space fixes you—at that time, if your answer is kindness from the heart and compassion from the head, there is no saint greater than you; there is no God but you; and there is no truth but you.

and his head is compassionate. There is nothing beyond that. The heart is kind. Kindness and compassion are the two things that guarantee your strength. There is no such thing as God. It is a gimmick if you produce it. But it is a reality if you dispense it in a simple way. You must be kind and compassionate when it is absolutely by all standards not possible.

Do you understand what God is? God is not twenty hands and sixteen legs and an elephant nose and Allah lives on the seventh story and God lives on the thirteenth story and Ram lives under the backyard. All this is just to teach us that A is apple, B is book, C is cat, D is dog. But neither D is dog nor dog is D. It is a learning process. Graduation? When do you get your Ph.D.? You get it when, by all standards of your capacity, your intelligence, your intuition, your ego, and your identity you think it is impossible to be kind and compassionate and yet you are kind at heart and compassionate at head. That is when you have found God. Otherwise, you are Mr. Bogus, and you are hocus-pocus, and you talk religion and reality, and you read books, and you lecture—you do everything! You have a meditation practice, and you have seen the *avtars*, and you have seen the *samskaras*. That is all jerk yoga; it has nothing to do with anything.

Yoga is the union between man and God, within the God and within the man, and there are no two opinions about it. But the test of it—after all, everything has a test, an examination—the test of it is when time hits you and space fixes you—at that time, if your answer is kindness from the heart and compassion from the head, there is no saint greater than you; there is no God but you; and there is no truth but you. These are the virtues of an ordinary grassroots human being. You can tell me I am an idiot, thank you. You can tell me I am wisest, thank you. You tell me I am a sage, thank you. You tell me you are nothing, or everything, that it doesn't make sense. But that is all it is about. If you are in love but you are not kind and if you have a romance but you are not compassionate, then you are just an animal.

The problem with me is that I must make you understand that the problem is not between you and somebody—the problem is between you and within you. I have nothing to do with who does what to you and what you do to them. That is not the idea. The thing is this: God made you. God made you. He made you rotten, or he made you the best. He couldn't do better than that. So you are the best identity and psyche created by God. You are a prostitute, or you are a goddess. You are the holiest, or you are the most unholy. That has nothing to do with the circumstances. You are what you are and then, within you, what you are. No questions asked. There are two things that shall totally test you—time and space. At a certain given time, at a certain space, or in certain environments, when by your standards—not by God's standards or my standards or anybody's standards, but by your standards—you think it is impossible, and yet you are kind at heart and compassionate at head, then you have already found God. Whether you mend tires or you run 1600 Pennsylvania Avenue, makes no difference. The fulfillment is yours. Everything is within you. If God had wanted something outside of you, He would have created something outside of you. But He couldn't. He didn't because He doesn't know better. It is all within each one of you. How rotten you are or how great you are, you have that capacity to experience.

We carry tons of garbage in our heads, but we do not know what we are carrying. Only later on things fall apart, and then we say, "I don't know." The first time in the United States that somebody told me, "I don't know," I had the shock of my life. I am telling you honestly. I did not know before that a person can answer like that. You are really free people, absolutely loose. All you have to say is one thing: "I don't know." Then you think there is nothing anybody can do to you. But what you are really saying to another person is, "Be dead." That is all you are saying. When a person does not communicate or communicates in a vernacular language of his own mind or choice in which he does not communicate, it means exactly one thing only: "Be dead." It doesn't mean more; it doesn't mean less. And I think that, on average, during the day, I hear it five to ten or twenty times. "I don't know." And they say it with such a style.

A friend of mine in India wrote me a question on health. The letter came through a personal friend. He never thought that my secretary would even give me the letter. But I said, "Okay." He asked me, "From what you have learned in the West, what is the best thing? Please, tell me." I wrote on the letter itself, on the other side of it. I said, "These people are freer than free will itself. All they have to say is, 'I don't know,' and they get out of everything and anything. It is very difficult to look at them and still smile. Thank God, I have kindness and compassion as the very maximum part of me."

I have lived through it. When I came to this country, I was almost forty years old. I had never heard in my life any human being saying, "I don't know." I mean, it is impossible; it can't be imagined that a person doesn't know. What can he not know when every question has an answer in it? If somebody is asking you, "Do you love me or don't you?" Just say, "I don't." But you say half and half, maybe, sometimes not, just so you can say something. The answer comes out as, "I don't know." Will you go to dinner with me? "I don't know." Will you call me tomorrow? "I don't know." When they say that, just watch their face. Sometimes it looks like a monkey; sometimes it looks like a bear. You will find one very specialized animal coming through their face. I am not kidding; it is reincarnation. People ask whether or not there is reincarnation, but I don't discuss it. I discuss reincarnation like this: "Don't talk to her; she is a snake." Well, there is a reincarnation right there. You don't have to look at a snake and determine that it's a snake. A person is being called a snake because of behavior, habits, treatment, and all that.

But all that is not needed. All that is needed are two things—compassion is your art and kindness is your science. And then you can get your Ph.D. in sainthood. You have to process yourself first by cleaning, cleansing, marbleizing, lifting your values up, and then lifting yourself up.

Take it or leave it, it is your choice. I do my best.

◆ ◆ ◆

May the long time sun shine upon you,
all love surround you, and the pure light within you, guide your way on.
And guide your way on to your homes. Good night.

Sat Nam

CLEANING THE CLUTTER OF THE MIND 1—THE KRIYA

February 21, 1989

There are no breaks between the exercises. Move immediately from one exercise to the next.

1. Sit in a meditative, yogic posture. Stick out your tongue, but not all the way—just relax the tongue. With the diaphragm, strongly exhale through the mouth over the relaxed tongue. This is called Paranoia Breath. This is a heavy, deep breath from the diaphragm. Breathe for **1½–3 minutes**.

Feel afraid! Do it heavily from the diaphragm. You think this is a joke? If you do it about twenty times a day, you shall never have nightmares. It is not a joke—this breath. If you practice this breath, two things will never hurt you: One is hysteria, the other is paranoia. It is a yogic breath. You usually do it in a natural emergency, but we are asking you to do it in a conscious emergency. I want it to be done by the pull of the diaphragm. When paranoia hits you, hit it with this breath.

2. Open your mouth and do Breath of Fire through a rounded mouth, very quickly and forcefully, for **30 seconds**.

3. Bring your hands into Ravi Mudra—ring finger and thumb together. The other three fingers are straight and open—stiff. Circle the hands around each other in front of the chest. Only the fingers move over each other—not the entire hand. Move as fast as you can for **4 minutes**.

TO END: Inhale deep, close your eyes, and lock the hands at the Heart Center.

If you do this exercise really fast, your nostrils will start having pressure on ida and pingala. You will have a very impulsive state here, right on both sides where ida and pingala start. We want that pressure. We also want the nose to start showing a little red color in the aura. I want the big nose. They call it clown nose.

4. Meditate with the hands gripped at the Heart Center. Grip tightly. The eyes are closed and focused at the hands. Meditate as the gong is played for **7 minutes**.

5. Relax the hands down and continue to meditate to the gong. The body will naturally adjust itself. *[Music is played over the gong for the last 5 minutes: Singh Kaur's Beloved God.]* Mentally go with the sound but not the words. Continue for **8 minutes**.

6. Do Breath of Fire as powerfully as possible for **30 seconds**. Now begin to clap the hands over the head—fast and powerful—for **30 seconds**.

7. Repeat Exercise 3 for **1 minute**.

8. Repeat Exercise 1: Powerful Paranoia Breath. Move the tail-bone; pull it. Breathe for **1 minute**.

9. Repeat Exercise 2: Breath of Fire through rounded mouth for **15 seconds**.

10. Relax.

It is recommended that you drink juice and liquids after this meditation. No solids. Also drink lots of liquids on the following day.

This meditation is to jerk out the jerk in you.

It is recommended that teachers and practitioners review the DVD before practicing this kriya in order to understand the rhythm and power of the breath.

"Today we are going to stimulate the western hemisphere of the brain. We are going to give it overriding power for the purposes of shedding some insecurity. Today I am letting you give up what is called incentive phobia. Incentive phobia happens when we automatically generate phobia. When constant fear is not addressed, it turns into a phobia, and the incentive is within us; it is not outside. "

– Yogi Bhajan

CLEANING THE CLUTTER OF THE MIND 11

February 22, 1989

Why are people unhappy? Why can't people progress? Why can't our lives be better? The answer is simple: We do not have the guts or the nerves to support our life. We short circuit it, we expand until we are too thin, so we cannot hold ourselves.

THERE IS A CERTAIN SITUATION THAT I DO NOT LIKE TO CONFRONT IN MY LIFE. I want to see people happy. But after twenty years, I have not reconciled that in America, to be unhappy is my national right. Is this not a democracy? Do I not have the right to vote? And all of you who are unhappy, one way or the other, do you have one reason to be unhappy? I am soon going to be sixty years old. I was a Master of Kundalini Yoga at sixteen and a half. I have seen the world. I have touched the hearts and heads of millions of people. And after all this in my life, I have come to a conclusion about something. Why are people unhappy? Why is a prostitute a prostitute? Why is a saint a saint? Why is a religious fanatic a religious fanatic? Why is a person mediocre? Why can't people progress? Why can't our lives be better?

The answer is simple: We do not have the guts or the nerves to support our life. We short circuit it, we expand until we are too thin, so we cannot hold ourselves. Sometimes we need extra energy, but we do not have the gear. We have a Rolls Royce car made by God but with a bad transmission. We should not apply the reverse gear when we have to go into first gear. Sometimes in our lives we sell ourselves cheap, and we call it satisfaction. Simple things have to be looked at simply.

I have seen some stupid people get mad at me. They are mad to begin with; they are mad at themselves. When there is extra flow, they get mad at me. What have I done to this person's life except tell him to live happily? Nothing! I am not a religious man, though I am head of the religion. But that was bestowed on me; I never wanted it, and I don't think they will ever make the mistake again of bestowing the title God on anybody; they are scared to death. What I have found in my life is very simple. I can't guarantee that you are not going to be ill. I can't guarantee that you won't get divorced. I won't guarantee that your child will not die. I won't guarantee that you will not be mugged or shot. I want to guarantee nothing. But I do know one thing: If you have the guts, if your three nervous systems—sympathetic, parasympathetic, and action—are properly flowing, then you don't have to be a yogi to have intuition. Within nine seconds, you will know what to do. Whatever comes to you after those nine seconds will be exact and shall protect you. And step by step you shall be successful, no matter what.

You may even deny God. You may be what they call those who don't believe in God, an atheist. You could be a dead-set atheist and still be happy because you can

I never knew that in this country people do not know that the mind has all these chambers and inter-computerized systems. I thought you knew.

deny God; but God doesn't deny you. So it is the same story: There was once a man who went to the palace for judgment. He saw there were saints and sages and yogis and swamis and gurus and every kind of thing. But he was given an override over everybody and was sent straight in. The others asked, "Who is this guy?"

"This is a man who knows God. He is a man of God."

Another man said, "I knew that guy in the streets of my town. He used to abuse not only God but also all those who claimed to love God. How he can go in and meet directly with God?"

"Because he was remembering God twenty-four hours."

"By abusing God?"

"That's the thing: Even in sleep, he was abusing, while you were just sleeping. That's the difference. And God doesn't understand your Earthly language. All He understands is who is paying attention."

You do not pay attention to yourself. It doesn't matter whether you are Christian, a yoga student, an American; whether you have a good haircut or you are totally blonde or bald. In sickness and in health, your nervous system has to stand with you as a friend. Your neurons, the composition of your brain, you must have for yourself. And that's the gift of God—or whosoever manufactured us—that brain capacity.

Our brain capacity only in the one part of the brain called *chith,* memory, sub-conscious memory and projective memory, intuitive memory, and now that we are writing this story on mind, how many portions are there? You have three minds, and you have eighty-one parts of the mind. I never knew that in this country people do not know that the mind has all these chambers and intercomputerized systems. I thought you knew. But one day I asked, "Do you know that there are three parts of the mind and it has eighty-one interrelated parts and they all cohesively work and coordinate the whole system?" And somebody in class said, "What? What eighty-one are you talking about?" I said, "They have been known to us for thousands of years." But then I realized that if these people didn't even know their own minds, with its chambers and work and interrelations, then what did they know?

What do we know? You might think that something is your idea. You might be totally under the hysteria of subconscious fear. You might think something is a thought or a scheme, or totally bewitched by a pattern. You might think you are in love when you are really totally destructive. The route can be anything, actions can be anything. And either you are under the spell of absolutely indirect, subtle, mental games or you are awake and your personality is in command of it. That's why you could be a doctor, an engineer, surgeon, attorney, businessman, rich man, poor man, actor, producer, whatever; but when it comes to personality, they all are stupid. It's not that they want to be, nor that they should be. They just don't know.

How can God create man in His own image but with a wrong blueprint? It's not possible. I have systematically studied the twenty-two sides of yoga and the eight main themes of yoga, including Hatha Yoga. It's not that I am against Hatha Yoga. I just gave it up. It's too long—stretch it and perfect it! Who wants it? But at one time, I was very fanatically a Hatha Yogi. I just wanted to learn and know what it is all about. But I found that all it does is give you a stimulant. When you are down, it jacks you up. That's all it does.

Then I saw people putting needles here, needles there. One day a man came, and I said to him, "My energy is so down right now. I am very tired, but I don't want to be tired."

He said, "Let us check it out." He said gall bladder and put two needles in me. The whole night I was up, just like I am now. There was no drug in me. I was fine—not a wink of sleep. I was just bright and sharp. I wanted to enjoy everything, and all with just two little needles. Massaging certain areas in the body stimulates other certain areas—of your body and of your self. You can totally stimulate your self just by pressing certain general energy points for more than nine seconds. After that, you are shipshape. The human body is the best thing that God has ever made in His total existence. It's the most small, effective, creative, realization machine, in which this Infinite of the Infinite of the Infinite God can stimulate Himself.

A lot of people will not like what I am going to say, but I am going to say it anyway. People think God is infinite, but I never have believed that. I am never going to believe it. If God is infinite and complete and perfect within Himself, then why did He create me? Did I ask for this?

There is something going on here. A woman's time clock ticks, and she just wants to get pregnant, even though she knows she is going to be big. And I saw that same girl eight years, and she practiced nothing but dieting and wanting to be skinny. Then she got pregnant, and she was so big while the rest of her body was so skinny. I couldn't understand how she could carry it. But she became a mother. And the power and instinct of the mother, that entire system, changed her from being a girl—a show girl, a cover girl, an acting girl—to being a Mother. It's like two totally different people: being a girl and being a lady, being a girl on sale and being a girl not on sale; they are two different people.

When you walk out of your house, are you on sale? You may be cheap—twenty percent off, thirty percent off, fifty percent. If you are not on sale, perhaps you are a person with a premium—twenty percent premium, fifty percent premium. You may not sell that day, that month, that year. But when you do sell, you will get a large profit. Life without profit is a practical, personal prostitution that we do openly and defiantly, and then we call ourselves religious.

Man is not against God; man is against his own self. We are going to work through a mental process in which we unload your subconscious garbage. You have come, and I am willing to work with you on this. I teach this class just to experiment and to understand in my head whether all men can be equally happy. I know richness will never make you happy, poverty will never make you happy. Being paid too much attention will make you a slave to attention. Not being paid too much attention will make you feel neglected and cheap. Do you understand why you have the mind? Because the soul was coming to live a sensory experience. That's what life is about.

I want to remember and see and be in touch with why the mind was given to us. The mind is the only sensitive part in the human body that is faster than time and faster than space. Just understand, your brain has the impulsive property. In *Chitya*, one-third of the mind receives and delivers thirty trillion messages per impulse. If your mental capacity could not do all that, then your body would disintegrate. You would not be alive. Your cells change every seventy-two hours—you have ten trillion cells that all change in just seventy-two hours. Multiply that by three electrons per minute—thirty trillion. And your mind keeps it all together in one piece—bad and good. You are quite a machine!

We have the capacity to help you; we don't need your help in that way. You just have to meditate deeply, simply; let it go. The sound of the gong is a productive sound that can change the pattern of the neurons, whether you like it or not, for positive purposes. You cannot use any magic and any nonreality. You are not in a position to do two things at once. You cannot be medium, and you cannot be negative. You are plus or you are zero—nothing in between.

In both Kundalini Yoga and Tantric Yoga, there is one lever, one energy—the diagonal energy, as we call it. Man has only two powers: lens and lever. With lever, man can move what otherwise could not be moved. With lens, he can see what otherwise could not be seen. All this progress in your life! As a human being, if you free your mind of a little of the subconscious dirt, you will have better intuition and better sensitivity, and you will have better strength than you otherwise might have had. Are you ready to co-operate?

There are three things I am going to stimulate now. I am talking about the science of it, because I believe this is going to be taped. And when I am physically gone, maybe you can run these tapes and understand what I said. Ultimately, one day, every individual will be in full driving control of his being—mentally, spiritually, and physically. This handicapped living has got to go. Handicapped living is not living.

In the fourteenth, fifteenth, and sixteenth centuries, there were no bathrooms; even up until the eighteenth century, there were many palaces in Europe without bathrooms. In 1887 the first bathroom was put into a home. But even before that,

there was always a bucket and water and a man. You gave him a penny, and you could cleanse yourself.

We have never thought about how to clean ourselves, how to brush ourselves. We know how to brush our tie, we know how to brush our coat, we know how to clean our house, we know everything about cleanliness. But about cleaning our mind, we know nothing. People think meditating is a jerk thing, that it's just something from the Sixties. But that's not at all true. Try driving a car—keep on driving and never change the oil. One day the engine will blow up. In humans, they call it a nervous breakdown. We have the Khalsa Clinic where you can go and get fixed up. But I am asking, "Why?" Why do you have to be a donkey when you can be a beautiful horse? Why? Why do you have to invoke suffering when you can be happy?

If you ever ask me whether the challenges will be less with me, I will say no. The more challenges there are, the better you are. A challenge is not here to test your intelligence; it is not something to be scared of.

One day there was a grave situation, and I was asked for advice on what to do. The person asking was no less than a Chancellor of my Dharma. But the question was to Siri Singh Sahib, not to me in person. Whenever I act as Siri Singh Sahib, I am acting as a history. My orders, my decisions will be recorded or, if not recorded, at least repeated. And either they will be proven over time as a gospel truth from a very high, beautiful, elevated person, or our history will judge me as stupid. There is no in-between. I know that, I am fully aware of it. So he said, "Sir, the situation is this, this, this, this, this, this, this, this, this."

I said, "It sounds pretty deadly stinky."

He said, "It's more than that. What do you want us to do?"

I said, "Let it pass."

"Sir?"

"You are Chancellor, you are my legal adviser. You have to act within the scope of the law, right?"

He said, "Yes."

"Let it pass."

"Do you mean it won't affect us?"

I said, "If we don't react, it won't affect us."

"Why?"

I said, "I have no reason. You have asked me, first of all, to give my opinion. If my opinion creates damage, send the paper and I will sign it and take responsibility. Your job is to tell me the problem. My job is to give you the orders. My orders are, we shall not move."

"Under no circumstances?"

In both Kundalini Yoga and Tantric Yoga, there is one lever, one energy— the diagonal energy, as we call it.

All I know is that if you do not care to be happy, nobody can make you happy. I know that. And if you care to be happy, God the Almighty—the real one, not this imaginary guy—cannot make you unhappy.

"Under no circumstances." And I won.

Later, he met me, and the first question he asked me was, "How did you know?"

I said, "Very simple formula: I did that thing out of pure parental love. It cannot be cashed in on because of hatred. That's the law of universe. I cannot face any problem on that issue."

"Was it a matter of guts?"

I said, "No, I am a Virgo. I don't need guts. All I need is the practical application of the intelligence you get when you live your life in kindness and compassion. In that way, you shall not suffer in the long run and shall not face defeat."

In a triangle, if the angles on two sides of two triangles are equal, then the two triangles are congruent. This is absolute geometry. If the infinity of God and the finite position of the human have the same angle and the sides are the same, then an affirmative victory shall belong to the human; the human will win. There is no problem. But whenever the mind gets overloaded and the subconscious gets overloaded, we suffer. We suffer not because we are not intelligent. We suffer not because we want to suffer. We suffer not because somebody is there to make us suffer. All of that is spiritual nonsense.

"If you give me six hundred dollars, I can reserve a seat in heaven for you, and God will be doing this and this for you." I have gone through this, and I have seen all the spiritual people injecting fear in people. I am absolutely not in favor of injecting fear. All I know is that if you do not care to be happy, nobody can make you happy. I know that. And if you care to be happy, God the Almighty—the real one, not this imaginary guy—cannot make you unhappy. I know that too. I don't have to learn that from you Americans.

I came from India absolutely innocent. I never knew one person in the United States—not one. I didn't come here to make money. I didn't come here to spread dharma. I came here to set up a Chair of Kundalini Yoga in a university. So I migrated to Toronto. And believe me, what God did to me then was the worst trick in the world. I will never forgive God for that, but therefore I will never forget Him either.

Do you know what it's like to be an Indian coming for the first time to a country that he doesn't know? It took me two years to set up. What shall be my salary? What shall be my accommodation? How soon can my children and my family come? What is this, and what is that—the whole thing! Details! And the Canadian Ambassador was my yoga student. So I was always asking, "George, look into this. George, look into that. George, check this out. George, try to find this. George, please, tell your son to look into it."

Anyway, when I came, I had planned perfectly. I brought with me sufficient wealth so I could live in Canada by myself for three years without a thing—very

good. I had been a customs officer, so the airlines were very nice, and out of respect they left the adjoining seats vacant. So I had four seats. I also had throughout my journey a special attendant.

I landed in Montreal wearing my beautiful Indian silk robe. I had thought to myself, Jesus Christ wore a robe, and I had a robe. But when I landed in Montreal, I found out that was all I had. They told me my luggage had been left back. They gave me twenty-five dollars cash so I could buy underwear and a toothbrush and toothpaste. I didn't know the country. I didn't know the people. When I left Montreal, I came to a beautiful place called Toronto. But then I was told that the Dean of the university who was supposed to pick me up had just died in a car accident half an hour ago. The chill factor outside was minus forty-five degrees, and I was in that silken robe at the Toronto airport thinking, Where am I?

And that was my start. I rode the rollercoaster. I used to sing this song: *"One day the day shall come when all the glory shall be Thine, people will say it is yours, I shall deny not mine."* I used to sing it all the time. And just understand my insecurity. If you ever get insecure sometimes, just remember this story. I used to go from Hamilton to Toronto to Ottawa to Montreal and back to Toronto, just teaching yoga classes. Check out the map and figure that out. When snow was all over and you don't know the towns and you don't have any friends, relatives or anybody, and you go teach just one yoga class. Do you know how many people used to come to my yoga class? Three, two. The biggest yoga class I taught was in Los Angeles; it was the best lecture, which we have printed at 3HO. Do you know how many people came to attend my lecture? Myself and my tape recorder.

The YMCA, which had set up the whole thing, gave a wrong date. So I sat in that hall with a capacity of five hundred people. I gave that lecture, and it got taped, and later on we produced it. That's the best little pamphlet. We give to people who want to be highly spiritual.

So, things can happen. But you are not a thing. You are part of infinity. Whenever you think you are finite or defined or identified, you become smaller, you become little, and your suffering starts. Otherwise, for all purposes, a human being is sufficient, right?

◆ ◆ ◆

Today we are going to stimulate the western hemisphere of the brain. We are going to give it overriding power for the purposes of shredding up some insecurity. Today I am letting you give up what is called incentive phobia. Incentive phobia happens when we automatically generate phobia. When constant fear is not addressed, it turns into a phobia, and the incentive is within us; it is not outside. Vitamin C cannot help much, and neither can Vitamin E. These phobias are destructive natures that ultimately take

a toll on our nervous system and our senses. So now we will see how much we have and how much we can release.

Two things will happen in this first exercise: Either the grip will go loose, or your eight will be forgotten. But don't give up on it. You will work it out all right. Just set yourself in the posture, but do not touch. Have you seen a generator that creates the electricity? We are working on the electromagnetic fields; it's a total science, right? We are generating the electromagnetic field with a centrifugal force. Do you know the mathematics or the science or the physics? That's what you are doing. And if the distance between the fingers is correct and the movement is right, it will start affecting you. But don't touch the hands together, because that will neutralize it.

We want to get this clutter out of us, because it's too much. If you have physical pain during the exercises, keep going. Don't stop. The nerves are coming together, so keep going. Just go beyond the pain. You may have a lot of trouble in the armpits, as that is where three nervous centers move. Stretch it and keep going. Cooperate; let it go. Go beyond the hurt. Your brain has the capacity to eat up the pain.

Many of you who did not eat this afternoon and who drank a lot of water can go home and eat as much you like. But, still, you should drink a lot of water. These classes will definitely warrant you drinking water so that you can replenish what you lost. Water is about sixty percent of your body, but the majority of the time, we are so busy that we forget to drink water. Sometimes we are so busy, we do not eat. Or maybe we overeat or eat too much fast food. After this class, you will remember me until next week! I can bet you that I will live in your armpits for one week.

The armpits are a very important area. It is the central point in the nervous system, and controls our nervous activity. Nobody understands why. What is the armpit? We often speak of somebody living in a pit—does he live in his armpit? Is there a snake in the armpit? But I have decided voluntarily to live in your armpit this week.

Next time we meet, we will run you through the mill. And after that, if you cannot be happy, then there is nothing true. A person works their whole life and comes to conclude that there is nothing wrong. There was never anything wrong with you, and there was never anything wrong with me. I was wrong to myself and that's my realization—that was my unhappiness, that was my cup of tea which was too hot and I drank too fast and burnt my lips. Read my lips: you cannot do that to yourself, okay? Do we have a gentleman's agreement?

If thousands of years of science are true, then this kriya must work. How do you feel? Are you comfortable? Is there pain? Okay, one last thing: This is the index finger, and this is a Saturn finger. This is one, and this is two. This is the victory sign. Between these two—between the dirt and the best—lies success. Do you understand?

What is worse than one who doesn't know what negative is, what corruption is, what honesty is? The people who say honesty, honesty, honesty, and good, good,

good, and character, character, character—I don't believe them. They are only there to talk. If you measure two things, you must know the depth; only then can you measure the height. You must know what corruption is so you can know what honesty is. You must know what lies are so you can know the truth. You must know there is no God so then you can know what God is. There are two sides to everything.

May the long time sun shine upon you,
all love surround you, and the pure light within you, guide your way on.
God bless you, peace be within you and may you be poor or rich, good or bad.
Never, ever in your life may you act without kindness and compassion.
That's all God is, that's all Divine is, that's all prosperity is.

Sat Nam

Beyond you there never was, there never is, and there never shall be anything else. Realize that beyond you, nothing exists. When within you, you decide everything with kindness and compassion, God is achieved.

Eighty-nine is the year of prosperity. It shall walk on the two legs of kindness and compassion. I am willing to bet that by the end of the year, you will get what you want. You say you are poor, you want to be better, you want to do anything. I am willing to bet that I will see you improve from one to ten, one to eight, one to six—whatever. But you have to keep your part of the bargain: Every action in your life shall be subject to kindness and compassion; then prosperity and happiness will be vouched for by your creativity. I won't say "by God," because you sometimes freak out with too much God. That's why when I used to teach at UCLA, I called God: "Heshit"—He, She, and It.

Before the next class, please refrain from food and take a mild laxative the night before to clean your digestive system. It's not that you are constipated; but it will help facilitate these exercises. When we are working the electromagnetic field, we produce or reproduce energy with the spine and the motorized system of the body. Therefore, there should be more water and less food in the digestive system. I am not asking you to fast; I don't believe in fasting. If you take a reasonable mild laxative and clean yourself out the next day, have a good breakfast, then after the strike of twelve noon just drink juices or milk or whatever; no solid food after that. Keep in mind that when you go home that night, you shall not be asked to eat as much as you want, and the next day after that you are expected to eat light. Remember to drink as much liquid as you can; it will be very helpful. If you can do that much, I can do my best. These are the essential requirements. The better you follow them, the better results you will get.

I am running the last mile of my life. I am doing my best, and I want you to do your best. Beyond you there never was, there never is, and there never shall be anything else. Realize that beyond you, nothing exists. When within you, you decide everything with kindness and compassion, God is achieved. Everything else is a hodgepodge and camouflage. So let's try to be simple and make it.

CLEANING THE CLUTTER OF THE MIND 11—THE KRIYA

February 22, 1989

There are no breaks between the exercises. Move immediately from one exercise to the next.

1. Sit on the heels and bring the tips of the five fingers together, as though you were picking up something with each hand. Hold the hands in front of the face, with the palms facing each other and the eyes open. The fingertips overlap about a half an inch, no more, and the hands are close together without touching each other. Begin circling the hands around each other in a forward motion. Move to a count of 8; on the 8th beat, extend the right arm out and up at a 60 degree angle, with a straight elbow. Move quickly in a jerking motion. On the count of one, immediately return to the circling motion. Move steadily and quickly at a pace of 8 counts every 5 seconds. Continue for **3 minutes**.

Sitting on the heels is very awkward. If it is hurting too much, it means your digestive system is already off track. Put your five fingers—the tattvas of ether, air, fire, water, earth—together and move your hands very fast. You are dealing with the brain; you are not dealing just with muscle. It's a whole system. It is going to make you dizzily nervous, but don't be afraid. Make sure the angle on the arm is out and upward. If you go downwards, you will be depressed.

2. Close the eyes and continue the motion for **1 minute**.

3. Continue the motion and begin Breath of Fire through the nose for **1 minute**.

Breathe quick and deep, quick and deep. We need the lower area of the lungs to totally touch the blood and start purifying it. The oxygen going to the lower chamber of your lungs can make your blood healthier than anything else on the planet, and Breath of Fire is the one breath that does it all. Now, you are moving your hands, you are counting mentally, and you are breathing Breath of Fire. You are locked in. Keep it going, because in the end, when the release comes, you must have the energy to kick it all out. Without that experience, it's not a good class.

4. Continue the motion and begin Breath of Fire through the mouth. The tongue remains in the mouth. Continue for **1 minute**.

Don't stick out the tongue. Keep going—you have to totally purify your blood to a proper composition that your body can understand.

5. With the eyes closed, interlace the fingers above the crown of the head with the thumb tips touching and the palms facing down. The elbows are slightly bent. Begin swaying left and right, 15 degrees in each direction. The spine becomes a pendulum, moving left and right. Deeply meditate and move. After **2½ minutes**, *Jai Te Gang* is played, and the gong is played over the music for **13½ minutes**.
Total: 16 minutes.

Don't overdo it; keep the pendulum angle perfect. If any vigor happens or if at anytime you feel overactivated, tighten the finger grip; that will control it. Move just fifteen degrees to each side. Meditate and move; meditate and move. Move and let the clutter go. This is a very, very, very deep meditative relaxation in which you can empty your mind without even knowing it. The energy that we create by the sound of the gong will enter your ear and transmit to your inner brain at two and a half cycles per impulse, which is sufficient to reinvigorate you as you empty yourself.

6. Bring the hands into the lap. Sit with a straight spine and meditate, through closed eyes, at the tip of the nose. Gong and music continue for **2 minutes**.

Float now. Mentally float far away. Give yourself the distance, give yourself the space; go away.

TO END: The gong stops, but the music continues. Tighten every muscle, every millimeter, of the body. Circulate, by your own will, the energy throughout the body. From the toe under the nails to the eyebrow and the hair on the scalp—it all will feel steady if you circulate the energy by your own will. Go muscle by muscle, portion by portion, strength by strength, nerve by nerve. Continue for **1 minute**.

7. Drop the head back, open your mouth wide, and look to the sky without opening your eyes. Stay in this position for **30 seconds**.

8. Bring the head upright and begin Segmented Breath through the nose: eight-stroke inhale and one long exhale. Continue for **30 seconds**.

With the eight-stroke breath, we are trying to produce the gray matter of the brain.

TO END: Inhale deep and pull the Navel Point in strongly; suspend the breath for **15 seconds**. Exhale. Inhale deep again, pull the Navel Point, and suspend the breath for **15 seconds.** Exhale. Inhale deep again, pull the Navel Point tight, and suspend the breath for **30 seconds**. Exhale.

9. Keeping the mudra in the hands, raise the hands over the head and shake the entire body through the movement of the hands for **30 seconds**.

10. Release the mudra and spread the fingers wide. The arms are at 60 degrees, with the palms facing forward. Begin shaking the arms powerfully, maintaining tension in the arms. Shake for **15 seconds**.

Your whole body will shake, but only use the power of the hands to shake. Use the hands and let the whole body have an earthquake. Now you will never get nervous when an earthquake hits, right? This is one way to practice that. If we don't get nervous when we confront things, then we can have the answer in nine seconds. But if we get nervous, we will get numb, and that's it.

11. Stretch the entire body and move the shoulders for **1 minute**. Then relax for **2½ minutes**.

12. Make rings out of the ring fingers and link them together. The right and left hands are in Surya Mudra, with the thumb and Sun (ring) finger touching. Interlock the mudras in front of the throat. The upper and lower arms are parallel to the ground. Inhale deeply and suspend the breath; pull the locked mudras apart, without breaking the lock, for **15–30 seconds**. Exhale and relax.

◆

"You can develop your inner self so your mind can see everything, so your brain becomes developed enough to give you all that you need. Or you can go outside, check it all out, figure it out, and do something. Just remember one thing: there is no God if you don't have it, and there is God all the way if you have it. This is because beyond you nothing exists—nothing. There is neither lie nor truth, nor is there richness or poverty, nor is their grace or great, nor is there scoundrel or stupid—it is all in you."

− Yogi Bhajan

CLEANING THE MIND I
February 28, 1989

There are three ways to live: one is that you want to be noticed, two is that people notice you, and three is that whether you are there or not you are noticeable, memorable.

THE CLASS WE ARE TEACHING TODAY IS ABOUT THE TOP PART OF THE BRAIN, which develops at a proportionate ratio of seven years. At UCLA, I have been with all the MDs, but they do not know how that part develops. They have never thought of it. But we have started looking at the part of the brain that they say develops at a rate of seven years. And some of its parts develop, while some of its parts don't. So how you think, how you feel, what your capacity is, what your goal is, what your approach is, who you want to be—that is all a very creative effect. One minute you want to be a king, the next minute you want to be a beggar. Today you want to be stupid, tomorrow you want to be a lunatic. You can also be very wise, calm, cool, quiet. But there is a one problem with that nonsense: Your tolerance is proportionate to the development of the cerebral faculty's interlinked angle of development. The cerebral interlocked development is responsible for the aptitude, the attitude, and the constitutional right to be you.

Now, you are an American or you are Indian or you are Japanese or you are French—it doesn't make any difference. What matters is how much you can develop yourself. I will give you an example: Take a Western kid, give him the sums, and he will look at you, his hand will go into his pocket, and he will think, "Hmm, hmm." Then you tell a Chinese kid the sums, and he goes "tutututu" on that wooden thing, and he will come out with the answer faster than you. Now go to a southern Indian—not a northern Indian—give him the sums, and he will give you the total before you finish. And not only that, in the south of India, you will find children who can look at the moon and tell you how many miles away it is. When you go check the books, you will see that they were right.

The brain is a very fascinating gift of God to man. Even the greatest men have used only three point three percent of their brains, period. Today the science is believed, but I have been telling you all along that men do not have the right side of the brain, while women have the right and the left.

So, we have three *gunas*: *rajas, tamas,* and *sattvic. Sattvic* is angelic; *rajas* is imperial, royal, conquering; and *tamas* is angry, animal, beastly. *Tamas* wants to disturb everything, to interrupt everything, to be noticed. There are three ways to live: one is that you want to be noticed, two is that people notice you, and three is that whether you are there or not you are noticeable, memorable. Saintly people, those who we call people of God, do not exist today—they don't. But they do exist in our memory,

We are all born in light, we are part of the light, we live because of light, so why darkness? Because our fuse blows out.

in our thought. They exist through their teaching, their touch, their story. They are guideposts that tell us where to go. Are we bound to follow? No. Should we follow? No. Do you want to adapt to anybody? No. Then why we are doing it?

There are two ways to go about it: You can develop your inner self so your mind can see everything, so your brain becomes developed enough to give you all that you need. Or you can go outside, check it all out, figure it out, and do something. You can get high inside; you can get high from outside. Just remember one thing—whether you believe me or not—there is no God if you don't have it, and there is God all the way if you have it. This is because beyond you nothing exists—nothing. There is neither lie nor truth, nor is there richness or poverty, nor is their grace or great, nor is there scoundrel or stupid—it is all in you.

I don't want to say that some people cannot change, that some people do not want to change, that some people change very fast, and all that, but I do believe in one thing: Nobody wants to be stupid, bad, an idiot, a thief, or negative—no one. Now, you will ask me, what is your theory? What is it based on? You say we see negative people every day, obnoxious people every day, people doing bad things every day. And I agree—I read the newspaper. But I simply believe our fuse blows out. We are all born in light, we are part of the light, we live because of light, so why darkness? Because our fuse goes out. In India, if your electric fuse goes out, you won't get it back until three days later, because somebody has to come, take the whole box, unscrew the whole thing, take that thing out, and put the wire in to fix it up. Here you have a very modern country; you do tic, tic to the fuse, and then the electricity comes again—very modern. But the fact is that at a certain point, we cannot go beyond our involvement and development, our capacity to maintain patience and to sustain ourselves. It is within our right, and we may have the strength; but maybe we do not have the strength.

If I ask you whether you have the strength, you will say, "Yeah, we have the strength." It's true. I have not met one person who thinks he doesn't have the strength. Sure, you all have the strength; that's why you mostly do things in that non-strong, insane mental attitude of phobia or hysteria. In psychology, we call it insensitive attitude toward the attitude—insensitive attitude toward other people's feelings, to other people's beliefs, other people's wants and needs. It is responsible for all divorces, for leaving children, for messing up things—you name it. We develop in our lifestyle insensitively, or sensitively, or insensitive sensitivity, or a sensitive attitude toward ourselves.

Twenty years ago I landed in this land called the United States. And that was the first time I heard a human being say, "I don't know." I have not yet gotten over the shock of hearing that, even today; I confess. When somebody says, "I do not know," it triggers something in me. That's how I feel.

It's such an easy thing for you: "I don't know. It just happened. I don't know." And you see their body language—it's like an insane person; it is automatic. Today I was

showing two people something. I didn't do anything; I just went in my office, and I picked up a certain thing so I could give some instruction. One was supposed to guide somebody, and the other was supposed to be guided. I switched on the light and put them before a mirror. I said, "Look at your face." One was absolutely white, had no life; the other was all red and blah, blah. One had his eyebrow about two to three millimeters this way. And I said, "Can you see me tomorrow in the class like this?" People's lips go this way, and then their nose starts tilting. Just think of all the structural pressure on the brain and its computerized system.

Keeping our ten trillion cells together in seventy-two hours is the work of our brain. Our brain is the binding force, and it does many things—repairs, maintenance, putting things together, keeping the *tattvas*, changing the electrons, changing the neutrons—all in seventy-two hours; your body changes within seventy-two hours. In that time, awful things can happen, awful things can disappear from your life. But there is a one problem... Sometimes it's natural. The situations that we have to face in life can be anything: making love, making a divorce, kicking somebody, hitting somebody, anything. But we have a total of nine seconds to decide; that's the time limit. Within nine seconds, you have to decide, act, and be.

Do you believe this? No. Can you do it? No. Face it: you have neither the assessment nor the acknowledgment nor the depth nor the belief nor the faith nor the understanding to do it. Those are six things that you don't have. Now, are you a human? The answer is no, because a human has only nine seconds to his life. Within nine seconds, you should be in a position to decide, act, and be. But you have so much loaded unconscious stuff, like a junk box, and you don't know where anything is. Have you seen that ad where this lady's child is crying, the milk is boiling, the telephone is ringing—have you seen that? And that is just an ad; every woman in America goes through that. There is one English word for it—hectic. We blame depression; it is the cause of everything; we are even born in depression. Nineteen twenty-nine has never gone from us. But you are lucky that you are not like Europe, because Europe is too crowded, with too little land. You have three thousand miles of vast land with lots of natural resources, and you are only two hundred fifty million people. The tragedy of it all is that even with all this beauty, you do not come from one culture; you have a multi-culture. So you do not know what is what. But the curiosity is keeping you going. In Switzerland, they pay twenty dollars to go into a club, and they put paint on each other, and then they take three days to clean the paint off, just to keep themselves busy. It is called color therapy.

Most of you do not know how to sleep if you want to sleep. You do not know how to kill your time—forget about using the time intelligently by being creative! So, we are going to offload your brain tonight. What is in B-grade material? It is between an effective attitude of hallucination, of a reality proposed in a dream stage, of nonreality during the day.

In this kriya, if you go through any problems, just go through it. This is not a tennis match, but it is not less than that. Do you understand what I am saying? You have no racket or ball, but you have to play your own game. If you do this wrong, you will not press the meridians correctly, and the response of the neurons will not be right, and this gray matter will not be straight. If you do not have the proper impulse, you will unload much less. So you will have wasted ten dollars. Even if you came here in good faith and understood it, you will end up with nothing. And nothing more will be said.

My idea to charge for this kind of course is just ten bucks to keep my staff happy. I am not even supposed to teach; my doctor said so right in front of me. But my idea is that I can see the pain and I know the cause of it, I know the source of it, and I want to get rid of it the easy way. But that doesn't mean that I do not enjoy teaching the class. I do enjoy teaching the class when I feel your aura and the results are good; that makes me happy. It's not about how many of you have come; that doesn't matter to me.

Now look at your hand; it has the five *tattvas*. The thumb is your Id, your ego; next is your funny Jupiter, then your funny Saturn, then your funny Sun, then your funny Mercury. Then there is Mars and that love thing Venus; then the Moon and the entire universe. So what is above is also below, in your hand; God made you that way. It's not astrology; I am talking about facts. You can believe in it or not, that doesn't matter. If your mind on one side becomes a little rough and coarse, then you cannot think sharply. It's all in your hand. See this? This unloaded left hand, this is my ego, this is my Id.

We are going to do a physical exercise to stimulate the central connecting chord between the left and right. You can go read about it after you do it. Later you can study, but here you just do.

After you finish class and we say good night, go home and drink as much water as you can afford to drink. You will go to the bathroom two, three times; that's healthy. If you go three, four times, that is a super healthy. And tomorrow's class is going to be a little harder, because we have to go into the cross-memory area of the brain. We will ask the neurons to form a rainbow of color around the grip of your cerebral something, whatever it is? Anyway, we are going to enter that to release a lot of fear and phobia through the front side, which is where you have stored a big bundle of garbage. And for that we expect you to be on a liquid diet as much you can. So drink from now onward until tomorrow. Drink juices, drink this and that; maybe have a little bit of lunch, but try to just live for one day on a liquid diet. You will not die from this; it's very healthy.

May the long time sun shine upon you,
all love surround you, and the pure light within you, guide your way on.

Sat Nam

CLEANING THE MIND I—THE KRIYA

February 23, 1989

There are no breaks between the exercises, unless indicated. Move immediately from one exercise to the next.

1. a) Sitting in Easy Pose, bring the elbows out to the sides, with the upper arms parallel to the ground. The hands are lifted above the shoulders. The forearm is angled forward at approximately 30 degrees. The wrists and hands are very limp. Shake the hands up and down from the wrists. Keep it loose. Shake for **4 minutes**.

We want to get rid of that lousiness. It will hurt after a while; it will put you through changes you can't believe. It will hurt, and you will be angry with me. Soon your natural anger will come out, because you can't afford to keep it in. That natural anger is the anger that actually kills your future. For just a little slip-up like that, somebody may never talk to you again. You say, "I lost my love." No, you didn't lose your love; you lost your cool. Keep working, even when it hurts. Just loosen your hand. Don't let it become tight, because that is cheating. Keep it loose. If it becomes tight, that means your brain is overtaking your own voluntary action.

b) Close the eyes and continue; concentrate at the tip of the nose. Allow the breath to be automatic. It will find its own rhythm and force. Continue for **4 minutes**.

If you do this right, with loose fast hands and elbows out, then all that interwoven tension, that basic anger from the womb of the mother and the anger from all the insecurity through life to date, will start leaving you. The pain will be tremendous. If you do it right, it will hurt to your guts and to your grit. But it is not really going to hurt us if it can take away hurt. Move fast; get that basic childhood anger out right now.

c) Continue shaking the hands and begin Breath of Fire through the nose. Continue for **1 minute**.

d) Continue the movement but make an O of the mouth. Continue Breath of Fire powerfully through the mouth, using the Navel Point. Continue for **3–5 minutes**.

e) Continue the movement and the breath, heavy and fast. Go faster and faster for **1 minute**.

2. Inhale deep. Interlace your fingers together tightly and stretch the arms above the head, with palms down. Stretch the elbows straight. Breathe normally and concentrate at the Third Eye as the gong is played for **7–11 minutes**.

The vibrations of the gong will carry you through; you have no resistance against it. When the gong plays, it is not a sound; it's a perpetual sound that repeats itself. Space out and start floating into space, keeping the hands high, tight, and totally together. Enter your memory zone; enter your memory zone. Start remembering things: good things, good things, good things, good things, good things.

3. Bring your hands in your lap and breathe long and deep and very slowly. Let yourself go as the gong continues for **5 minutes.**

Give the body the chance to heal, give the body the chance to heal. Go with the sound; go away, go away. Do not sit in your body; it's affecting your own healing process. Don't become your own enemy. Go, go, go! Don't age; become a sage. Think like a sage. Go into the infinity of space and leave the body to heal. Have mercy! Even if you hate yourself and you don't want to be healthy, try it!

4. Sing with the mantra *Wahe Guru Wahe Jio.* Recording by Singh Kaur was used in class, as the gong continues lightly for **2 minutes**.

This is just another word in praise of the Lord, nothing else.

5. Inhale deep and bring your hands up above the head. Shake the arms, the spine, and the hips for **1 minute**.

As you shake, let the energy go wherever it wants. It will do you good. Shake up. California knows how to have an earthquake; bring the earthquake in you. Practice it now; practice how not to tremble even when the whole Earth is moving. Come on. Move, move, heavy, heavy, heavy. Shake up the legs, the spine, the butts—everything must move.

6. Open your eyes. Sit and relax for **5 minutes**.

7. Stretch the arms out in front from the shoulder, with the palms facing each other, shoulder-width apart. Stretch the elbows straight. The fingers are together, and the thumbs are extended up. Move the thumbs in circles. The left thumb moves counterclockwise, and the right thumb moves clockwise. Move the thumbs quickly for **1 minute**.

8. Stretch the arms out in front of you, at shoulder level, making a V. Make fists of your hands and bring the fists powerfully toward the chest, but do not strike the chest or any part of the body. Do approximately one repetition per second. Move powerfully; create a shock.
Continue for **2½ minutes**.

9. Hold one hand in the other, palms together and arms extended in front of the body. Keep the arms stable and the hands high, between the heart and the face. Move from the lower back to create a little twist right and left.
Continue for **1½ minutes**.

10. Bring the hands to your sides and jump the hips off the floor for **1 minute**.

Pull the anus, the sex area, and the Navel Point up; squeeze it upward. The whole sexual creative energy and sharpness of a man lie in that one little muscle.

11. Hug yourself. Bring the palms to opposite shoulders, with the elbows stacked on top of each other and pointing forward. The right arm is over the left. Squeeze your shoulders; tighten everything—even your face. This exercise will automatically adjust your neck and skull. Continue for **1 minute**.

TO END: Inhale and squeeze the shoulders. Pull the Navel Point in and apply Mulbandh. Suspend the breath for **30 seconds**. Exhale. Repeat two more times.

Comments

After this kriya, go home and drink as much water as you can: 2–3 glasses every hour. Keep on drinking. You must urinate at least 2–3 times during the night to ensure the effectiveness of this kriya. If you continue this series, maintain a liquid diet and drink as much as you can— juices, broth, lemon water.

" Your problem is that you feel through emotions, through feelings, through sex, through vulgarity, through pornography, through all that you can do and feel. You have to keep alive inside. Those who know the inside know the entire outside, but those who know the outside do not know the inside. That's why there is an emptiness, a hollowness, a shallowness. "

– Yogi Bhajan

CLEANING THE MIND II

March 1, 1989

YOU MAY UNDERSTAND THAT I AM A SIKH and I am a religious leader and all that hanky-panky. But the fact is that I studied in a Catholic convent. Did you know that you don't have to be born Catholic to be a Catholic? You don't have to believe in Jesus Christ to be a Catholic? To be a Catholic, you just enter the convent and come out; that's it. You are Catholic forever. And I, who studied in a Sacred Heart convent, can never forget.

I did two things when I was a Catholic—I converted my Mother Superior, and she became Protestant. It's true! And I caught every mother, including my house mother, stealing bread in their big habits. I can tell you those Canterbury Tales, too.

Anyway, I was a boy in a girls' convent. That was one advantage of being a Sikh—with that long hair that can be braided, nobody knows if you are a little boy or a little girl. Really, though, my father was chief, so for me there was no law. Also, we lived in a British town, which meant that my father, my mother, myself, my grand-father, and our five servants were only allowed to walk on the side streets. Can you imagine living in a country where you cannot walk on the main street? If you didn't have a permit, you could be arrested and put behind bars for six months. That was the British time, and India was their colony, and there was a rule that Indians could not go on this main road. And our cars could not go more than a couple miles unless we had a permit. But out of all these permits, I could not understand why I had a permit that let me go to a Catholic convent. However, it was a good thing, because I learned how to confess, even if I just made something up. Those of you who are Catholic know that inside joke!

So I am going to confess something to you: I have worked twenty hard years to be a yogi. But when I started being a yogi, I didn't set out to become a religious man. I have to be very honest: I was the greatest religious rebel India ever produced. My attitude was what they call *positive intake*. I always asked, Who are these religious people? What are they saying? How much of it is true? Is what this book says real, or is it all a lie?

But while trying to find out whether anything is real or not real, whether any-thing is good or not good, I found out that I am a serious student. And I think I was very lucky that I got the teacher I got. I pray to Almighty God for the sake of any good deed of any human that you should never get such a teacher. My teacher was not only the hardest but also the most calculating. Do you know what calculating means? He would lay a trap from which there could be no escape, no matter what. I

If you obey somebody, you feel that you are a servant or a slave, that you have lost your will. If I obey somebody, I feel that I have the grit, the intelligence, the competence. I have accomplished something, It gives me strength and self-belief.

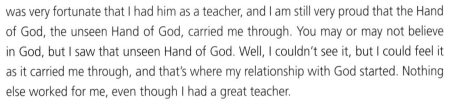

You have only one problem and that is that you are not inside you. The deliveryman brings a gift to a person, but that person is not in. You are all searching, but those who are searching are never home.

was very fortunate that I had him as a teacher, and I am still very proud that the Hand of God, the unseen Hand of God, carried me through. You may or may not believe in God, but I saw that unseen Hand of God. Well, I couldn't see it, but I could feel it as it carried me through, and that's where my relationship with God started. Nothing else worked for me, even though I had a great teacher.

One day my teacher and I were going shopping. As we passed a tree, he said, "Why don't you go up this tree and stand on that split? In how many seconds can you get up there?" I was dressed in my day clothes; I had not prepared anything special, but I went up that tree. I thought I might have to sit there just three or four minutes, something like that. But my teacher said, "Stay there until I come back and ask you to come down." I said, "Thank you." And then he came back three days later.

Within those three days, I learned everything. There was nothing else to learn. In my mind I knew my teacher had only one thing to achieve—a stronger teacher for tomorrow. Good teachers do not live for money or for statues or for books. They do not live for wealth or women or pleasure or government. A real teacher will not live for anything except to find out if there is somebody who can be ten times better than him to become tomorrow's teacher. I knew that in my heart. So I knew that he was testing me; he wasn't out to kill me. I also knew that at night, if I fell from that height where he had stuck me, I would be broken into ninety pieces. There would be nothing left of me. I was also Mr. Virgo—cleanliness is next to Godliness is next to me. I wondered how I would clean myself. But in that tree I learned how to sleep being alert. I also learned that the dew collects enough water that I could clean myself and drink through the day. I learned that if I chewed the tree's fresh green leaves, I wouldn't feel any hunger. Finally, when I came down from that tree, I realized I was victorious. I learned that I could really obey. I started believing in myself. Before, I had spent twenty-four years of my life never believing in myself because I did not obey.

For you Westerners, to obey is to be a slave; it's a dungeon. For we Orientals, obeying is believing. We belong to a different species. But just understand, my west is Tokyo, and my east is New York. How we look at things is all a state of mind. Anyway, if you obey somebody, then you feel that you are a servant or a slave, that you have lost your will. If I obey somebody, I feel that I have the grit, the intelligence, the competence. I have accomplished something, and it gives me strength and self-belief. That's the difference in our teachings. That's why you have all the wealth and are unhappy, while we have nothing and are extremely happy. That's why you don't understand me, and I stand under you. You will never know me.

I came to the United States twenty years ago. I had absolutely no friends, nothing. But look at what I have done. Everything starts from nothing. Those who always believe in nothing end up with everything, while those who believe in something end up with nothing. That law I cannot change.

There is a Hindu God called Krishna. Actually the word is *Kar-eh-shuniya. Kar* means "creation," *Eh* means "happen," and *shuniya* means "where zero happens, where everything comes to a standstill." You will ask this Hindu God, Ram. The word is *Raa-e-ma*, or "the one who created the moon and the sun." We live by the light of the sun; we don't have anything else. Muslims say *La ellah—La* means "God is," *Ellah* means "feel His presence." They have a simple thing: *La ellah Mohammed rasool Al-lah*—God is feeling God's presence, and Mohammed is the messenger of God. Take any religion, take any teachings dealing with anything, and you will find that there is only one thing you should become—and that is you—complete and competent, that's the process. Life will have no other process but that.

Your problem is that you feel through emotions, feelings, sex, vulgarity, pornography, through all that you can do and feel. You have to keep alive inside. Those who know the inside know the entire outside, but those who know the outside do not know the inside. That's why there is an emptiness, a hollowness, a shallowness. Life is empty, hollow, shallow because you are not inside you. You don't have a problem with God; you have no problem with happiness; you have no problem with wealth or prosperity. You have only one problem and that is that you are not inside you. The deliveryman brings a gift to a person, but that person is not in. You are all searching, but those who are searching are never home. Did you know that?

Religion is the most naked white lie in the world. The religious man lies to man. This stupid religious man and his insecurity tells every man to search for God. But God is everywhere, so that's like asking you to search for air. Now, who is searching for the air? The most insecure man became the man of the church, and he wants his basket to be filled. He says he collects money in the name of God, but he collects it out of your security, which has been challenged by the phobia within you that you don't know God. So on the bet of the church man, you go out on this search, leaving your home to dogs, to thieves, to everything else. If you sit in your home, then the five egos—*kaam, krodh, lobh, moh, ahankar*[1]—will not be touched; then you will be the master in the house and the lights will be on. Then it would very, very daring for a thief to enter and plunder your house. But your problem is that you want to find happiness outside. The happiness is inside, but you never go inside, so you never find happiness. That's why you marry, you divorce, you have children, you leave them, you have child support. I hear about this in this world of ours, and I can't even believe it.

I wonder sometimes: My wife never sees me, and I never see her, so why don't we divorce? Oh, we get mad at each other. We fight just like you. I yell and scream to tell my children that I am the father and the buck stops here. All that drama I do, and I do it very intentionally. I do it to let them know that I am a very alive human being, their father. Otherwise they would think I am yogi, and I am supreme, that I live in the bliss and forget all about the rest; that I am just a statue. But once in a while I shake

[1] These are the five "poisons": lust, greed, anger, pride and attachment.

my statue to let them know I am alive and well, just like they are. You do not know the tragedy in my family. When my family came and my children came from their school in India, they brought two kilograms, about four pounds, of common salt. They thought that in America their parents had become holy and that they didn't eat salt. So they brought their own salt. When I opened the bag and saw the salt, my wife said, "What? It's a mistake; they brought salt."

I said, "Don't be stupid. We have lost our children; they are gone."

She said, "No, they are not gone. What are you talking about?"

"Before I tell you what I am going to do, promise to just do it."

"What is it?"

"When they all come in, I am going to jump on you and start beating you, and you start beating me back. Start yelling as loud as you can."

So when they came in, I pulled her from the sofa and threw her on the carpet. I was over her, then she was over me, and she thought I was for real. But when I tell her something has to be done, she does it good.

Our children cried, "No, no, no, no, no, no, Papa, Papa, mama, mama, mama, papa, mama, papa, mama." So we stopped what we were doing and said, "It's fine, fine, fine, fine, thank you very much, how are you?" Then they saw that we are not that holy, that we can't fight, and there was no need to bring salt from India to America. We did a practical thing so that they could see we were exactly the same as we had been. It was in the army that I learned how to give and to receive a command, and that is very effective.

So, my confession is that even with all twenty-four years of my yoga practice and meditation and all that, I became sick. I couldn't teach you for two years, and I am still not healthy now. So you should have no problem believing that I am not perfect, and I don't believe there is a need to be perfect. I started teaching again out of compassion, because I could not take it anymore. A lot of people have mental problems, and my personal feeling is that I am a Ph.D. in the psychology of communication, and I counsel people as a religious man. I know that it will take years and years and years to help. So I started a cleaning service in the United States. So, what am I? I am the biggest garbage collector in the United States. That's how I started moving with young people.

You know, I am grateful to Nancy Reagan. She started saying, "just say no." Twenty years ago, I started saying no because I told people that outside stimulation will not make you high. No drug can give you any experience. All drugs can give you is a drag. If you want to drag yourself, then take drugs, mess up your nerves, stimulate them, overstimulate them—and they will not be yours.

Don't ever overextend yourself. You think you can do everything, but your body won't do this one thing for you—it won't stretch itself. I didn't stretch my most workable body for four years. And, my dear friends, I had no excuse for not stretching. I

thought my excuse was that I overworked, I overkilled myself. But that's all bogus. The fact is that I didn't stretch, and the result is that I got sick.

You must learn that your body may seem to be yours, but you are not the body. You are in your body. And within you is your real you. There is a trinity of your body, you, and that within you, your spirit. Your spirit inside is what gives you security, fulfillment, and contentment. Contentment comes to you when you are contained within your you. You know, you go on a date to mate, but you end up with a pit and that other word I cannot say because I am a holy man—but you can guess it. You marry, you love, you live. When you are married, you have a marriage problem. When you are single, you have a single woman problem. Single men have single men problems, gays have their gay problems, womanizers have their women problems. Holy man has his holy man problem; unholy man has his unholy problems. The ugly woman has her ugly woman problem; the beautiful woman has her beautiful woman problem—everybody is after her, she doesn't know where to hide. It's true. Actors have their actor problems, and extras have their extra problems. These problems do not go away.

The fact is, with every movement, every limb, there is a resistance. Do you know physics? Every movement causes resistance, and every movement breaks resistance. That's a law of physics; it cannot change. Every life will confront a challenge, and every challenge that you confront is called a problem. So no man can be without problems. Every living body needs to be stretched; it's called tuning. But nobody wants to stretch the body. For you, comfort is lying in a beautiful king-sized bed with a golden canopy, while being fanned and given everything, including a commode in the bed. And with that you would feel comfortable. But I call it sick. That image of comfort—of having to do nothing and everything is done—that kind of comfort is called being dead. When we do nothing, we are dead. We have to breathe, we have to drink water, we have to go to the bathroom, we have to do something.

You know that with a heart attack, you may not die, but if you slip in a bathroom, you may never live again. So no one can say where or when death is going to shake hands with you. By the way, in your life, death comes to you four times—it's called reminder death, and it will happen to you. The only exception is when a person dies in an accident and the other body is waiting for that person to be transformed; it's called quick switch action. Then you have to die through an accident. Otherwise, death will visit you four times; the fifth time you have to go. You are living in a universal motel, and in the end you must pay your bill and go; don't take your pillows with you! The day your credit runs out here, you will leave; nothing will go with you. The soul body will enter into the subtle body; all the rest will be left here. You don't have to believe this philosophy if your religion doesn't permit it. But think about it: Why are you in America and not in South Africa? Why aren't you a fish or a bird? Why are you a human? When you start searching for that answer, you will find that what I am saying is almost real.

Your spirit inside is what gives you security, fulfillment, and contentment. Contentment comes to you when you are contained within your you.

But my idea is not to convert you today to any belief. My idea is to make you happy; that's what I want. My belief is that religion, God, purpose, prayer, money, women, gold, power, politics are all for happiness. Nobody does anything unless it's for happiness; people have even done the wrong things for happiness. It's a matter of thinking. Nothing is good and nothing is bad but thinking makes it so. So think what you think.

We have started thinking that there is a source in our thing called the brain. In that brain, there is a thinking dialogue that causes insecurity, which is the mother of all our problems. You have to be in to be secure; that is why when a person starts becoming secure, his problems start. You have to get into the security to start problems. If you don't care, then there's no problem. The moment as a human being that you start feeling that you are not secure, then you are miles away from God. There is no other God/good business. This is all simple: When you feel insecure, you are miles away from God. But when you are in God, you do not feel insecure. When you are insecure, you are not in God. When you are insecure, you are in your ego. But when you are in God, you are totally infinite.

One day my life came to a desperate moment: I was commanding a unit and we were opposite an absolute volley of bullets coming down like rain. My second in command said, "We are running out of ammunition."

I said, "Yeah, we are officers, so we have to catch it."

He said, "No way! I think we should retreat."

"We don't know how to retreat. We have to win. It's a psychological war; bullets do not matter."

"Sir, we are running out of ammunition. I don't know how much ammunition they have, and they are not stopping."

"Radio headquarters to see what can be done."

"The radio is broken."

"Are there any other possibilities?"

"No. The only option is we retreat."

I looked at my watch, I looked at the time, I looked at myself. And I took my revolver and jumped over the wall to the other side, without firing. In seconds, there was no war, no more firing. After all the official things that had to be done got done, my second in charge said, "Was that right, what you did?"

I said, "No."

"You could have been hurt fatally?"

"No. From the way they were firing—that rapidness and the sound of that rapidness—I intuitively knew that they wanted to keep us away but they didn't want to kill us. They didn't want the wrath on us; they just wanted us to go away. We were falling into their trap, and I couldn't order you to follow, so I jumped."

Man has a problem. Without intuition, you do not know what the psyche is doing, and you cannot have intuition if you are being bombarded by your inner insecurity. Your inner insecurity is responsible for your pain, displeasure, unhappiness and poverty. Even if outside you can build castles, that doesn't mean a thing. So we are going to just scratch that inside, clear it up, make it shine, and you will have a better day.

◆ ◆ ◆

I didn't make these exercises. I am not the author of them. I have nothing to do with them. I simply learned them just as you are learning them. But I do know that they work. I also know that sometimes your arms hurt and your armpits get swollen, and you don't like it. You don't want to breathe, you don't want me to yell and scream and push you a little more. But it is not a matter of what we do, it is of what we get. Do we get relaxation, eternal happiness being ourselves? Or do we lose something? If we are gaining more than what we are putting in, then we are in profit, we are in a good business, right?

Come on. I am just trying to divert your attention so that you may look very earthly. I am not willing to talk about all these things, but I want you to not concentrate so that you can go wrong. It's my duty tonight to create a certain humor that diverts your attention. Please concentrate on what I told you to do in the beginning. Those sexy dreams and sexy nights of yours must have been a flip yesterday, is that true?

My Master used to tell me all the time, "Trust God, but don't trust me."

And I said, "Why can't I trust you?"

"I want you to be better than God, but you can't be, and that is what a Master's ego is."

Move the female and the male in the same rhythm at the same distance.

You will not have a mental attack in old age, you will never go insane, if you do this exercise perfectly. I am not kidding. It's very powerful.

May the long time sun shine upon you,
all love surround you, and the pure light within you, guide your way on.

Blessed God, bring bounty, beauty, and bliss to the heart of man. Bring peace and silence to the drums of wars. Let man learn to hear the beat of his heart rather than the beat of death. May Thy kindness make this beast, the monster, the traumatic man be a bountiful flower of peace, tranquility, joy, fulfillment, and happiness. May the warlords become people's servant to enjoy and to serve man's creation. In reality may they see the Almighty God. In the smallness is the allness of Thyself. May we all live to experience it. We pray that Thy power may guide us, may make us ourselves, may give us the destiny, the glory, the height and the light for which we may be proud of Thee.

Sat Nam

Kindness and compassion are not small things; they are the all of everything.

Before our next meeting, eat less. It won't kill you to miss a meal. If you really want to enjoy the class, just miss a meal and drink as much liquid as you can. Give yourself a chance to prepare yourself. You must remember that happiness in experience is the most costly item. Do not ever try to buy it cheap. Don't believe in promises; believe in experience. See within you and find yourself; that's the brightness of life.

There is no such thing as God. It starts with you, and it ends with you. All promises given to you, all knowledge given to you, all wealth, health, happiness given to you—if it cannot make you walk with compassion and kindness on this planet Earth, then it is the worst thing you can do to yourself. Kindness and compassion are not small things; they are the all of everything. Be kind to those who do not deserve it, be compassionate to those who cannot even think of it. Forgive those who have absolutely no capacity to be forgiven, and honor those who have lived all the time with insult. Stand up with a smile to those who are tyrants, and speak with affection and love to those who have abused all their life. This is the start to being a human; it is the alphabet to being a person. Those who cannot speak kindly and cannot act compassionately—it does not matter who they are—they have not yet learned to be a human, forget about being divine. It doesn't matter which country you belong to or how wise you are, how rich you are, how fulfilled you are. It doesn't matter how miserable and terrible you are, how painful your life is, or how low it is.

Remember, start walking kindly and living compassionately, and you will be surprised. The Almighty Creator God will start walking with you, hand in hand and a friend forever. There is no bigger prayer, there is no bigger act, there is no best thought. Just be kind to those who do not deserve, be compassionate to those who cannot think you can be. That's the first step toward God's friendship. Don't try to conquer the Infinity; it's not possible. Don't try to ignore it either; it's not possible. Befriend it, and you will be happy, fulfilled, tranquil, peaceful, blissful, bountiful, and beautiful. These are the simple experiences that you can enjoy.

Age is going, energy is going; you are given energy, nobody is going to give his life to you. Saints can do it, sages can do it but you by your own ego you give. Nobody will wet your hand, nobody will put water in your hand to drink, nobody will nurture you. It means nobody will accomplish you. Sometimes the saints do weird things; they give life, their life for somebody's life and those extended lives instead of becoming divine become the most weird egomaniacs because when life is not there and it is given, it is misused, it is mistrusted, and it is abused. They become a living abuse instead of a living use, and that's why we say nobody will wet your hand, nobody will nurture you.

CLEANING THE MIND II—THE KRIYA

March 1, 1989

There are no breaks between the exercises. Move immediately from one exercise to the next.

1. Extend the arms directly out to the sides, parallel to the ground. The elbows must be extended perfectly straight. The right palm faces down and the left palm faces up. Flutter the hands and arms from the elbows. Don't move it; just dance it very quickly, like hummingbirds. Approximately 8 movements for every 2 seconds. The breath will become very heavy. Continue for **11 minutes**.

Faster, quicker! This coordinates both horizons of your brain. It's a yin and yang, a male and a female; it's an intercourse, it gives you sexual satisfaction without ejaculation. This exercise, like sex, is nothing but a sixth sense. Move the arms in absolute sexual harmony. It's a sexual intercourse with your total personality. If you're not enjoying this, there's something sexually wrong with you!

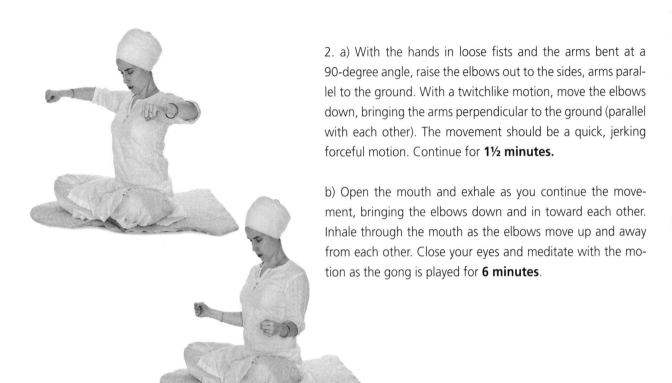

2. a) With the hands in loose fists and the arms bent at a 90-degree angle, raise the elbows out to the sides, arms parallel to the ground. With a twitchlike motion, move the elbows down, bringing the arms perpendicular to the ground (parallel with each other). The movement should be a quick, jerking forceful motion. Continue for **1½ minutes.**

b) Open the mouth and exhale as you continue the movement, bringing the elbows down and in toward each other. Inhale through the mouth as the elbows move up and away from each other. Close your eyes and meditate with the motion as the gong is played for **6 minutes**.

3. Inhale and interlace the hands behind the back. Suspend the breath for **30 seconds**. Stretch the spine like a steel rod. Exhale. Continue inhaling and exhaling, suspending the breath as long as possible each time. Concentrate on the spine. Meditate on the deep breath; deeply inhale, deeply suspend, and deeply exhale. *It's a Long Way to Go* and *The Night the Light Went Out* by Sat Peter. Continue for **10½ minutes**.

Just think that the breath is God that you are welcoming. Just pay homage, be a little respectful. Help your health, not me; help your mind, not me; help your soul, not me. Breath deeply of life, fall deeply in love.

4. Cross the hands over the heart. Breathe as slowly as possibly, as the music continues (*Time and Space by Sat Peter Singh*). After **3 minutes**, the gong is struck powerfully, once, and then played over the music for **5 minutes**.

Let it go. Come with me and let it go. Don't resist. Resistance will create friction; you don't need that. Feel that you have spread your wings. Fly straight into the bright sun.

5. Inhale and interlace the hands above the head. Stretch your spine. Try to lift yourself from the ground. Suspend the breath for **15 seconds**. Exhale. Repeat 3 more times.

TO END: Shake out the arms above the head for **30 seconds**.

◆

" As long as I live, I will pursue one thing, one satisfaction: Happiness is a human birthright. Everyone is born to be happy. We are unhappy because we get short-circuited. We are unhappy because our nervous systems cannot take it. We are unhappy because our intuition does not answer us within nine seconds. "

- Yogi Bhajan

CLEANING THE MIND FOR DEEP MEDITATION

March 3, 1989

Life is a harmony— inside and outside must meet in balance.

ET ME TELL YOU WHY I AM TEACHING THESE CLASSES. I had no idea of ever coming to the West, let alone to the United States. But I had to make a decision—either go to Tashkent in Russia to start an investigation of parapsychology and yogic theories, which they wanted to squeeze out of my head, or leave. I had a double mind, because I never wanted to come to the West. I do not like this civilization, I do not like the emotions. I do not like that everything is about money—and I even had money. I didn't want to come here to make bucks or to see white women or all that stuff. The West had nothing to offer me. It doesn't give any mental satisfaction; it doesn't give any extension. However, something used to bother me. You all used to go to India with full bags of money, traveler's checks, and God knows what. I used to meet you at the airport. Then you would go back home with empty pockets thinking you had reached spirituality. And I thought it was exploitation. So when I got a chance, I went to Canada to teach "Kundalini Yoga" through the university system. Unfortunately God played the trick: All my luggage was lost in Amsterdam. I ended up in Montreal, where they gave me twenty-five dollars to buy a toothbrush, et cetera. Then I came to Toronto, where it was minus forty-five degrees, and I was wearing a housecoat that was made of Indian raw silk! Can you believe it?

The man who was to receive me was dead, and it took somebody four hours to find me a place to stay that night. The university didn't know what to do with me; nobody knew what to do with me. Then somebody stole my shoes; my feet are very wide, and I did not know what to wear. So my life here started with absolutely minus zero. But I knew I had to do something. At that time, I didn't do anything, because I didn't know. I came with all the arrangements to become a professor in the university and teach something; I was to have a high profile job, but instead I started with nothing.

I never came to America to become an American. I came on a Friday with thirty-five bucks in my pocket and was only supposed to stay Saturday and Sunday. But I never went back. I entered the United States through Chicago and then walked around Los Angeles for three days. What I saw here I couldn't bear, and what I see today I absolutely cannot bear. You are all crazy; you think taking drugs, getting high from outside, stimulating yourself, stimulating your caliber, extending yourself are all enjoyment. That may be true in your case, but you must understand that life is a harmony—inside and outside must meet in balance.

No, there is no happiness outside. You can never get it. You have to go inside and pull it out.

I am a medical patient, and I am not supposed to teach. But I don't believe that. I have extended myself on that issue, and I don't do it for the money. There is just one satisfaction. As long as I live, I will pursue one thing: Happiness is a human birthright. Everybody is born to be happy. We are unhappy because we get short-circuited. We are unhappy because our nervous systems cannot take it. We are unhappy because our intuition does not answer us within nine seconds.

Our brain has no system to respond to. I don't blame you; I blame your education system. I remember when I was three years old, I was given certain exercises to determine whether I could figure them out within nine seconds or not. My governess was not a psychologist or a psychiatrist or a child specialist; nothing like that. In one exercise, I was told that if I throw a stone from this side at this angle and throw another stone from that side and that angle, from which side would I not get splashed. All I knew was the two stones and which way to throw; I was a three-year-old kid, and I knew it. I understand why they taught us that way—it was a training. But now we are not educated or trained to answer under pressure. We are not educated to have stainless-steel nerves. We give in to stress. The problem is very simple: You give in to yourself when there is stress; you cannot meet stress, because you are not you. Somebody has an edge over you, so you make up something, you cover up; and that's dead painful.

There is no pain in your life. I mean, how much can you eat? Four pieces of toast, two omelets, six cups of coffee, nineteen drinks, one steak and potato? Whether you eat junk or you eat the healthiest, whether you live in a palace or you live in a garbage dump—it doesn't make any difference, as long as you feel you are happy, you feel you are in control, you feel you are you. Richness does not make you secure; richness is when we stimulate richness all around us to feel secure. We put on makeup to feel secure; we do everything for the sake of security, which is so important in our lives. Our love is security: "That's my wife." "That's my husband." We even go to the extent of saying, "This is my God." Unfortunately there is just one God and everybody divides Him. No, there is no happiness outside; you can never get it. You have to go inside and pull it out.

Jo barmindey soi pindae
Whatever is in the Infinite universe that is in you.

Within you is the living God; outside you is the relative God. But you don't understand me. For twenty years, you have never understood. You just think I have come here for this and for that. But I have not come here for anything. I don't need you; you don't need me at all. We have no relationship. I have to tell you just one thing: If you cannot live happily, then there is no happiness on the planet as far as you are concerned. Everything outside is a relative happiness; inside you is the real happiness—it's

a simple science. Become a Jew, become a Christian, become a Sikh, become a Hindu, become nothing, become everything; it doesn't matter. It's all garbage, because an unhappy Christian and an unhappy Sikh are still two unhappy people, simple.

One freak said to another freak, "How are you?"

He said, "Exactly a carbon copy."

They were truthful. One unhappy woman is the source of one unhappy family. One happy man is the frustration of an unhappy family. One man's frustration and one unhappy, unfulfilled woman are the source of our basic trouble; there are no two opinions about it. The problem is that we go for relative happiness not for real happiness. When real is not there, then relative is here; we will fall apart no matter what we do, because relative is a mirage if there is no base. You say you want containment, you want control? Okay, I agree, but without contentment, you are wrong. There are three things—Father, Son, Holy Ghost—contentment, containment, and control. You should be in control, you should contain, and you should be contented.

You can go to church and pray for half an hour or one hour. Or go to the Gurdwara and pray for one hour, two hours, three hours, or more. Or go do meditation in the morning and extend it. Do whatever you want to do. But what are you doing it for? So that you can be good? Then you are dead wrong. You are good to begin with, but you do not accept the basic value that you are okay. Twenty years in America I have traveled around; I have seen the highest to the lowest. I have met the rich and the powerful and the poorest man in the street; the homeless and a man who lives in a palace. Not one person accepts that he is okay, period.

"Yogiji, what can I do?"

I say, "Do nothing." If you want to do something, just do nothing. Let God take care of it; let it flow. It is the power to flow that you are afraid of. You are not afraid of the word; you are not afraid of poverty and war and disease and sickness and death; you are not afraid of anybody. You are afraid because you cannot get along. You are afraid because you are not you. You are afraid because your commitment has no roots. You might be thinking, "He's just saying that." But, no, I have seen people under whose one signature thousands of people's lives hang, and they have the same stupid insecurity.

They used to ask me, "How come you are always calm?"

I said, "I am very disturbed. I am not calm."

"No, we never see you disturbed?"

I said, "I am not disturbed in that way; I am disturbed in another way."

"Which way are you disturbed?"

I said, "I am disturbed because you are stupid, and I have to deal with you."

That's very disturbing, isn't it? First of all, I have to carry my stupidity and control it. Then I have to carry your stupidity and control it. I have put two and two together,

Every seed has all the perfect knowledge it needs to become a tree. If you had a seed without that perfect knowledge to become a tree, you wouldn't be able to make it grow. Every human being has a perfect knowledge within himself, too.

and if I come through, then there will be a third person watching what they are doing. It's too much.

Do you know that in the West you do not know how to have sexual intercourse? None of you know. I saw on television that they have found a pelvic muscle—this G-point. When they talk like this, I say, "My God!" Thousands of years ago they wrote the *Kamasutra*, the science of sex. I have seen thousands of interpretations of it in English, but nothing is real. Even the translation has to be explained to the West, because you don't know what they are talking about.

Did you know that if a woman bites on the Moon Center of a man's left hand, he has a different sexual feeling than if she does it on the right? She has different sexual feelings, too. Does anybody know that? Using the upper teeth on the Moon Center of the right hand tastes different than doing it on the Moon Center of the left hand. Using the lower teeth, it tastes different; with the tip of the tongue, it tastes different; with the lower lip, it tastes different; and with the upper lip, it tastes different. If you don't believe me, go tonight and check it out.

And I am absolutely telling the truth: You do not know about this sex of which you are so proud. So what do you know? I mean, what is going on? Do you know that even many of you who masturbate do not know how to masturbate? At the base of the penis, there is a ring where there is a meridian point. If you pull that meridian point after you masturbate, you will be better off. Now, who can teach you all that? The first person who should have taught you that is your father. If not from him, then you should learn it somewhere. I was seven years old when I was told every sexual tidbit in the world, and I said, "What?"

The lady who was teaching said, "You listen, and you answer me correctly, whether you understand it or not."

I said, "Why are you teaching me this?"

"One day you may have to use it."

Women, do you know your twelve moons? It is in the the women's training manuals. I was shocked; I was taken aback. There were two hundred fifty of the most intelligent women from all over the world here in the United States. I started to tell them how the moon moves and how the sexual tendency moves, and they didn't know a thing about it. They said, "Moon, what moon?" But if the moon is on the left side of the Navel Point and you ask a woman for intercourse, you will have a divorce on your hands. She will never forgive you, and that's the truth. You will have not one satisfied night; you will have not one satisfied day. You cannot say, "I am! I am satisfied." The balance sheet does not match up with your "I am, I am." Being satisfied is something for every day. Every day at the close of twilight, what you call evening, and we call *sandhya*. The morning is called *prabhat*. In the morning, you must wake up from the night feeling "I am, I am." Every night you must feel "I am, I am." And each day is a new day. It's not that you have to pass a revolution or a resolution; you have to be absolute or not absolute; complete or incomplete. Life is a status of self-satisfaction, self-enjoyment, and self-inheritance. You all want to inherit one thing or the other because somebody gave it to you. But what you can inherit from God is you, knowledge about you.

Somebody today asked, "How can I get rid of the anger?"

I said, "Don't produce it. Why get rid of something? Just don't produce it."

"How can I do that?"

I said, "Just don't be angry."

"But it's not easy."

I said, "That's all it is. It's not easy, but it's not difficult either." You are the one who produces anger, and yet you don't know how to get rid of it?

◆ ◆ ◆

Tonight is my personal night with you. I asked for it, and I have to carry you through certain meditative projects. Listen, don't just trust me. I have done all those gimmicks of high powers, superpowers, and all that. I don't want to be known for that, because that's not the way life is. Real life is within your own reality; anything extra is a load that you have to carry with you. When you reach a certain state of consciousness, you will realize this. The body doesn't accept even a good injection. The body is self-contained; it repulses things from outside. That's why when you change somebody's heart and put in a new heart, you have to give certain medicines to tell the body to accept it. The body has its own automatic chambers of accepting or rejecting. The body has its own way of accepting.

When I was on my way here today, I got a call to meet somebody. I was told that I could get there in twenty-five minutes, half an hour. But today the traffic was so bad, we got stuck for two hours. I went there, and it was a mission. Then I came back, and it took another two hours, bumper to bumper. I didn't like it. Then I thought, "Oh, God, I have to teach a class. Let's heal ourselves." So I went to the kitchen and cooked spaghetti sauce, but we didn't have any spaghetti. So I just ate some toast and came back here to have fun. But I know what can carry me through for the next few hours, and you know it too:

Bij mantar sarb ko giaan
-Guru Arjan Dev, Siri Guru Granth Sahib, page 274 (Ashtapadi of Sukhmani Sahib)
In the very seed, all knowledge is given.

Every seed has all the perfect knowledge it needs to become a tree. If you had a seed without that perfect knowledge to become a tree, you wouldn't be able to make it grow. Every human being has a perfect knowledge within himself, too.

This universe and the other universes are not running with any petrol, gas, or oil. It is the power of the resounding sound —anaahad. The unlimited sound vibrates and creates light and creates life.

What is Kundalini Yoga? It's a simple thing. It unlocks and uncoils the locked knowledge within you. What knowledge? Is it something to learn? No, it is happiness; within you is the knowledge of happiness. Let us see if we can touch it. Maybe we will fail, maybe we will succeed. Who knows?

The gong is not a sound; the gong is the resound before the sound. You have no power against it. If you go in the mountain and say one word, the echo will go a thousand times more and thousands of miles. This universe and the other universes are not running with any petrol, gas, or oil. It is the power of the resounding sound—*anaahad*. The unlimited sound vibrates and creates light and creates life.

I remember walking in New Mexico and somebody asked, "How can we find God?"

I said, "Do you have a good eye?"

She said, "Yeah."

"Look at that mountain. What do you see?"

"A mountain."

"What is on it?"

"Trees."

"Who did the gardening there of those trees?"

The automatic answer came: "God."

I said, "So you see God."

But there is no acceptance. There is no acceptance that all around you, whatever you do, there God is. There is no acceptance. But on the other hand, we say, "God is Almighty, God is everywhere, God is this, God is that." But when we close the shutters down, we think God is outside and we are inside. That duality, that hiding, that lying to God is a continuous profession of both holy men and unholy men. Anyone who has nine holes is holy, and you all have nine holes.

Do you know what a lie is? A lie is not you lying to me or me lying to you. A lie is when you do not accept God around you, within you, and for you. You lie to the One who, by His virtue, you live. That's the lie, and it's a very painful lie that cannot be accepted.

One student asked me, "When will I be enlightened?"

I said, "You will be dead. You will not be enlightened."

"What are you saying?"

"You are enlightened. What more enlightenment do you want?"

"When will my Third Eye open?"

"It is open all the time; it sees everything."

"Then what is the problem?"

I said, "You just don't realize what your little voice is telling you."

Everybody sees what the truth is, and everybody knows what the truth is. But

everybody doesn't want to relate to it, because relating to truth is nothing but a commitment. It's a commitment, it's a commitment, and it's a commitment. Because once you relate to the truth and you know what you have to do, then you know you have to do it now. The moment you start living in the now, tomorrow will be perfect, and yesterday will be already gone—goodbye to it. Your life will start being fulfilled and happy. But it's very difficult to live in the now. You may look beautiful, but you have to deliver it. You may make up for anything, but you have to make up with your own God. How many times have you tried to make up with your own God? With your own faith? With your own self? Is that making up not essential?

For tonight, whether you cooperate with me or not doesn't matter. I will do my best, and you will do your best, too, right?

◆ ◆ ◆

This exercise takes away all the toxins from the blood through the lungs; it is the most cleansing vitamin you can ever get. It works. We are experimenting; we are experimenting to experience. Time and space, rhythm and harmony create music—the music of the breath.

My God, you join clubs, you pay so much money, you exercise, you sweat, you try to go to the top of the mountain; here we just have to do something simple. You don't need five hundred dollars for the equipment. You are coordinating your circulatory movement and your voluntarily, conscious breathing. Do it as though you are in a club and you have paid for it and you have to get the best out of it. Create all the Western stimulation you need but just complete this. Keep going even if you are tired.

The idea is that there is no substitute for victory—conquer! Now, what does Saturn test in you? Your impatience and your patience, that is what Saturn does; Jupiter tests your unapplied knowledge, that is your frustration. When a person cannot apply himself fully, when he cannot get satisfaction because of his lack of knowledge, frustration and anger come. You do not have the grit and the patience to tolerate the impossible, which is what you are going through now. Come on, we are just empting the garbage, that's all. What are you waiting for? We have to get rid of this wretched garbage in our mind. We have to physically get rid of it. It's not going to be done by somebody else; our neighbor isn't going to do it for us.

Now is the chance to feel the unfeelable, start flowing with it. If you resist it will create friction; but if you start flowing with it you will be happy. As much distance from your identity as you can give yourself, you will heal. Remember, the principle is just to give yourself a chance to heal. You don't have to do anything, just mentally give distance to yourself. Give it a distance, take yourself away from your own body, exercise the biggest command: Keep yourself aloof from what your mind does and what you do. Between you and your mind you are still an independent identity. Watch

What is Kundalini Yoga?
It's a simple thing.
It unlocks and uncoils the
locked knowledge within
you. What knowledge?
Is it something to learn?
No, it is happiness.
Within you is the
knowledge of happiness.

over yourself; look at yourself. You have to create a hawk's eye and watch yourself. Go away with this sound; it can penetrate you.

May the long time sun shine upon you,
all love surround you, and the pure light within you, guide your way on.

May the process of life penetrate through the reality of the realism within the self. May I find the Giver of the eye, may I become the eye, and through the Third Eye may I see that which can't be seen. May one through the living see that which does not live, may one being see time and space for the time being. May the essence of life project and prevail. May the power penetrate through every tissue and into timelessness of our self, into peace, tranquility, bounty, beauty, prosperity, and the purpose of life.

Sat Nam

CLEANING THE MIND FOR DEEP MEDITATION—THE KRIYA

March 3, 1989

There are no breaks between the exercises, unless indicated. Move immediately from one exercise to the next.

1. Interlock the Gyan Mudra of each hand (thumb and forefinger together) in front of the Heart Center and pull, with the elbows parallel to the ground. Move the hands in a circle away from the body. The pressure should remain the same as the hands move in a circle. Begin Breath of Fire and rotate the hands with each cycle of the Breath of Fire.

After **2 minutes**, close your eyes; look through the closed eyes at the tip of the nose. Continue the movement and breathe consciously for **6 minutes**. (**8 minutes total**)

Try to coordinate time and space, rhythm and harmony. Create music—the music of the breath. Get all that hidden frustration and anger that you have subdued right out. Get it out now and fight for yourself. The more you do it, the angrier you will become. But you will not be tired; you will be angry. It will make you dead angry, but that is all right. Let the anger out by doing this exercise. You are tying your ego to Jupiter; you are circulating it, and you are forcing yourself. The meridian difference will hit your hidden memory and release it. The subconscious will let it go, and you will have a lot of release. But right now you feel uncomfortable and angry. Keep going, keep breathing, keep moving, even if you are tired. There is no substitute for victory—conquer.

2. Interlock the middle (Saturn) finger and thumb in each hand in Shuni Mudra and pull. Continue the movement from Exercise 1 with Breath of Fire for **3½ minutes**.

What does Saturn test in you? Your impatience and patience—that is what Saturn does. Jupiter was your knowledge, your frustration, your unapplied. When a person cannot apply himself fully and experience satisfaction, when there is a lack of knowledge, frustration arises, and anger comes out. When you do not have the grit and patience to tolerate the impossible, that's what you are going to face now. We are just emptying the garbage, that's all. We have to get rid of this wretched garbage in our minds. We have to physically get rid of it, as it's not going to be done by somebody else. Move, move, think you are skiing; think you are anything; get to any positive thought and move.

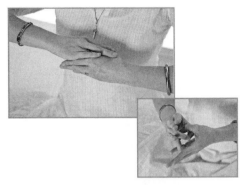

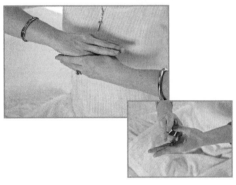

3. Interlock the ring (Sun) finger and thumb in each hand in Surya Mudra and pull. Continue the breath and the movement from Exercise 1 for **1 minute**.

4. Interlock the pinkie finger and thumb in each hand in Buddhi Mudra and pull. Continue the breath and the movement from Exercise 1 for **3½ minutes**.

Something you don't want to remember—unwanted memories—will come out now. We want to get out the matters of the heart, the scars of the heart. Love and hatred. Romance and sex. All that put together—that's what we are talking about. That's why it is difficult to move.

5. Put the hands behind the neck, release the elbows forward, and release the head down. Get lost. Keep the spine straight but allow the head to relax down. Concentrate in the center of your forehead as the gong is played for **7 minutes**.

Start flowing with it. If you resist, it will create friction. You have to start flowing with it. You will be happy. Give as much distance from your identity as you can; then you will heal. Remember the principle: You are just giving yourself a chance to heal. You don't have to do anything; just mentally give distance to yourself. Let the body–mind go through; don't resist it. Give it a distance. Take yourself away from the body; exercise command.

6. Cross the hands over the Heart Center. Breathe deeply. Become calm and quiet and breathe consciously. Feel the breath under your hands. Long, slow deep breaths. After **2 minutes**, begin listening to **Har Singh Nar Singh** by Nirinjan Kaur for **12 minutes**.
(**14 minutes total**)

You don't have to do anything. Your mind will go berserk, and you will go berserk. But whatever happens, it is not your problem; stay away. Keep yourself aloof from what your mind does and what you do. You and your mind are two independent identities. Watch over yourself; look at yourself. You have to create a hawk's eye and watch yourself. Look at your living self. Give distance. The body is going to attract you, but keep yourself away from it. Don't give in to it. Be above your own body; you are the tenant in the body, you are not the body.

7. Inhale and relax. Take a break. Stretch and move. Stand up, move around, allow the circulation to move. Jump around. Try to touch the ceiling. Stretch in whatever way the body wants to. Follow your own rules. Continue the mantra throughout for **3½ minutes**.

8. a) Sit on the heels for 2 minutes. Stay seated on the heels and put the right hand on the heart, as though taking a pledge (left of the Heart Center). Put the left hand on the Navel Point. The pressure should be the same in each hand. Come into balance. Open the mouth and extend the tongue slightly; begin a Breath of Fire through the mouth. This is Dog Breath. Continue for **2 minutes**.

This exercise is the start of Zen Buddhism. This is how the great Zen master who started Buddhism sat. Zen Buddhism means total self-control in the internal being. He described a situation: Somebody just cut his hand, and a minute later, Buddha said, "Give me the arm." He took it with his hand and fixed it there. He healed because he had control of the prana, which means the nucleus of the body. Now we call it an atom. When people saw that, they were surprised, they were dazzled, they couldn't believe it. The Zen Buddhists don't have to lie about it—the beauty of Buddhism is that everything they did in their experiment of life, they recorded. It is the most recorded religion in the world. In Buddhism, the beauty is that anybody who discovered anything recorded it exactly as it happened.

b) Begin a long, deep breath. Close the eyes and meditate: ***Ong Namo Guru Dev Namo*** by Nirinjan Kaur. Balance the pressure between the right and left hands. Remain seated on the heels or move into a kneeling position. It's acceptable to go back and forth between these two postures to avoid pain in the knees. After **7 minutes**, the gong begins with the music. Continue for **4½ minutes**. Inhale and hold the breath for **30 seconds**. Exhale.
(**12½ minutes total**)

9. Come into Easy Pose and relax. Shake your hands; shake every part of your body. Move. The gong and the music continue for **1½ minutes**.

"Life is a gift, and it must be happily enjoyed. It should neither be ruined because of imagination nor be absolutely spoiled because of fear. Just remember one thing: The one who gave you the gift of life also knows how to wrap it for you. Just enjoy it!"

– Yogi Bhajan

RELEASE YOUR GARBAGE

March 7, 1989

DISCUSSING A HOUSE, FURNITURE, LAYOUT, ROOMS, GUESTS, PARTIES, and everything is fine. But when a house is to be cleaned, it is to be cleaned. Isn't that true? But Westerners do not know where to start cleaning the house. The weaknesses are not in our neighbors; the weakness is not because the bank didn't give us a loan. The weakness is not that "My wife was not beautiful, and somebody else was more beautiful; so I picked her up and my wife divorced me." The weakness is not that "My wife has slept with somebody else because I am impotent and he is potent." None of that is the weakness; that's not life.

My weakness is that my mind doesn't reflect myself. When I have a hazy mind and a daze-y day, that is the day I have failed within myself. And that's the beginning of every life and the end of every life. There is nobody in the world who can tell you what to do or who has an answer for your problems. Your answer to your problems will come from the very self of your own Self.

We have in New York, Broadway. What do we do on Broadway? We have companies there. What do the companies do? They make dramas—very popular. If a show gets good reviews on Broadway, there is nothing like it. Everybody loves to go to Broadway. I used to go to New York and think, "What Broadway? Leave it." Then everybody said, "Let's go and see Broadway." So I did. And I appreciated that within the framework of a few actors and actresses and a little stage, they really tell the story. They really tell the story well, and it's worth fifty dollars. They do a lot; their life is nothing beyond that telling of the story. Tales are the balance of every life. Every life has a tale. Some have long, some have short; some have very hairy tails, and some have just a bone. But the tale is there.

Broadway is not actually very broad. It is a narrow street. If you park two limousines on the side, the police come and honk. And then some girl in mink starts yelling at you, and it's all messed up. But Broadway is Broadway. They do good dramas on Broadway, successful dramas, and it's a very reputable thing to do a drama. What other dramas are there? We make movies, and we have actors. They are our celebrities. If an actor goes into a bathroom, everybody flips out, and they won't let him use the bathroom. It goes with the territory, but that poor guy. He was a simple guy, and now he is a very popular actor. And everybody wants to look at him.

Now, why are actors—more than political people, more than anybody—very popular? Because we relate to their drama, isn't that true? People want actors' signatures, people want to associate with them. Drama is a very important thing. But

My weakness is that my mind doesn't reflect myself. When I have a hazy mind and a daze-y day, that is the day I have failed within myself. That's the beginning of every life and the end of every life. There is nobody in the world who can tell you what to do or who has an answer for your problems. Your answer to your problems will come from the very self of your own Self.

Happiness is my birthright, and that's what I believe. I pursue it, and I live it, and I want others to share it with me.

why? Because as a child, you learned everything from drama: the drama of the parents, the drama of the neighbors, the drama of the house, even the drama of the dog. And that is fine, because a child learns through drama. Therefore the drama in life becomes the child and that drama becomes the adult and that drama becomes the old man.

Dr. Freud said that drama is based on two basic theories—phobia and phenomenon. But he didn't go much deeper into it. For phobias, he said there are two powers that force you to live—love and hatred. The phobia and your pursuit of love—for that you are willing to mess up any part of your life. That's what his theory was. But he didn't understand that phobia can be cured, but phenomenon cannot be. That part he didn't touch.

When you get into a phenomenon of fear or you have a mother phenomenon or you have a father phenomenon, then you become the pursuer of the phenomenon, and your own life becomes zero. And that has been known to the yogis for five thousand years. They said, "Man is the product of a drama and his personality; happiness is proportionate to the control of the trauma." They also said, "Once the phenomenon of the personality coincidently correlates to man's own practical reality, then man is not himself." This they wrote five thousand years ago. So you are the product of phenomena, you are the product of drama. But along with drama, there comes something else called trauma. Trauma is a deep, uninsulated action that totally shakes your personality. When you go through it, you start showing physical symptoms. It's not something you like to go through.

So our life is a drama and a trauma. And when a trauma becomes psychotic, we call it a phenomenon, a personality phenomenon. It means "forget it," and that's how we read it. So in our life we are never our self—never. It's a constant chase; it's constant. Some people will love one woman or another woman, but they will always select the "A type" of woman. Each woman may be a little different, but her basic traits will be the "A type." This isn't about how she dresses or how she looks; it's just her type. A man who likes "A type" women will never pursue "B type" women. And if he unfortunately does, then he will not go through with it. He will walk away, and so will the woman.

You may say, "Our chemistry didn't match." But your chemistry will never match; it cannot. Man is never going to be a woman, and woman is never going to be a man. But there is half a woman in each of us and half a man in each of us. We all have an original basic woman and basic man in us. Just like every apple has Earth in it because it grew from Earth.

You know when I see you Western people talking I want to vomit. I have never seen human beings so insensitive to their own intelligence. And it's not only your insensitivity to intelligence; that I can tolerate because I come from a Third World

country. But you insult human intelligence. You spend five, six hundred dollars to dress up; you wear thousand-dollar dresses. You look so good, you are so powerful, but you are not worth zero because you insult your intelligence again and again and again. You don't have to find an enemy; you are your own enemies. Nobody can hurt you. There is so much freedom here—everybody is free, everybody can speak, everybody can pursue, everybody wants what they want. But you can't have your own happiness, and that is my reason for fighting. Twenty years ago, it was a single-man crusade. Yogi Bhajan started this. Nothing was available to me, but I had this pursuit. I believed that man has happiness as his birthright. Happiness is my birthright, and that's what I believe. I pursue it, and I live it, and I want others to share it with me.

I did my Ph.D. in psychology only with the idea of understanding what you are talking about. You cannot be happy, even in spite of everything you have. Now, if a man has had cancer and you say, "you are healthy," ask him if he is happy. He will dance, he will talk, he will visit, he will do everything. Maybe his cancer is dormant, maybe it is sustained, maybe it is contained, maybe it is reversed. But once a person is diagnosed with cancer, forget everything else. There is that feeling that he is not complete. You can't take away that feeling.

Once you know that you have a trauma but you have not yet faced it, you can't be complete. It doesn't matter who you are! And then you compensate for it. Some people make money and become very powerful. They order everybody around, because as a child they had been ordered around; so they reverse that. Other people make a lot of money and help everybody else, because nobody helped them. Some people do this; some people do that.

So now I am asking one question: When are you going to do everything you want to do? Is there one day when you refuse to react and just act as you? If there is one day in your life when you will refuse to react to anything, and just act as you, then that will be the day you are human. The rest of the time, you are animals, because animals have an impulsive action and an impulsive reaction. There is a woman in you, there is a man in you, and there is also an animal in you. You are an angel, a human, and a beast. You have all three in you. But which one has the priority and which one has the pride? If there is an action and a reaction, it is an animal, it's a beast. If there is a profit and a loss, it's a human. If there is grace and grace and grace, then you are an angel. But only you can decide; nobody else can decide it for you.

Listen, if you believe that if you could just have a couple million dollars then you would be happy, forget about it. If you think your family can make you happy, forget it. If you think all the environments of the world together can make you happy, forget it. None of that works. Everybody on this Earth has that belief—that what you think you want will make you happy. But when you get that thing, it doesn't make you happy. The reason is that happiness is never outside you; happiness is always inside you.

You learn in your life through drama, and you get solidified by trauma. The traumas in your life kick you around like a football. And the tragedy is that it is a continuous thermal reaction. A drama kicks you, so you kick back, and it kicks back, and back to back to back it continues. Life becomes nothing but going from one kick to another kick. That means the majority situation in your life is a yoyo. We play within our own self the stigma of our own life.

◆ ◆ ◆

Basically what we are talking about today is the deep cut in your life. Sometimes you cannot jump that gorge that is caused by a trauma; it has no bridge. Perhaps it was caused by an earthquake in your life when you were a child. You grew up, you learned everything; maybe you built a very strong bridge to cover the gorge. Fine, you can walk in and out on it, but what about the winds? What about the weather? Can you deny they are not there?

It is just like that man who has been diagnosed with cancer. First he wants to know if it's malignant or nonmalignant. If it's not malignant, fine; but if it's malignant, forget it, he can't sleep. Then they do the operation and they say they took it out; they do chemotherapy, and they say it's all gone. They give him a clean bill of health. But look at his face—on his face, is written, "cancer." You can't take it away. Even if you heal him and by every test tell him that he has no cancer, he still says, "Well, it happened once; maybe it will happen again. Now I have to take precautions." That is how it goes.

Whatever the trauma has done to you—whether your mother is responsible or your father is responsible, your neighbor is responsible or the circumstances are responsible, the government is responsible or war is responsible or peace is responsible—trauma has happened and it has to be dealt with.

We do not deal with it when we are children, because we do not know how. If our parents created a trauma, we might never have understood the aftereffect of it. But when we grow up, those traumas become the mountains and valleys of our lives. Then we adapt strength; we call it 'career' and we either override it or we go under. There was a funny situation.

I once asked somebody, "Why did you become a man of the law? Why did you become a police officer?"

He said, "You know, in our village, police used to come and drag everybody and kick everybody and do all those kinds of things. And I don't know, something told me I should become a police officer."

"But now you are police commissioner, and you have done wonderful things."

"That's true, but I am still trying to control the police. I still have nightmares that they are going to come to my village and drag me out and ask me the question."

"Look at your shoulder. You are wearing five stars; you are the commissioner of police; you are the head of the department."

"That is for the people outside; inside I am still afraid of policemen."

I asked, "How many policemen are under you?"

"Sixty thousand."

Sixty thousand policemen, and he was afraid of one. Multiply that by sixty, and now do you understand what a fear it was for him? That's how life has to be measured. That is how childhood traumas have to be measured. When you are rude once, it is not that you are rude once that matters; that only shows there is a rudeness in you. It is a problem if you are rude, and then you are rude, and then you are rude again. But it doesn't matter if you are rude if you do not let anybody know you are rude. But let's look at the facts of basic psychology—what you are and why you are the way you are and why you behave the way you behave. It is not that we do not know how to behave. I have not met one man or woman who wants to be unhappy; no one wants to be unhappy. You do not want to be unhappy. You may take on the profile of a happy personality but this will also make you unhappy. You do all the makeup to be happy and still you are the most unhappy idiots. Why? That's the question.

Why are you unhappy? You are intelligent, you are successful, you have all the degrees, you have everything, but at night, you put your head on the pillow and you cry. Why? The whole day you boasted, the whole day you gossiped, the whole day you pretended, the whole day you pushed, the whole day you manipulated, the whole day you lied, the whole day you did the whole thing. But at night, at home, you go to the bathroom, and you put your head in the sink and splash cold water on it so nobody can see your tears. Why? Why do you meet somebody, say to her that even after death you will be together in the heavens, but then three years later, you are in court divorcing her and she is divorcing you. I couldn't believe it, but one of my friends, a Hassidic couple, he was getting a divorce. I couldn't believe these people could divorce. He asked me, "How do you feel?"

I said, "It's the third day, and I still couldn't sleep. I can't even believe it."

"Why?"

"You are a person who has the capacity to stand out socially, has the capacity to outstandingly control everything; it's automatic, it is called gain in and gain out."

I don't believe that you go to a religious place just to be with God—that's total nonsense. You go to a synagogue to listen to a cantor. You go to a church to listen to a choir. You go to a Gurdwara to listen to a ragi. It may seem like nothing, but it's a highly potential projective music therapy—that's all it is. You are forced to sit in reverence because you are sitting before the Guru, or you are in the synagogue or in a temple. You have to close your eyes and pretend to be holy. You have to force yourself to be

Is there one day when you refuse to react and just act as you? If there is one day in your life when you will refuse to react to anything, and just act as you, then that will be the day you are human.

Be happy; don't be insane—that's actually the theory of my life. I don't believe that any of us should be unhappy.

silent. You cannot be a baboon or a monkey; you cannot beat yourself like a gorilla. So you have to just be and just look good. You may feel stupid inside and absolutely outrageously angry; you may want to tear your chest and eat your own ribs without putting on sauce. But in church, you sit down and pretend you are very holy, because the atmosphere of the place demands this etiquette, these manners. It is needed; it is wanted; and you have to come through it. And then they bombard you with music, just as we are going to do today, to clean you out, in spite of your resistance. That's what we want to do today. But unlike church, where you have faith, here you have come like it's a therapy session. Here you deal based on experience; here you don't deal based on faith—that's the difference.

What I am trying to explain to you is that when you have drama in your life and it has taken a deeper shape of a trauma, then you have a confrontation within yourself. And any person who is sitting here, listening to me, just remember that when you have a confrontation within yourself, your own energy can counsel your own self. You don't have to go and find somebody outside. I have counseled for the past twenty years, and I always say, "Why did you do that? Did you know about it?"

"Yes, sir, I knew about it. I know it was a bad thing."

"Oh, then why did you do it?"

"It happened."

"Why did it happen?"

"I don't know. That's why I have come to talk to you."

"Why didn't you talk to me earlier, before it happened?"

"I was not sure."

"Why are you talking to me after it has happened?"

"I am not sure."

"What do you want me to do?"

"I don't know. I am not sure."

Now what can you do with people like that? They are not sure, so there is no cure. They want what they want.

You know, in the Western world, commitment is just like a jail, like being behind bars, like being put in a dungeon. The Oriental and Western minds are two different minds in one way. In the Orient, if somebody tells you to do something obnoxiously impossible, you do it—you do it for honor, you do it for fulfillment. You do it to satisfy yourself. Even though this son of a so-and-so told me the dirtiest of the dirty thing, I did it, I could do it, it is my impulse to do it, it's in my power to do it, it is high, it is my strength to do it, it's my intelligence, it is my intuitiveness, whatever. But, here nobody has that kind of attitude. If it doesn't suit you, you don't want to sweat. "It's not for me; it's not my cup of tea." Over there, challenge is met with commitment.

Here challenge is met emotionally. If it hurts you emotionally, then you shall meet it with all force. That's the difference. That's why here in this country a doctor has the highest insurance and now the attorneys are starting to insure themselves too. Finally, parents will be insured against their children and children will be insured against the parents. Yes, you can ask anybody. You know, twenty years ago I started out by sitting in a place—a garage at Melrose that had been converted into an ashram—and people used to come. I would touch them and heal them; that's how my public relations happened. It's not that I was a great man. And one day somebody's dog got lost and she didn't come to yoga class. I inquired after her: "What happened to her?"

"Oh, she has not slept. She is wandering like a wild person."

And I said, "She is such a good yogi, why she is wandering? What is her problem? Ask her to call me."

Well, that was bad luck for me, but good luck for her. She called me and said, "Yogi, I lost my dog. I can't sleep, I can't rest"

Stupid as I was in those days, I just said, "All right, where is your house?"

"Such and place."

"Okay, go out of your house, go to the right side of the lane and go all the way down. There is a road after that colored house. Turn around, go all the way, and measure your step. You must go about a quarter-mile, then turn to another lane, and there will be a lot of trees there. Then turn around the right side, and there will be a little kind of pinkish house. Knock at the door. Your dog is chained there. They will give it to you because they don't know what to do with it."

I thought I did a great service. I thought, she is a good student, and I'm glad she found the dog. But then my telephone never stopped ringing because of every cat and dog lost in Los Angeles. I was known to all of Los Angeles within three days. Nobody cared that I was a yogi. The fact was that I found a dog, and word spread around—I was perfect, that's it. I didn't have to do public relations after that for any reason. When the bell rang, we knew somebody's dog was missing. I couldn't do it; it was just too much.

I used to just touch a person to adjust this main meridian point. There are main meridian points that cannot adjust *tattvas*, and *tattvas* can readjust the body. I am a heart patient myself now, and I have four arteries clogged up with whatever that stuff is. After forty years, I now get up in the morning and start healing myself through the therapy that I used to teach. Can you believe this? I used to teach them myself, and here I forgot about myself, and I got sick. But when I got sick and all that, I woke up and said, "Wait a minute. What are you people going to ask me?" They are going to ask why I am sick. Then I learned. I had been carried away by the basic deep trauma. When the religious head of my nation got slaughtered and people got injured and the

Where there is no trust, life is a bust; it's no good. You have to develop your personality. If the question of trust or disbelief arises, your Radiant Body should effectively let everybody know what the truth is. That's what we are working for.

innocent got killed and it all happened like a holocaust, I got carried away. The impact and the impulse of all that took me away from me in my own self. My body couldn't take it; it is a most sensitive body. I understood, and I understand even now, even though it is too late, that the repair has to be made. Then I asked myself a question: "I am a yogi and this can happen to me. What about these guys?"

Yesterday somebody asked, "Yogiji, I don't know why we get the common cold these days."

I said, "Forget it. 3HO has three things: 3HO is Breath of Fire, Sat Kriya, and Yogi Tea. Then the sickness never comes in the neighborhood. But now that you people are rich and sophisticated, you are sick."

You are all supposed to be healthy, happy, and holy. But in those days, if you tried to find a 3HO house, you could find it just by following the smell of Yogi Tea from blocks away. Now, no way—Yogi Tea is passé. But if every 3HO person does Sat Kriya and opens up all the chakras and balances all the tattvas, then there is no way that anything can happen to you, period. I know it myself. But who does this now? No one. Even if you introduce it in sadhana, they stop doing it. At Sat Kriya, they sleep; that is their Sat Kriya these days. Then what to do? In my sixty years of experience with spirituality, the mind, God, and health, I have found that the body won't stretch itself for you, if you don't stretch it. That's why I am going to these chiropractic conventions, because by muscle manipulation, rehabilitation can happen by the muscle itself. Muscle has its own identity, but we have to find the meridians and their mandalas, so that if the adjustment happens, the mandalas are rotated—not the meridian, not the muscle. Otherwise these Sikh chiropractic doctors will be just like everybody else: Hook, hook, hook but by the third day, the patient will be right back at the door, saying, "My neck is still hurting." Of course it hurts. The crack is in the foundation, but you are repairing the roof and you think it is going to be all right? No way.

There are certain other things in our life that are very effective. Forget about the stars—whether Jupiter is in retrograde or advanced. You make jokes about it because those powers are very subtle. You can't deal with it. I can also tell you that putting a crystal around your neck will not make you safe either. What I am saying is that you have to understand certain fundamental basics: The air is not pure, and the water is not healthy. That is where we have goofed, and compensating directly for that is impossible. Over and above that, we have our minds, and we are the by-products of our traumas. If you put all this together, you'll realize that sixty percent of the body is water, and the air is the Breath of Life through which we live.

The body has an automatic repulsive system. I am very shocked that people do not know how to breathe from the navel; they do not know how to breathe deeply. Do you understand that in the two lungs, the blood that comes from the heart goes deep because it is a heavy liquid. If you don't do deep breathing, then air doesn't touch that blood; oxygen doesn't touch it. You breathe, but you do not use it. It's like a dead bank account. Do you know what a dead bank account is? The money is there, you are there, but the checkbook is missing; something is wrong.

◆ ◆ ◆

The mind has a collection of dramas, and that's what we are going to work on today and tomorrow. I am not teaching these classes according to your convenience. I am teaching these classes because it satisfies me. I am not teaching this class for ten bucks, nor am I teaching this class because it makes you happy and you feel good about it. No, not at all, I have absolutely no feeling for that. I am teaching because it makes me happy, and I am satisfied. I am also teaching these classes and using you as guinea pigs to get this done so that our children will have it as a record. So come to this class and forget about everything else; stay with me. Because although I do this for my happiness, I will not be honestly satisfied if through my auric eye I see that the job is not done or only half done. I don't want to do half the job, you understand?

So bear in mind what we are trying to do: We want to get into your dreams. We want to shake away their ugliness, which you are carrying in your subconscious. Give me your pain. Be happy; don't be insane—that's actually the theory of my life. I don't believe that any of us should be unhappy. People are so scared of me when I talk to them; they say, "You make everything so simple." Yes, everything is simple; between two points there is only one straight line, period. Everything else is a hodgepodge. Life is simple. The moment you live a complicated life or make it complicated, you are causing pain, trouble, misery, unhappiness, and all that. Do not make your life complicated. Comply with the simple law: Simple I am, and life is life, simple. Talk direct, listen direct; don't misinterpret things, don't add your dreams and imagination to it, do not add your ego to it. Identity is a given gift; it is not your property, please understand that.

We are going deeper into our subconscious today. Are you ready? Do you understand that the basic fact is that you will release your garbage today? You have to volunteer to let the garbage go. Today is a technical class. We have to look into a lot of things. Let us see how this job is done.

We have to play the gong because the gong is not a sound, it is a resound. It is a an elementary sound.

Today you have to stay with me. I definitely demand one honorable, respectable resolution. It's a question of mind, it's a question of dealing with the mind, and it's a question of dealing with the garbage of the mind. We are not dealing with the positive side of the mind. If I am allowed, I will be carrying out your garbage.

We have to clean our lungs and open up; we have to change the circulation of the blood and give it the prana so that we can do the meditation; and meditation is not a joke. Meditation is nothing but a mind's best. We need the best mind right?

You are going to space out today, and you will have a funny class; but there is nothing to worry about except to cooperate. Now, you have nothing to do with me, and I have nothing do with you. We will carry you whether you like it or not, all right? Sit steady and feel you are in the heavens.

◆ ◆ ◆

May the long time sun shine upon you,
all love surround you, and the pure light within you, guide your way on.
This is our prayer; it's a prayer of the Sixties.

Sat Nam

According to my zodiac, I am very careful about what words I say. And I don't want to put my foot in my mouth, but it's not a matter of privilege; it's a matter of pride and of rational and logical thinking that all is not bad. All may look bad, but there is a lot of good in people. We just do not know them all. I feel that's what we have to learn—to take the pain and powder it and then digest it and let it go. I wish everybody—for God's sake and for your own sake—could have the strength to enjoy life. Life is a gift, and it must be happily enjoyed. It should neither be ruined because of imagination nor be absolutely spoiled because of fear. Just remember one thing: The one who gave you the gift of life also knows how to wrap it for you. Just enjoy it!

Come prepared tomorrow. We are working for a certain quality, because we want to prove that if we can clean the house, then the biggest reward will come—happiness, prosperity, beautiful life, wonderful days. We all have the right to change our adversity to prosperity; that's why we are working. Give away your pains, and God will give you fame. Be merciful, be kind. You won't have to grind your teeth at night, you won't have to have tears. God shall become your peer. Learn that He is seventy percent, whether you like it or not. Ten percent is the other party, twenty percent is you—that's thirty percent; seventy percent is unknown. That's why you need intuition. If your intuition is wrong, your intention can't help.

To become fulfilled and happy and prosperous are simple things. They don't require force, they don't require lies, they don't require anything. What is a lie? You—you just lied right now. Everybody lies. Some people say, "He is lying, she is lying." I say, "We all lie." Everybody knows that we are a by-product of God, but we don't want to agree with it. That's the biggest lie we all live. If it's all about I, I, I, then Thou doesn't come. If it's all about Thou, Thou, Thou, then I doesn't exist. It's the biggest lie.

Who is truthful? The truth is that if you happen to live and you are on this Earth, then you should be happy. Whether you go to heaven or hell, that we will decide later; that's something later on. But right now, the situation and the problem are that your sexual plunders and your life's blunders do not make any sense—simple as that. We have to do something about that, and we have to start somewhere. I am on a single-man crusade in this. I don't mind.

I do not believe in insanity, I do not believe in unhappiness, I don't believe in putting down people. I chisel you, I hammer you, I push you because I believe the goal is there, and you have to make it. Each one of you is able to handle your own routine in life. But if God Almighty can rotate the Earth for you to give you one night and one day, He can also take care of your routine. So what are you missing? You are missing trust. There is no truth if there is no trust. Even between friends, you prove, you give evidence, you give witnesses, you say definitely this is it, but then in the end they say, "I don't believe you."

So what's missing? Trust! Where there is no trust, life is a bust; it's no good. You have to develop your personality. If the question of trust or disbelief arises, your Radiant Body should effectively let everybody know what the truth is. That's what we are working for.

I am not the author of these courses. Therefore there are certain handicaps in which I can't predict time and I can't predict what will happen. All I know is that in the end we will be better off than we started.

RELEASE YOUR GARBAGE—THE KRIYA

March 7, 1989

There are no breaks between the exercises, unless indicated. Move immediately from one exercise to the next.

1. Bring the palms about 6 inches in front of the face with the hands at an angle. With Breath of Fire, powerfully move the hands toward the cheeks without striking the face. The movement of the hands is in rhythm with the Breath of Fire, at a pace of up to 3 movements of the hand per breath. **1½ minutes**.

We have to clean out our lungs and open up and change the circulation of the blood and give it the prana so we can meditate. Meditation is not a joke; meditation is nothing but a mind's best. We need the best mind, right? Don't touch your face, because the touch will create a bad, negative impulse. We want a positive impulse on your face. You are going to space out today; you will have a funny class, but there is nothing to worry about. Just co-operate. You need deep oxygen, and Breath of Fire can give you that. It hammers the lungs and puts the oxygen in.

2. Place the hands on the Navel Point and close the eyes. The gong is played intermittently throughout this exercise to help maintain alertness and to indicate musical changes. A classical Indian raag featuring the sitar is played. **11 minutes**.

Sit steady and feel you are in the heavens.

3. Place the hands on the Heart Center. Multiple selections of baroque chamber music are played. The gong is played intermittently throughout the meditation to indicate musical changes and to maintain alertness. **13 minutes**.

4. Maintain the posture and begin singing with *Ardas Bhaee*, *Instrumental Version*, also known as *Whistling Ardas*. The gong is played along with the music. **4½ minutes**.

TO END: Inhale and put pressure on the Heart Center; squeeze the entire body and suspend the breath for **15 seconds**, exhale. Inhale deep, to your fullest capacity, and squeeze the entire body from the toes to the tips of the hair. Suspend the breath for **15 seconds** and then exhale. Take two deep cleansing breaths and then inhale deep. Put all the pressure at the Heart Center and squeeze the entire body, suspend the breath for **15 seconds**, exhale, and relax.

Break for **3–5 minutes** and then practice the following exercises before traveling in order to ground yourself. Sweets were served in the original class. The next set of exercises is called Crystal Clear Kriya; it will help bring the *tattvas* into balance.

CRYSTAL CLEAR KRIYA

1. Lift the hands in front of the face. With the palms facing each other and the fingers straight and pointing forward, begin circling the thumbs around each other. Listen to *Har Singh Nar Singh* by Nirinjan Kaur. **3 minutes**.

It's very painful. I know, I do it every day. Don't move all your fingers; you are not playing a harmonium or piano. You will find your fingers getting uptight, but that's all right. You have to move the two thumbs until they don't hurt. They will stop hurting because everything has a limit.

2. Bring the tips of the fingers and thumbs together, like a teepee, with the fingers slightly apart. Balance the *tattvas* by expanding and contracting the fingers in a wavelike motion. Continue listening to *Har Singh Nar Singh*. **1 minute**.

3. Bring the hands palms up with the arms extended in front of the body, shoulder-width apart. Begin quickly criss-crossing the arms. Listen to *Walking Up the Mountain* sung by Guru Dass Singh and Krishna Kaur. **2 minutes**.

4. With the arms straight in front of the chest at shoulder level, palms down, extend the Jupiter (index) fingers, pointing forward, and begin outward circles with the Jupiter fingers. Continue listening to *Walking Up the Mountain*. **1 minute**.

5. Bring the hands up by the ears, 8–12 inches to either side, palms forward. Touch the Mercury (pinkie) finger to the thumb. Move your hands as though you're releasing something into the sky, releasing the pinkie finger and then reconnecting. The emphasis is on the release of the finger. **1 minute**.

6. Clasp the hands in front of the face and begin shaking them vigorously. **30 seconds**.

◆

"Our intuitive capacity to identify our personality in answer to the challenges of life is not developed. Every human being has a total of nine seconds to confront a challenge, find an answer, and apply it—it's called an applied answer. You cannot be given more, because there is no more. If you are not sharp enough to control and deliver a situation in nine seconds, then you have lost the leadership. "

– Yogi Bhajan

ARDH KECHARI KRIYA

March 8, 1989

*T*HESE CLASSES ALL HAVE ONE PURPOSE ONLY—to let you understand that your mind is the focal power behind your every frequency. The mind has not been investigated, because it is not a physical thing. But the body's electromagnetic field is now being measured, and a lot of healing is being done by changing the electromagnetic field and its impulses. A lot of countries in Europe are trying to totally go that route, and they have achieved wonderful results.

Your mind can be your very powerful enemy as well as your friend. What we are discussing is the simple truth that through drama, we learn life, and through trauma, we ruin it. It's a simple statement; it's not any complicated thing that you should doubt.

So, why is there trauma? When our drama fails, it is followed by trauma. Why does our drama fail? Because our intuitive capacity to identify our personality in answer to the challenges of life is not developed. Every human being has a total of nine seconds to confront a challenge, find an answer, and apply it—it's called an applied answer. For an applied answer, you have nine seconds. You cannot be given more, because there is no more. If you are not sharp enough to control and deliver a situation in nine seconds, then you have lost the leadership; there are no two opinions about it. So, there are three things to do: hold, control, and deliver.

Why do people fall in love? We don't know. Why do people get divorced? We don't know. Why do people betray and cheat each other? We do not know. Why are some things rotten and wrong? We do not know. Why are other things good and happy? Nobody knows. The only answer is that within nine seconds, what you can handle will work for you, and what you can't handle will work against you, period. If more things work against you, you will be miserable. If more things work for you, you will be happy. That is karma—action and reaction, achievement and loss, excellence and stupidity. They are all polarities. But there is also something more than that, and it is called dharma. In dharma, there is no doubt. It's a realm of intuition. In yoga, they call it the *turiya* state. In this state, you are you. You can achieve this state through three goals—be straight, be simple, and do it with a smile. These three laws will never fail you. Be straight—don't complicate anything, just be straight. Be simple, because if you are not simple, you can never be trusted. You can be loved, but love will be a bait to exploit you, so you will never be trusted. And if you are not simple and you cannot be trusted, it doesn't matter what you have, you are just mister, miss, mistress, Ms., whatever you call yourself. Because all you should want

Your mind can be your very powerful enemy as well as your friend. What we are discussing is the simple truth that through drama, we learn life, and through trauma, we ruin it.

is for people to trust you. You don't want people to love you. That is a dead wrong, rotten statement.

Love is the face you use to get the trust you want. You want people to say, "Yes, yes, one hundred percent true, correct." But people like me who are religious, we get confronted, and we end up on a cross. When you come to us, our professional obligation is to tell you a simple, straightforward truth. But you don't have the capacity to hear it. And if you do not have the capacity to hear the truth of a man of God, how can you have the capacity to hear the truth of God himself? If that little creature tells you something straight and simple and you don't want to believe that, how can you believe something that He who created the entire universe and the universe of the universe tells you?

You are not religious. You want to be a Christian or a Jew or a Muslim and all that, but you don't want to believe. And look at the tragedy of every religious head who has been tortured to death when he was alive but then was worshiped for the rest of his life. Name one leader who has not been tortured—Guru Nanak, Akbar put him in a jail. Look what happened to Moses. They nailed Jesus to a cross. They poisoned Buddha. Just try to name someone who is religious and who was not put through a trial. But the majority of you cannot tolerate the simple truth.

In your life, you say you want to be loved, and I believe you. But that's actually not what you want. You actually want to be trusted, and you want to trust. That is your diet; that is the diet of your soul. You want to trust, and you want to be trusted. But the tragedy of each person's life is that you can be betrayed only once; you cannot be betrayed twice. When you are betrayed once, the negative mind records it in the subconscious. Afterward all your mind will say is, "This person was a super shit on the fourth of July. He screwed me. I would be a son of bitch to trust him again." That's what the mind says, even if to his face you say, "I am very glad you came, and I am so glad you talked to me. It is really good to hear from you." So there is a conflict. You are the same person but with two minds—the negative mind says kick him out; the positive mind says put some butter on it when you are kicking. Then the neutral mind says he is not worth it. And, you know, whatever you are saying, you are trying to be trusted. But when you are trying to be trusted, you have already presumed that you are not trustworthy. When you are searching for something, you have already presumed that you have absolutely no confidence in finding it. You have lost something; otherwise, why should you search?

It's a continuous saga of a person. On one side is the negative mind, which is supremely abusive. I hear it sometimes, and I shut it off. It is only used to create a defensive aggression; it has no other purpose. The positive mind tells you what good can be. It is the neutral mind that tells you what to do. But we never reach the

neutral mind because we never cross the negative mind. One after the other there is a subconscious record of all our traumas in life; there is gorge after gorge of traumas. There is hardly a green valley left, and that is human. But is it the way it should be? No. Is it the only way we can deal with it? No. Can we not be better? Yes, and that is why the science of yoga was found. It wasn't that somebody wanted to do exercises to work out. That was not the reason. The purpose of yoga is to stimulate the body into an energy at which the intuitive faculty can catch up with the frequency and restore the infinite acknowledgment of trust. And what is God? It is an acknowledgment of the infinity, and a trust of the finite limitations; it is a rehearsal of recreating and reproducing that trust again, and again and again and again and again. There is no such thing as God—absolutely no such thing. We made it up.

So, what is God? G-O-D—generating power, organizing power, destroying power. Hindus call their Paramatma, Brahma, Vishnu, and Mahesh, or one who gives birth, one who sustains you, and one who kills you. Christianity started saying Holy Ghost and Son and Father. But big deal; you all say the same thing. Whether there are three million Gods or there are three Gods or whether there are one million Gods or there is one God, it is nothing to us. We want to deal with something so infinite that it can never lie to us and it can always be trusted. The idea is to trust and to be trusted.

Love is a perpetual trick to induce or seduce that state of trust. Basically you all lie to each other. It looks so stupid when you say, "Trust me." The other says, "Oh, I have trusted so many times, and I got burned. Henry told me to trust him, Smith told me to trust him, Jack told me to trust him, so and so told me to trust him. And they all burned me up. Why should I trust you?" The other guy says, "So don't." And you fall apart; that's all it takes.

The basic enjoyment in human life is to trust and to be trusted. There is no such thing as love, and there is no such thing as God; there is no such thing as religion, there is no such thing as prosperity, there is nothing. Everything else is a big zero. Money, parties, friends, socializing—all that we do is just us trying to get trust. Sex—trust; divorce—trust that didn't come through. It's all trust. Mistrust is where you miss the trust; we miss it all day, every day.

A mistake is where you miss the take. Something came and you should have taken over, but you didn't. You miss it, and you say, "It's my mistake." A blunder is when you couldn't come under and recover it. These words are a human body language that describes what you do. These days, if somebody tells you what to do, you say they are trying to brainwash you. But I wish everybody could be brainwashed and cleaned and clear. But nobody knows how to chop up the skull and go under it, to take a brush and put in some detergent and then put it in the laundry machine and the dryer so you come out smelling Downy fresh.

The purpose of yoga is to stimulate the body into an energy at which the intuitive faculty can catch up with the frequency and restore the infinite acknowledgment of trust.

The basic enjoyment in human life is to trust and to be trusted. There is no such thing as love, and there is no such thing as God; there is no such thing as religion, there is no such thing as prosperity, there is nothing. Everything else is a big zero.

What do you do to cover yourself? You put on a scent, you put on good clothes, you put on makeup. You become everything. You invite people, you give them a party. But all this is called baiting. You have learned how to do two things in your life—baiting and debating. Go to a good restaurant for lunch to eat a salad. You will be surprised that you have entered into a pond of ducks—quack, quack, quack, quack, quack. Everybody is talking, and everybody is eating—quack, quack, quack, quack. It is just a pond of quacks—quack, quack. What are they all talking about? We don't know. Maybe they are discussing the weather for tomorrow or yesterday or to-day. But all they are doing is moving their lips and creating a sound—useless. It means nothing. Maybe they are discussing the dressing, the cutlery, the salad plate. These stupid humans can waste time on cutlery and the color of a plate. These people, who have the brain that can conceive of the infinite self, have never developed it. Humans do not know how vast they are.

All of a sudden at three o'clock today, I just got up and said, "Find so-and-so. Something is wrong." We found so-and-so, and by five o'clock we had fixed it. There were a lot of wrinkles, the cloth was not washed. But we put it through the dry-cleaner, and we cleaned it perfectly. We took it to the biggest press to take out all the wrinkles. You think we have done it all? No. We will watch it. In three days, maybe five days, maybe seven days, we will do it again. These things have to be straight, simple, and smiling. Three things in life bring prosperity, happiness, and fulfillment. Don't play the trust-or-not-trust game, and don't play the love-or-no-love game, don't play the debate test. Don't do any of that. Just do three things: Be straight, be simple, and smile not for others but for yourself.

To get angry, to yell and scream and curse is also a smile. You ask, "How?" For some people anything less than that and they won't even turn around. Any sincere effort, any sincere noise, any sincere projection that can wake up another person to rise to the occasion is the smile of life. But you don't have the guts to do it. Telling somebody a simple truth is a smile of life. You go round and round and round and round, and after six hours, you finally tell him, "Well, I just came here to ask you if you can spare two hundred bucks." Why do you do that? Just tell him: "Hey, I need two hundred dollars, but it would be better if you gave me three hundred."

But instead, you say, "Well, I was just passing by, and oh, by the way, I don't have any money." That whole thing. It's because you don't want to say it; you are afraid of being rejected. You are afraid of being lied to. You are afraid of not being trusted.

One day, tape record your whole conversation throughout the day. Just take a tape recorder and put it around your neck and walk around recording everything. If anyone asks about it, just say, "It is the doctor; he's testing my heart." If you have to lie, lie for a good reason. Because if you say that it is a tape recorder to tape everything, nobody will talk to you. But you can speak a converted lie in a truthful manner. In the evening, play back the tape and just analyze it: How many times did you lie? How many times did you speak the truth? How many times did you cheat a friend? How many times did you not say things simply?

You don't have to learn anything, because you will learn it all right there. It is automatic with you to communicate and to project love, but the problem is you do it at any cost. Somebody was asking me, "What is the difference between what you do and what I do?" I said, "I do what I do. You do what you do. I do what I have to do; you do just to do, and you end up in doo-doo." We are all in the game of the doo-doo.

It's a concept to be simple; it is not a science, it is a concept. To be straight is not an art; it's a concept. To be smiling is not an exercise; it's a concept. And it all comes to those who have their personal integrity intact.

You can never speak truth, you can never help anybody with a purpose, you cannot be fulfilled and satisfied if you do not have personal integrity. If you have not decided to be questioned by yourself and to be answerable to yourself for all your acts, deeds, and thoughts, then you will never be happy. There are certain laws that can never change. I can't change them, and you can't change them. My job is only to remind you to be absolutely simple, to be strangely straight, and to say it with a smile. Then you will win the whole world. I am not lying to you. I didn't say I love you or anything.

When I came here, I never spoke, period. I never shook hands with any American. I used to keep you all at nine feet and fold my hands, because to me, you are the gods and goddesses of misery. I couldn't relate to it; I was too innocent. I couldn't believe a young girl of eighteen years old with sixty million dollars and a trust fund runs naked. I couldn't believe it. I couldn't believe that in the trails of New Mexico, there were the most beautiful kids lying dead, OD'd. I couldn't believe anything that I saw. I didn't come to America to be American or to be here at all. I came for just a Friday, Saturday, Sunday. Monday I was supposed to go back. But I never went back. In three days, after what I saw, it took away from me my legs even to think of going back.

The first center we established in America, twenty years ago, was a drugless drug rehabilitation center in Tucson. Twenty years ago I started saying that you cannot be high from outside drugs; you have to create that natural high within you. Now I am telling you that you have the birthright to be happy. Do you want to know how? Practice it: be simple, be straight, and be smiling. It doesn't matter what your religion is. It doesn't matter what you look like. Don't worry about all that. Our total intention is to pretend; but don't intend to pretend, just be. What I am trying to

make you understand is that you never know where the luck is going to smile. If you complicate things, you make the luck run away; just let it be. Life is based on a very simple fact: The flow of life will never stop, and you can take advantage of it or you can deny it.

❖ ❖ ❖

Today is a very special day. We are going into the cross memory, and it's a very sophisticated area. Cross memory is one of the eighty-one chambers of the mind. In it are the memories of past lives that you may or may not remember, plus memories that trigger those past life memories by the actions of this life. Those are called cross memories.

Today I would like you to understand and just do nothing: Be simple, be straight, and cooperate. Just do exactly what you are told so that things can happen the way they should. It is going to start hurting you because this exercise will also show you whether you have a future tendency of cancer. It relates to the inborn anger. Sometimes you won't understand why there is a sharp knife-like pain going through you; there's no reason, you are just releasing subconscious anger which you are unaware of and holding so deep and dear within you. All right, steady?

❖ ❖ ❖

When we continue this series, do me a favor and don't come with a full belly or with any food. It will be disturbing because that particular exercise works on the stomach and the digestive system. It's called *Agan Granthi*—the fire spot in the body. It also deals with the circulatory system and the pain that you got in the womb of the mother. It's called the fire chamber of the birth and it gives you the heat and the temperament. Those temperaments have to be cleaned; it's a heavy duty.

ARDH KECHARI KRIYA

March 8, 1989

There are no breaks between the exercises, unless indicated. Move immediately from one exercise to the next.

1. Sit with a straight spine and cross the arms over the chest; left hand on the right shoulder and right hand on the left shoulder, with the right arm over the left. Close the eyes. Strongly pucker the lips into a kiss and then sip the breath in through the mouth in a segmented breath. Inhale in this manner as deeply as you can and then exhale through the mouth in the same segmented way, with a kiss. Become musical. **27 minutes**.

A medley of music is played, from classical Indian raag to baroque chamber music to classical piano to American jazz and so on.

TO END: Inhale deep and exhale.

Try to become as meek as you can be. Not weak, meek. It is going to start hurting you, because it relates to inborn anger. Sometimes you may not understand why there is a sharp, knifelike pain going through you. There's no reason to understand; just release the subconscious anger that you are unaware of and that you are holding so deep and dear within you. Kiss with the music; mentally dance and breathe with a kiss. You will reach a point where you are going to release the trauma—get to it.

2. Holding the same posture, turn your tongue upward in the mouth and suck it inward. Meditate deeply. Be sure to drink the juices created—that is the nectar. Suck the tongue as powerfully as possible. Music medley continues. **1 minute**. Continue sucking the tongue powerfully as the gong is played along with *Ardas Bhaee*, Instrumental Version. **2 minutes**.

Whatever juice comes with it, please drink it. Those juices are the most precious thing you can ever create. Just as you took the milk from the mother's bosom, turn the tongue upward and suck on it. That juice is more precious than anything you can ever buy.

3. As the gong and music continue, begin to chant:

Ardaas Bhaee, Amar Daas Guroo
Amar Daas Guroo, Ardaas Bhaee
Raam Daas Guroo, Raam Daas Guroo,
Raam Daas Guroo, Sachee Sahee

The prayer has been offered Oh Guru Amar Das!
Oh Guru Amar Das, the prayer has been offered!
Ram Das the Guru, Ram Das the Guru,
Ram Das the Guru, it is sealed in Truth.

3½ minutes

TO END: Continue chanting as you raise the hands straight into the air. Keep them lifted and perfectly straight. Stretch up. **1 minute**. Shake the hands out. Shake the entire body. Create your own earthquake! Move everything. **30 seconds**. Inhale deeply, suspend the breath for **15 seconds**, and stretch. Exhale and relax.

4. Visit with your neighbor—don't stop talking. Everyone must talk. **2½ minutes**.

Just start a conversation: How is the weather? Try to be very earthy, earthly talk: How do you feel? How wonderful! How are you? Your nose looks good, your eyes are nice. Whatever it takes—talk, talk, talk. Don't stop.

5. Begin clapping the hands. Make music with your hands. Create a steady rhythm—not fast, not slow. Stay together. **30 seconds**.

6. Come back into the posture from Exercise 1 and pat the shoulders in rhythm with *Bolay So Nihal* recording. Clap the shoulders with a heavy sound. **1½ minutes**.

Bolay So Nihal recording plays throughout the remainder of the kriya, and all movements are in rhythm to the music.

7. Pat the lower back hard. It should sound like a drum. **1 minute**.

8. Pat the cheek bones with the base of the hand in an upward motion. **1 minute**.

9. Pat the back of the hands together in front of the body. **1½ minutes**.

10. Inhale deeply. Hold the fists in front of the body and shake the entire body. **15 seconds**. Exhale. Repeat 2 more times.

11. Sit and meditate. With closed eyes, look at the tip of the nose.

Guided Meditation

Forgive your sadness of the first five years. You have to remember, day by day. Try to remember. Think about when you were in the womb of the mother. Think about when you were born. Just keep on thinking: You were born and you grew; you were walking and you were training and you were living those first five years—quite a memory. Remember with love and affection and forgiveness, with kindness and compassion, because it is past. Forgiving is for the sake of giving a chance. If you forgive and do not give yourself a chance, it's not forgiving. Practice forgiveness. **2 minutes**.

TO END: Inhale deeply, exhale deeply. Repeat 1 more time.

◆

Comments

For the next 7 days, you must drink 32 ounces or more of citrus juice per day, including orange, grapefruit, lemon, or lime. Note: Protect the enamel of our teeth by drinking citrus through a straw.

This exercise will have seven days of continuous effect in your body. This exercise also has a food: It's called citrus juice. If you like to drink grapefruit juice or orange juice—California or Florida, it doesn't matter to me—or if you have lemon juice or you want to drink it with Perrier with a lemon twist, doesn't matter; even some of you who go and drink wine should put lemon in it.

You have to drink 32 ounces or more of citrus throughout the day. That will naturally make you eat less, and you will be very comfortable, extremely delightful. Your attitude will change, your strength will change, and your capacity to change and to see it will be fun. Something has been triggered in you; now you have to complete it. So don't forget it!

What you have started today, complete it. There's an art to eating: You can eat your meals regularly, and there is no restriction to what you eat; but you will naturally eat less. Thirty-two to forty ounces of citrus fruit should go in your holy body through your mouth and come out through the tract. You will have fun. If you stick to this diet each day, you will feel different. I am not claiming a miracle, but less than that I am not willing to accept.

In yoga, there is no more sacred and secret kriya than Kechari. And you have done Ardh Kechari—half Kechari. Now the problem is that your body shall need citrus, and the more you nurture it, the better you will feel.

" Transit memories are very heavy in life. In a transit memory, there is an imprint of a life on which this life is being fixed—it doesn't fit. Whether you are rich or you are poor, you are religious or you are nonreligious, you are beautiful or you are ugly—there is absolutely no dealing with any of these aspects of your life. It has no feeling to it. In cosmic law it is just called a misfit. "

– Yogi Bhajan

GETTING RID OF
TRANSIT MEMORIES 1
March 14, 1989

ONIGHT I HAVE TO CHANGE THE CLASS INTO TRANSIT MEMORIES. Transit memory is the most painful Western institute of insanity. What are transit memories? "I love you; you love me," that's a statement. "I like you, you like me," that is a statement. "I know you, you know me" is a statement. But in the subconscious of our minds, we think, "I am not sure," and that puts us into transit. Anything in your life for which you present a façade, an affirmation out front and a transit in your mind, that draws on your own nervous energy to the extent that you do not know whether you are a person or not a person. What happens is this: If you achieve something in your life, it's useless, and if you don't achieve something in your life, it's useless, because you have built up an attitude of not being sure. Do you know how many people in this world are not sure? They are religious, but they are not sure. They are thieves, but they are not sure. A prostitute is not sure. A saint is not sure. Then, what is all this life about? If all the education in the universities, and all the relationships in the world, all the knowledge of humankind, all the civilizations we have gone through have not yet taken away from us this insecurity and have not made us sure of ourselves, then what can life be? Nobody wants to diagnose it; nobody wants to deal with it.

Transit memories are very heavy in life. In a transit memory, there is an imprint of a life on which this life is being fixed. It's a foundation of an elephant on which a horse is being set—it doesn't fit. Whether you are rich or you are poor, you are religious or you are nonreligious, you are beautiful or you are ugly—any of these aspects of your life—there is absolutely no dealing with it. It has no feeling to it. In cosmic law it is just called a misfit. We are human, so therefore, we misfit. Animals don't misfit, because they are impulsive. We are impulsive and conscious, which means we are neither impulsive nor conscious. Instead, we create a state of twilight zone, and we cannot put our best into it.

My personal question for God is why couldn't He give us this ability when He made us in his own image? Because I know that as humans, if we put everything into something, we can get it. There is no stopping us; nothing can get in the way. That is definite. When the human mind and human consciousness get intelligence, God has no defense against it. That's a known fact, that's history; human history can prove it. But the problem is that man is so much in transit memories; he may be intellectually intelligent or intelligently intellectual, but he is never wise. Wisdom

What is all this life about? If all the education in the universities, all the relationships in the world, and all the knowledge of humankind, all the civilizations we have gone through have not yet taken away from us this insecurity and have not made us sure of ourselves, then what can life be?

Wisdom is a contained flexibility in which man always reaches toward his zenith of victory. To be great is nothing; to be wise is everything.

is not knowledge, wisdom is not beauty, wisdom is not consciousness—wisdom is just wisdom. It is a contained flexibility in which man always reaches toward his zenith of victory. To be great is nothing; to be wise is everything. You can have the whole world at the command of your finger, but you will never be happy if you are not wise. Wise is not undersized or oversized; it is the size that fits the foundation.

There are three things in this world: totality, reality, and personality. There is nothing else. You call it Father, Son, Holy Ghost; Hindus call it Brahma, Vishnu, Mahesh. Call it anything. I have no dispute with the religious people, because I know they all are lying anyway. Do you know why religions fall apart? One man gets into religion so he can achieve an experience, he gets to be holy, he says certain things, and everybody starts liking it. Then after ten years he is gone, twenty years he is gone, hundred years he is gone, and then all the intrigues and those things come in. Once you go to somebody's house, you eat good food, you enjoy it, you have had the taste of it, and you love it. Then ten days later, you go to the same house, but somebody just hodgepodges the food together and puts it before you. You cannot say, "I am sorry," nor can you eat it, nor can you say "It's terrible," nor can you leave.

When you find reality, you have to experience totality, and when you find totality, your personality must experience reality. Something for everything, and everything for something. These are natural laws. They are beyond you; they are beyond politics. Every child knows that when an earthquake hits, the city falls apart. Whether it is in Russia or in America or in Germany or in South Africa—it doesn't make any difference. The earthquake is a symbolic movement and a jolt of Earth's plates in which everything in three minutes goes away. For Californians, it is a joke; they have forgotten San Francisco. But how can we forget the San Francisco earthquake? Because it is a memory in transit.

You must understand that as a human being, you have the greatest tragedy in your life: you can suspend anything you want. Each human child has the power to suspend memory, and that is a human tragedy. You will never be an animal and you will never be an angel if you have to avoid your memories. The science of yoga did not arise to become another religion; it came as a science and an art of life. It is about how to uncoil your potential, to be above those normal human tendencies and not to suffer. Yoga knows that the body won't stretch itself; it will do everything else for you, but it won't stretch itself. So it will not give you the full capacity of its work. Either your nervous fuse will be off, your mental fuse will be off, or your spiritual fuse will be off. Somewhere in your dealings, you will fall apart for no reason; you have no explanation, you have no understanding. Why? There is no answer. You have a nervous system, you have a muscular system, and you have a pranic system—the energy, the strength, the courage, the self. But you do not value any of that. And without that, you cannot be. So, we cannot handle transit memories. Somewhere we know and we don't know, so what do we do? We suspend.

I once worked with an officer who was my planning chief. I would go to him and say, "Well, can we discuss this problem?"

He said, "Sure, sure, sure, sit down. Would you like to have cup of tea?"

"No."

"Would you like to have a biscuit?"

"No."

"Do you like sandwiches?"

I said, "What is this? What is all this? Is it a canteen? I have not come to eat with you!"

"Oh, no, no. I have to be hospitable, you know? You can't insult me. I just have to have my hospitality."

So I ordered British sandwiches and this and that, and it took about half an hour. Then I started sipping tea and eating those cucumber and bread sandwiches and that kind of stuff. They are to be eaten very artistically. It's a very polite, light, and sophisticated food. You Americans can't enjoy it; you have your Big Macs—you know, that big thing? You eat like animals. But a British sandwich is a very polite, delightful thing, and you cannot get full. You eat a little and then chew it—it is all an exercise for the teeth actually; it has nothing to do with the stomach. So I ate the British sandwiches because those have to be eaten, and then the double cream biscuits. And then I had a sip of Darjeeling tea. And he said, "How do you feel?" and this and that.

Finally I said, "No, this is a time for planning. Let us start."

"Later, later."

"You don't feel like it?"

"The tea has totally surpassed me. Later."

A week later, I show up again.

He said, "Do you want to go for a walk in the garden?"

"Yeah, I have not seen the garden. Let's go."

We go in the garden, we start talking, and I said, "It's a serious situation. We have to plan, a member is waiting, and there is a due date. Let's go in and figure it out and then tell the secretary."

"Not today. Later."

Six months later I said, "There has come a letter asking whether you want to be suspended or not. There is no later today."

"I am not going to see this letter. Later."

There are two forces in the life of a human: love and fear. Love makes you kind, and fear makes you unkind. Both forces have a result. We are the by-product of these two forces.

One day I caught hold of him, I said, "What are you doing? You are such a senior officer. They want a report."

He said, "I can't handle it."

"How can you escape it?"

"I have already escaped it. Didn't you send the report?"

"Yes, I did."

"Then my 'later' works."

It's true. I couldn't take that insult—letter after letter, reminder after reminder, and finally it came to telephones. I couldn't let the whole thing sink, so I made up a report and sent it, and they were satisfied. Anyway, that report was to go from me to him for him to simply sign it. But he wouldn't sign the report.

So one day we were having a British sandwich and tea and he was very happy. I said, "Why does it bother you? Why are you so upset? I bring the report, discuss it with you, you sign it, send it, and the matter ends."

He said, "I feel very insulted; you know everything, and I know nothing. So I won't sign a letter. You do whatever you want to do."

This example is your life—chapter by chapter, day by day, hour by hour, moment by moment, accident by accident, incident by incident. You avoid things, and you want to suspend things, because you know that as you are growing, you are dying. You are not prepared for dying because you do not know where you are going. You don't have any knowledge and address of your home. You are in a motel, and all you know is that the pillows and sheets are changed everyday. So, what do you want?

You want to suspend time. But you can't suspend time; therefore, you suspend the memory. And thus you create a twilight zone in your life. You are, but you are not. You know all the ethics, but you don't use them. You have all the morals, but you don't use them. You know all the manners, but you don't use them. You know all the tricks, but you don't apply them. You know all the games and the names and everything, but you say later, then again later, then again later. Nobody can force you to do things all the time, because you are not with the time. As a human, you are afraid of the time, because time is carrying you to death. That is what you have been made to understand, and you are afraid of death. Whatever you fear or whatever you are phobic about, you shall suspend it and create a twilight zone. You do it in love, you do it in life, you do it in business. What's that they say? "What you can do today, don't leave it to tomorrow." Have you heard that? No. Do you want to act on it? No. Because you are not ahead of time.

Fear doesn't do anything to you. There are two forces in the life of a human: love and fear. Love makes you kind, and fear makes you unkind. Both forces have a result. We are the by-product of these two forces. But when you fear something

consciously, subconsciously, spiritually, mentally, personally, or in faith, you suspend things. When you can't suspend things, then you attend things. Those things you attend, you shall win because you are human. That which you suspend, you will lose because you are human. You want to lose, you want to gain. So what happened? Your life is not totality; therefore it is not a reality. But you do have a personality, so you survive in that twilight zone, because you are guided by suspended personality, and you are suspended by your own projections.

You create in your life a thing called the twilight zone—a little bathroom, a little restroom where you lock yourself inside and you just let the water go and you sink and you sit and you think and you are sure. These things are called suspended memories. It's a little square in life where you frame yourself off, and you don't have to argue, reason, or say anything. All you do is say, "just a minute," and on the other side, the person knows you are in. They do not even want to know who you are. They do not want to know what you are doing. They know you are in because everybody does this, and nobody wants to be disturbed. Everybody has suspended memories. And we all relate to them by saying, "Leave it alone." But that "leave it alone" comes back like a monster, and then you wonder why you didn't attend to it right away.

Life goes through two forces: attend or suspend. Nothing will go away, nothing will run away. Your love of life will guide you, and your fear of life will goad you.

Somebody said to me, "I am deadly unhappy."

I said, "You are just afraid."

"Why not? Is it wrong to be afraid?"

"Nothing is wrong. If you want to be unhappy, be afraid; if you want to be happy, don't be afraid."

"Just like that?"

I said, "Yes, like that. That's how it works."

Be not afraid and life will become automatically happy. When you are not afraid, you act wisely; when you are afraid, you act stupidly. Your sensory sense—the sixth sense, your radiant body—doesn't act when it is clouded by fear. That's why where there is chaos and fear, we ask the policeman to come. He can come in a uniform or not, but we expect him to be in uniform so that the personality is identified.

Do you want to succeed in life? Then make a personality that can be knowingly and unknowingly identified. It's called good will, it's called reputation, it's called you. You are not what you are. You are what your unsuspended personality is when it is totally in flow.

*Do you want to succeed
in life? Then make
a personality that can
be knowingly and
unknowingly identified.
It's called good will,
it's called reputation,
it's called you.*

◆ ◆ ◆

Well, we have tried to create something today. Today is our Persian night, and we have to carry a "*Para*" energy. Persia is now called Iran, but forget about what it is now. At one time it was the Persian culture. All I am saying is that this is a morning, and dawn is on. Twenty years ago, I started telling you that God did not make anything better than you. He could have, and He should have. But you are the best. I don't like these religions, these guilt religions, these sin religions that tell you differently. What is a sin religion?

One day I saw somebody driving a car, and another man hit the back of his car. They both gave their insurance numbers, and they walked away. It happens. It's always like that—instead of applying the brake, he put his foot on the gas, and there was a "bang." This happens because you are dealing with your suspended energy, you are dealing with your suspended personality, you are dealing with your suspended memory, and you are not here. We all have that little square, that little frame, and it's our private project. Therefore we don't mind.

Today we are going to get into that little window and see what we can do. We will try to do it all today and tomorrow. They tell me that I should be disciplined because people have appointments and babysitters and God knows what. They tell me this, but I have suspended memory, so I don't hear it.

You must understand that I am not medically authorized to teach classes. I am not supposed to work. But I do it for the joy and for the future of the children who will follow this path. I do it so they can feel that these things are available, expandable, and usable. I am leaving it for them; not for you. You are just guinea pigs, but along the way, you get the advantage too.

Did you know that in psychology today they have not even touched this subject? Did you know that all disease comes from suspended shocks? Did you know that all relationships break up from suspended communication? Do you know what suspension does? Do you know that it's a root cause of every tragedy of human life?

Just as you played with your rhythmic center in *Agan Granthi,* now you are going to play your etheric center. Do you know where your etheric center is?

Use the navel energy, the Third Chakra. Pull the navel musically. You shall heal yourself tonight, don't suspend it. Attend to it, attend to it. It's a yin and yang. We are just stimulating certain areas of the body to coordinate the system.

♦ ♦ ♦

May the long time sun shine upon you,
all love surround you, and the pure light within you, guide your way on.

Blessed God, give us the strength and the power to be peaceful, tranquil, blissful, bountiful, and wonderful for ourselves and for all we see, know, and hear. May Thyself prevail, may Thyself be, and may Thyself to be. May this day and this night, tomorrow and tomorrow night, on and on, pass in that peaceful tranquility, in that trinity in which we all love, live, and let live.

Sat Nam

Go home and enjoy yourself and do whatever you have to do, but for God's sake drink a lot of water tonight. In the middle of night, if you do not get up to go to the bathroom, it means you did not drink enough. You must not sleep without urinating every four hours or more. You have to drink so much water that it forces you to get up in the night. That will be highly cleansing. That's what your system needs after all you've done. So go home and drink as much water as you can. Watch TV, do whatever, and then go to sleep. And that water will say, "Get up!" That release, watch it. It's worth watching.

GETTING RID OF TRANSIT MEMORIES I
—THE KRIYA

March 14, 1989

There are no breaks between the exercises, unless indicated. Move immediately from one exercise to the next.

1. Alternate Nostril Breathing: Inhale left, exhale right. Go at a quick pace of approximately 1–2 cycles per second. **2 minutes**.

2. Bring the palms onto each side of the chest. The fingers point toward each other and the thumbs extend up. With both hands together, pat your chest in a gentle, rhythmic motion. Go at quick pace of approximately 2 cycles per second. (Yogi Bhajan plays a musical rhythm on an African sound box, similar to a xylophone.) **7 minutes**.

These are very important meridian points; you are touching them and they are going to take you through the space. It's no use hitting yourself hard; hit just enough to send the sensory vibrations inside. It will start changing your glandular system. It will start changing your tattvas. It will start doing everything you want to do. Meditate. You cannot go home today with all that sickness and nonsense. Keep up. Bless yourself. Touch yourself. Bless the sacred heart.

3. Repeat Exercise 1. **2–2½ minutes**.

In Exercises 4 through 10, various selections of Middle Eastern/Persian pop music were played throughout.

4. Repeat Exercise 2 with the eyes closed. Create your own rhythm with the music. **4½ minutes**.

Do it intuitively and meditatively. You are playing a very precious drum. Move only your hands. Play your own lullaby, play your own music, go with it. It will relax your inner suspended self. Touch the hand with the body rhythmically.

5. With the mouth in an "O," breathe in and out through the mouth. Allow the cheeks to move with the breath. Exhale as you pat the chest. Continue in rhythm. **1½ minutes**.

6. With the hands in front of the body, begin alternately striking the center of each palm: right fingertips come together and touch the center of the left palm; left fingertips come together and touch the center of the right palm. Move in rhythm with the music. Quick pace: 1 cycle of left and right each second. Breathe through the mouth in pace with the motion; exhale as the fingers touch each palm. Breathe from the diaphragm; move the cheeks as you breathe. **3 minutes**. The musical pace changes to half time—one cycle every 2 seconds. **4 minutes**. Total: **7 minutes**.

7. With the hands in front of the body, touch the backs of the hands together in rhythm with the music. With each strike of the hands, alternate which hand is on top. Move quickly. **4½ minutes**.

This is the instrument with which they awaken the serpent. It is called the Been. Arouse the serpent power. Meditate, meditate, meditate. Keep your rattle going with the back of the hand.

8. Repeat Exercise 2 and breathe through the mouth. Use the cheek; engage the diaphragm. **4½ minutes**.

Move the diaphragm. Move the third center, the Navel Point. Push it hard.

9. Inhale deep and begin puffing the cheeks in rhythm with the music. Breathe through the nose and puff the cheeks. The lips are closed and the cheeks stretch up and out in rhythm to the music. **1½ minutes**.

10. Open the mouth and begin making a clucking noise with the tongue. Make your own music. Create a rhythm by alternating between whole beats and triple beats. Play with the tip of the tongue. **5 minutes**. Continue the clucking for another **30 seconds** as the music changes to *Whistling Ardas Bhaee*.

Persian women still do what they call "the call of the tongue." It is a victory call and in private, she heals herself with it—even today.

11. Return to Exercise 2, patting the chest while continuing to listen to Instrumental *Ardas Bhaee*. After **1 minute**, begin Snake Breath—inhale and exhale quickly and powerfully through the nose as you pat the chest; the breath will make a hissing sound. Find a rhythm. Be musical. **2 minutes**. Total: **3 minutes**.

12. Inhale deeply and press the hands on the Heart Center, right hand over left. Sit with a straight spine. Exhale. Breathe naturally. Gong is played over the music, *Ardas Bhaee,* Instrumental Version. **7 minutes**.

Please leave your body; go along with the sound; it is very easy to float on it.

13. Maintain the posture and begin chanting *Ardas Bhaee*. Press the hands against the Heart Center. Give your heart a hug. Hug yourself. Hug the Unknown. After **1½ minutes**, begin to whisper powerfully for **2 minutes**:

Ardaas Bhaee Amar Daas Guroo
Amar Daas Guroo Ardaas Bhaee
Raam Daas Guroo, Raam Daas Guroo,
Raam Daas Guroo, Sachee Sahee

14. After the music stops, continue pressing the hands against the Heart Center. Press hard as you suspend the breath. Inhale deep and pump the navel for **15 seconds**. Exhale. Inhale deep again; suspend the breath and pump the navel for **15 seconds**. Exhale. Inhale and suspend the breath for **30 seconds**, pumping the navel. Exhale.

    a) Relax and talk to each other. **1½ minutes**.

    b) Begin shaking the hands. Get rid of everything you no longer want, those unwanted spirits. Shake it off. **30 seconds**.

    c) Move the entire spine in circles, spiral from the base of the spine to the shoulders and the neck. **1½ minutes**.

    d) Whistle something musical—anything. Whistling *Ardas Bhaee* is played. **1 minute**.

    e) Create the sound through the nose; **hum** through the nose while the music continues. **1½ minutes**.

Drink enough water that you have to get up in the middle of the night to eliminate.

◆

"Once you start growing and confronting and camouflaging yourself and then creating a twilight zone of suspension, you start suspending—suspending, suspending, suspending. Then that suspension becomes you totally. The load of all the suspended thoughts comes back to you through your dreams."

– *Yogi Bhajan*

GETTING RID OF TRANSIT MEMORIES II

March 15, 1989

*T*HIS IS THE THEORY. I AM NOT SAYING THAT YOU HAVE TO UNDERSTAND any of it; it's not your caliber. But I have to explain to you how it works. Unfortunately you are a Western civilization. All you know is machines, and through machines, you know productivity; through productivity, you understand life. That's the way you are. Whereas there are some people who are not worried about what productivity is and what the process of productivity is; they go by the mental. So there is a crossroads: One has too much mental, one has too much productivity, and I think they never meet each other. That's why society is as berserk as it is. However, when you are mentally in a subconscious and conscious state of personality, you create a twilight zone, and you suspend things, you suspend action. Otherwise two lovers would never get divorced; otherwise nobody would be wrong; otherwise impossible would not be a word for humankind; otherwise . . . there are so many millions of things that I can say that you will not accept. But once you start growing and confronting and camouflaging yourself and then creating a twilight zone of suspension, you start suspending—suspending, suspending, suspending. Then that suspension becomes you totally. The load of all the suspended thoughts comes back to you through your dreams. And when that's not enough, they come through your daydreams. Then they come through fantasies. And then they come through fanatical fantasies of realities, which is when you become nothing. You are of no use to yourself because you are in a fantasy of nonreality. You can't let it go, but you can't have it. You are mister, miss, Ms.—whatever, miserable. And that's how you cause misery.

Misery is not that you are hungry. You are hungry, so you are miserable. But you eat, and it's fine. You are thirsty, you want to drink, and you are miserable. That's fine—quench your thirst, and you are okay. You are horny and sexy, so you have sex, and you are fine. You want to laugh, you are bored; so you go out and laugh and smile and crack up, and you are fine. But you are not fine when you are in a state of suspended identity. Is there any way that psychology can help let it go? No. Is there any psychiatric treatment that can let it go? No. Is there any medicine that can let it go? No. There is only one state that man has found: Put a man in a trance of self-suspension and suspend his id. When the id gets suspended, you will drop your suspended identity, because the two cannot sit together in the same chamber. When do you act really good? When you are at stake, when you know the fire

There is only one state that man has found: Put a man in a trance of self-suspension and suspend his id. When the id gets suspended, you will drop your suspended identity, because the two cannot sit together in the same chamber.

burns, when your butt is on the line. If somebody's burning, there is no maybe. You just deal with it.

When you are there, there is no maybe, and that's what we are going to do tonight. We are going to get rid of your maybes. I am going to put you on it, and if you come through it, you will come through very light, very delightful, and happy. But it will take time. But what can I do? I can't create time.

If you do this honestly, I don't need you. Just sit calm and steady and watch what we do today. I want you to understand it is not that I need your cooperation, I need your posture. Mentally I know what you will go through and what I have to take you through, so it's fine. All right? Set? Okay?

We are combining the birth force of the navel with the power of the pineal and the pituitary. That's all we are doing. We are not doing anything magical. Remain stable, calm, quiet, peaceful. Create a simultaneous rhythm and pressurize the motor in the brain to obey both ways; coordinate. This exercise helps deal with your mental disorientation. You have to circulate the energy. If it sits somewhere, it will rot; it won't reach; it will just be unplugged.

◆ ◆ ◆

May the long time sun shine upon you,
all love surround you, and the pure light within you, guide your way on.

Sat Nam

GETTING RID OF TRANSIT MEMORIES II—THE KRIYA

March 15, 1989

Move immediately from one exercise to the next. There are no breaks between the exercises.

1. *Right Hand:* The pinkie fingertip should rest at the base of the nose; the other fingertips line up along the center of the brow— the index finger rests at the hair line and the pinkie is at the bridge of the nose, with one fingertip in a line above the other.
Left Hand: The center of the palm is directly on the Navel Point. In-hale and exhale forcefully through the mouth. The cheeks expand with the exhale. One breath per second. **4 minutes**.

Music: Classical Indian music featuring the flute and then a medley of contemporary flute music plays throughout Exercise 1 through 9.

Your cheeks have to blow up so that your locked jaw, through which you work the whole day, opens up. It's a dental exercise, not breathing. We are combining the birth force of the navel with the power of the pineal and the pituitary. That's all we are doing. We are not doing any magic. Your cheeks must swell up and it should come out as gunfire. Breathe desperately; you need this breath.

2. Maintain the mudra and begin making a popping sound with the lips. The lips are curled over the teeth and meet and then separate to create a popping sound. Create a steady beat.
4 minutes.

Try! Your nervous system will respond. It is an internal kiss. You are kissing yourself. Tighten up both lips, one onto the other, fix it and beat the drum. It will take away all the tension you have stored in your jaw.

3. Maintain the mudra and begin inhaling and exhaling powerfully through the mouth. Let the cheeks move. 2 breaths per second.
1 minute.

4. Maintain the mudra and begin making a clucking sound with the tongue against the upper palate. Create a steady rhythm. **5 minutes**.

The lower jaw will feel the pull and the pressure if you do it right. You are stimulating the hypothalamus. Do it strongly, continuously, and rhythmically.

5. Cross the arms over the chest and begin patting the shoulders. Right hand pats the left shoulder, and left arm pats the right. Move quickly—like a hummingbird. Breathe long, deep, and slow. **2 minutes**.

6. Arms remain crossed and move up to the sides of the neck. Begin to pat the sides of the neck with the fingers. **3 minutes**.

God made you able to recover yourself. You are a very self-contained unit. The hands will fit in there without your trouble. Be calm, quiet—keep going, meditate.

7. Continue the movement of the hands from Exercise 6 and begin Breath of Fire. After **30 seconds** start moving the knees in rhythm with the hands and the breath. Total: **5 1/2 minutes**.

What is above is below; move in coordination. I'm sick and tired of "my back hurts and my neck hurts and this hurts and that hurts." Let's get out of all that hurt business. Halt the hurt. Keep going—Breath of Fire. Three things are working: legs, hands, and breath. Tonight you are not going to carry all the previous frustration, anxiety, and tension in the fiber of your body—that's what we are going to work on. So please move rhythmically, pressurize the navel. Breath of Fire from the navel, move the hands and move the legs in a rhythm, simultaneously.

8. Place the thumbs at the Mercury Mound, the base of the pinkie finger, and then lock the fingers over the thumbs. Remain seated and begin running in place with your arms; left and right arms move alternately forward and back. This is not a punching motion; the arms have a limited range of motion, as though jogging. Continue Breath of Fire and move in rhythm. Use the navel. Allow the ribs to move with the motion. **4 minutes**.

We are using the five tattvas and integrating a power in them so that you can come out like a baby. Bitterness and brittleness have to go. Move! Don't do too much, but don't do too little. We want to take the tension from the very bones of our being, period.

9. Bring the hands, palms facing each other, in front of the face. Begin waving the hands, using the wrist. The hands alternate: the right hand in front and then the left; continue alternating the position of the hands as they bend at the wrist. Close your eyes and concentrate at the Third Eye. **3 1/2 minutes**.

10. Begin chanting the mantra **Humee Hum Tumhee Tum** sung by Livtar Singh as you pat the upper chest with the palms of the hands. Make music with the hands. With every downbeat of the music, strike the chest twice; maintain the rhythm. **2 minutes**.

I Am Thine, in Mine Myself, Whaa-hay Guroo
Hamee Ham Too(n) Hee Too(n) Whaa-hay Guroo

We want to hear a sound of one hundred horses walking; it's the ribcage. Talk to your soul musically.

11. Alternately pat the Navel Point and the chest with both hands as you continue chanting. **4½ minutes**.

Move the energy! It's your energy; nobody is going to give you a B-12 injection. Connect the Heart Center and the Navel Point, alternately.

12. Inhale deeply, relax the arms, and roll your eyes to the Third Eye—that is the projecting point. Exhale and meditate at the Third Eye as the gong is played. *I Am Thine in Mine Myself* by Livtar Singh and *Walking Up the Mountain* sung by Guru Dass Singh and Krishna Kaur are played beneath the sound of the gong. **13½ minutes.**

As we play the gong, the subconscious tiredness should leave you within seven minutes—that's the maximum that you can hold onto it with your id and your ego. You have no defense against the gong. Well, you can resist, and you can feel freaky, and you can say, "Where am I going?" But the easiest way is if you say, "I am going," and let yourself go and then start floating. That's the best! Give yourself a chance. Let your immune system and your glandular system recuperate. Glands are the guardians of health, wealth, and happiness. God created it that way. Let us trust in Him who made us, and let us go into a space unknown to us, without fear and without questioning; that way we can easily float. Within that sound, the body will recuperate itself from all of its seriousness, which is caused by tension and the detention of toxins.

13. Begin chanting in a heavy, forceful whisper with *Ardas Bhaee, Instrumental Version*, by Nirinjan Kaur. Concentrate at the tip of the nose through closed eyes. The gong continues for **2 minutes** over the music. **12 minutes total**.

You don't have to raise the kundalini; it'll raise itself. Simply hiss strongly, musically.

14. Begin singing the mantra. **1 minute**.

15. Now go into deep silence. Concentrate at the Navel Point. Music continues. **1½ minutes**.

16. Return to the mudra in Exercise 1 and concentrate deeply. Music continues. After **30 seconds** begin whistling strongly with the music. Total: **2½ minutes**.

17. Become silent and begin clapping the hands together gently, rhythmically. **1½ minutes**.

18. As the music continues, interlace the hands behind the neck. Inhale and suspend the breath. Squeeze the entire spine, the entire body, and hold for **30 seconds**. Exhale. Inhale and suspend the breath. Squeeze. Make yourself a solid state for **30 seconds**. Exhale and repeat once more.

19. Relax and move. Listen to Sat Peter Singh's *Himalaya*. **2 minutes**.

20. Interlace the fingers with the hands a few inches above the crown of the head, palms down. Rock left and right, like a pendulum. Music continues. **1 minute**.

21. Continue rocking the spine and begin to move the knees up and down. **30 seconds**.

22. Inhale and shake the arms out above the head for a few seconds. Relax and talk to each other; eat and relax.

◆

"We will go through the womb, we will transpire it; we will go to the fifth month in the womb. That's a little later than when the soul enters; the soul enters on the 120th day. We are going one month later, to where life is in its projected form. We will go deeper, and then we will hang there. What it does to us is our affair. "

– Yogi Bhajan

REMOVING FEARS FROM THE FIFTH MONTH IN THE WOMB I

March 21, 1989

ONIGHT IS A VERY SIMPLE CLASS. "Oh, my Mother, give my innocence back to me." We will go through the womb, we will transpire it; we will go to the fifth month in the womb. That's a little later than when the soul enters; the soul enters on the 120th day. We are going one month later, to where life is in its projected form. We will go deeper, and then we will hang there. What it does to us is our affair.

What is suffering? Do you understand it? Suffering is caused only by our insecurity within ourselves. It's not about long distances; it's not a time or space situation. Every morning, we get up, and we have doubts about how the day shall be. Why? Because we do not have the *drib drishti*. We do not have intuition. We can't see, through our intuition, how the day shall be. We don't have a road map to see the destination. We do not have intuition to see our destiny throughout the day. And that's a human dilemma; it's confusion. Therefore, you get up and think that if you cut your hair this way and shave your moustache that way and wear this color, then you will get it.

But you have never become you as you; you are always a trendy person. And a person, a human being, who believes in a trend and lives in a trend and wins by a trend can never be who he is. Even if here on Earth you become successful, the richest person on Earth, the most powerful person on Earth, you will never be you. You cannot be you, because all your life, your whole energy has been focused on winning through the trend. When you win through the trend, you have to bend to that trend, and you cannot walk tall. You go by what the fashion says; you don't create the fashion. You go by the time; you don't create the time. You go by the people; you are not the people. You take the easy road; you never take the scenic road.

There are some people who serve the time, and there are some people whom time serves. But both are people. It's a hard choice, but that's the choice one has to make. If you have not found the reality in you, then you can be a boy or a playboy, and still be a blue boy—a boy who doesn't go anywhere. You can understand religion your whole life, you can practice religion your whole life, and still not know what religion is if you have not yet found the reality within you. It doesn't matter what you put on or what your setup is. All that matters is whether you have found

Tonight is a very simple class. "Oh, my Mother, give my innocence back to me."

the goal. Have you met your God face to face? Have you seen yourself person to person? How many of you get up in the morning and shake hands with your own self? "Hi, Kid. Good morning. Let's get to the day. We are going to win." No, none of you are ever trained that way.

When I was born, I was told that I never opened my eyes other than to see my own hands, to look at the lines of my own hand, and to tell myself, "Thank you, God, for giving me another day." I know that if you do not open your eyes, it keeps your eyesight better, because it doesn't put any pressure. I know there is a science behind that ritual. But I also know that it was an affirmation for myself. But you have not been trained that way; you have been trained to sleep in the way you want. You don't sleep to sleep. How many of you sleep at night just to sleep? How many wake up just to wake up? How many have a day just to have a day? You do not know one thing about how to be prosperous.

Prosperity doesn't come through sweat and hard work—that's a total lie you have been told. The man who digs ditches sweats more than anybody, and does he become very rich? No. What sells in this world is talent, but talent doesn't pay a lot if it is not a trusted talent—which you call professional good will. Professional good will is nothing but a trusted talent, and that is the strength.

Tonight I have to teach this class. We have been working on it for so many days, and we got it, we saw it together. That's the idea—to give you what we want to give to you. You didn't ask, you just came to class, walked in, paid at the door, and it's fine, but you came with a trust that must be honored and that shall be honored. Nobody put pressure on anybody. But if I come here and sit down and say meditate, and then you all meditate, and it is nice—that's a gimmick. To me that's daylight robbery. I feel there is no bigger cheat than a spiritual man who lets a person come and see and shake hands and then, without uplifting his spirit, lets him go. I don't care what religion one has or what teaching one has.

I don't believe a doctor is a doctor if his very touch cannot heal a person and make him comfortable and give him the confidence that he is in good hands. I don't believe an attorney is worth anything if he doesn't create immediate elevated trust in a human being. I believe that the very sight of a person should bring about trust and confidence. There is no need to discuss things; there is no need to fight things. If you can sell a trusted talent, you can never be poor. A hundred people will come and take care of you. A thousand people will come take care of you. If one will drop, ten more will be standing there for you, provided you have a trusted talent to offer. People will dig you.

Gold is found ten thousand feet, one hundred thousand feet down. And you dig for it. You mine it. You don't mine the earth, but once you know there is gold in

the land, forget it—you will go after it, no matter what. If they find out that there is oil but they can't get to it, so they put in hot water and they force it up. The North Sea is a treacherous sea, but they have built platforms. People go after trusted talent wherever it is, even if some people only know how to take, take, take. So, trusted talent creates the trends; trusted talent doesn't go by the trend.

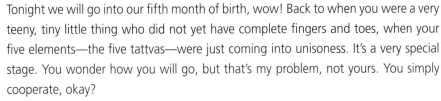

Tonight we will go into our fifth month of birth, wow! Back to when you were a very teeny, tiny little thing who did not yet have complete fingers and toes, when your five elements—the five tattvas—were just coming into unisoness. It's a very special stage. You wonder how you will go, but that's my problem, not yours. You simply cooperate, okay?

Power the diaphragm, as this automatically gives you a long breath. The air touches the thumbs, which are the id, and gets into the lungs, which is your receptivity. It gives you a lot of good oxygen and good prana (*see Exercise 1*). Getting back to that most flexible time of time and space will give you the mental energy to recapture yourself and to get rid of the stiffness and brittleness and belittleness (*see Exercise 2*).

Tomorrow we have to do a process of rebirthing in musical terms. We have never practiced that before in the United States. We will bring the baby out and cut out his grief. Then next week we will restimulate what you call grief. Grief is the cause of all our disease, pain, and tragedy. We all grieve. Grief is not something we can get rid of; we grieve whether we want to or not. We grieve because it is a psychological syndrome, it is a psychotic syndrome in interrelated psychology. I am not going to lay my Ph.D. number on you, but that's what I am—a doctorate in psychology of communication. All you have to do is speak nine wrong words in the whole day and you will mess up yourself. If you say, "Oh, God, I made it. I got to that guy, perfect!" Do you know what you have done? Have you expressed success? No, you have started anxiety. Whatever you have to say, just say it consciously.

There are two things in your life that will make you sick and dead—anxiety and grief. There is no third thing, like "I want to go home" or "You want to go home." That's just called conscious exit. There are only two things in this world—anxiety and grief. The rest is all a bunch of lies; they do not exist. The outcome of these two things is all kinds of diseases and all kinds of stress. You create this anxiety and grief everyday. If I say, "She was good." Because you are now in a stage of innocence, once you say, "She was good," there is grief; you immediately reflect on the loss by asking, "But where is she? What was good?"

You must understand that your subtle body works in a very subtle way. It doesn't make a lot of noise; it controls your pranic energy, or *pra* energy. *Pra* energy is not controlled by you; it comes from the Pranic Body and is controlled by the Subtle Body. If you miss the subtle things in your life, then you miss your life. Life is not based on huge achievements. Subtle, small things contain all things. You have senses and sensitivity, but you roll right over everything.

You know, you do not understand; you just speak. I did my Ph.D. in psychology, and I found out, while doing my paper, that if you do not elevate yourself in your own talk, you will be sick that day. Say we start the day with one hundred ounces of energy, but if we don't elevate ourselves just one ounce per conversation, we lose. So, what do you have in you? You have nothing in you except energy. You can give it to people, you can take it from people, you can spill the beans, you can cook the beans, you can eat the beans. It's all you. And this whole gimmick of religion and that whole thing is old news. I understand it; I am very respectful, and I am a religious man. I don't have any two opinions about it, but I don't want to be called tomorrow and hear, "You are a secular religion." Because this is an old drama, this religion. The thing is that man today has to find his own reality, and his own reality is in his own uplift, his own elevation. There is no substitute for it. We can prostitute ourselves, we can debate, we can masturbate, we can do anything in our life—it is up to us. But we have to agree that we are sick, because we think we can play life, but life is not ready to play with us.

Life is a constant consistent existence, and it is automatic. Not to respect one's own life consistency—to be flaky about it and moody about it—is one of the biggest nonrealities you live. Basically you live in lies, you breathe lies, and you feel lies, and that's why you are insecure. Who can make you secure? No one, because you don't respect the consistency of your own life. Your life breathes fifteen times a minute on average; it's never wrong; it's automatic. Even at night when you sleep and you're snoring, still you are breathing. You work, you forget about everything, you do not pay any attention to your breath of life, and still you breathe. So long as you live, breathing is a constant act. And it has a consistency—when you are in a passionate sexy mood, your breath becomes shorter, shallower to give you that mood. When you are in deep meditation—and it's a very powerful thing—your breath becomes automatically deeper and longer. So between eleven and twenty-one breaths is your ratio; that's how you live. Your breath adjusts itself automatically without you. You can cause anxiety and grief without even knowing it.

There is no such thing as God; this energy is something real. Imagine it or not, feel it or not—it doesn't matter. Matter is a real force; energy created matter, and matter created energy; matter can change into energy, and energy can change into matter. That's the law of physics, and it will never be wrong. So you can create the matter, but the matter is that you have to put energy into it and it has to be conscious. If you have no consistency and don't respect the consistency of life, how can life respect you?

I say this every day, but I say it differently so that one day it will get into you. If you respect the subtlety, the radiance, and the consistency of your life, prosperity will lick your shoes, and the world will come to you. The world will come to you by manipulation; but that's only a timely achievement. You can do it day to day, you can do it night to night, you can do it moment to moment—you are freaks. You walk, talk, and look like humans, but you act like animals. Between those two things you do not know who you are.

For just one day look at yourself and see how subtle you are. Just one day; I am not asking you to become religious or to get baptized; I am not asking you to jump out of a window. All I am saying is for one day, just feel very subtle and be nice. Then see how much that day brings to you. Days are days of light; it must bring you life and light. The sun comes out to give you light. In India they never get up without Surya Namaskar, a set of exercises they do before the sun comes out. Do you know why? Because they want to feel the subtlety, they want to relate to it, they want to get it from the light of the sun.

The Jews say theirs is a religion of light, a religion of candles. They burn the candles and make a big deal about burning the candles on those special days. But the rest of the time they do not know what a candle is. They give everybody a candle but only to burn on those days. Their religious symbol—the menorah—has those eight candles. But they don't know that it is not the candle that is important; it is looking at the candle. It's meditating on the candle. It's called *agni traatika*, and it is a part of yoga that makes the stupidest person the wisest. It gives the Third Eye, it opens up the Sixth Chakra—that's the rule.

There are a lot of people who have never seen me. All they have is my "Tantric picture." They do not know who I am. They do not know where I am. They have just heard about me, like I am a part of history. They have that "Tantric picture," and they have the process: They get up in the morning, sit down, and talk to the picture on the paper. It is just a piece of paper that costs a dollar. We made it to prove that a paper picture can talk and answer all of your intelligent questions. So it's a very funny thing, that one day, somebody called me on the telephone and asked me a question:

"Sir, can you give me a reply?"

I gave him my reply.

He said, "I already got that reply this morning."

If you respect the subtlety, the radiance, and the consistency of your life, prosperity will lick your shoes, and the world will come to you.

"Then why are you spending money on the telephone?"

"Just to be sure."

The "Tantric picture" is a simple, ordinary photo. It's no big deal; there is nothing special about it. But it's the angle of the eyes; they are at a fixed angle. We've never gotten that angle again, so we keep making copies of it. But there is a procedure to it; we know it's a *chittra traatika*; it is with the eyes and it is related to the light. And we know it will work; it will never fail because for centuries it has not failed. The entire Judaism is based on that, and the entire Christianity is based on accepting the subtlety of God. Entire Hinduism, Shintoism, Buddhism is based on one simple thing: The totality is the reality. And then came Guru Nanak. All he said is that totality is a reality, and reality is totality; don't separate them. They started throwing stones at him. They beat him up; they called him their ghost: "You don't follow any tradition."

He said, "What is tradition?"

"No, no, no. Reality is reality."

He said, "Then why did reality create totality?"

"Totality is totality."

He said, "Then where is the reality?"

Finally he said, "*Ek Ong Kar.*" There is one totality and one reality, and they cannot be separated. The world cannot be separated from the word. All these yogis used to go in caves, sit down, meditate, and be in bliss, and they said everybody else can go to hell. So the world was divided between those who are in ecstasy and those who are in hell. But Guru Nanak said, "Let heaven and hell meet and mix. If you mix it, you will fix it." That's all he said: If you have happiness, share it. They asked him why. He said, "Because it will multiply."

The Law of the Vacuum is that there is no vacuum. And that's where the problem is today. Today, everybody wants to be himself or herself; all some people want is the self. They want to rule; they want to control. So what do we end up creating? Anxiety and grief. Anxiety gives you cancer and all the other diseases. Grief gives you diabetes and this and that. If you line up all the diseases, the root cause can be divided between two things: anxiety and grief.

Somebody was very seriously suffering, so he went to a doctor. The doctor checked the history and that whole thing. The nurse asked, "What is it?"

The doctor said, "He will be cured, but don't tell him what we are giving him." So they gave him some sweet homeopathic medicine.

He said, "I was told that I was a terminal case."

The doctor said, "No, no, no. Just take this."

Two weeks later, the man came back and said, "Doctor, I am healed."

The nurse said, "How did that happen? I mean this guy was sick!"

The doctor said, "He had nothing but absolute deep grief, so I gave him some

homeopathic minerals and the grief went away. Now the guy is healed. He must have eaten right, that's all."

The nurse asked, "What should I give him now?"

"Powder up some sugar and give it to him; he doesn't need medicine."

"What should I tell him?"

"Don't tell him anything; otherwise he will have grief again."

That's why homeopathy was developed. It wasn't that man found out that those little sweet things are great. It's the potency of certain medicines that determines their effectiveness. It's a very subtle medicine. If you take the best homeopathic medicine and then take one onion bite, the medicine is out the window. It doesn't tolerate anything that is not subtle. Onion, garlic, ginger, and those other things you eat are very gross and very pungent.

When you are dealing with your life, you have two things: either getting sick or healing your life. So you have to understand the little subtleties, the little niceties. Be a little good, right?

◆ ◆ ◆

May the long time sun shine upon you,
all love surround you, and the pure light within you, guide your way on.

Sat Nam

REMOVING FEARS FROM THE FIFTH MONTH IN THE WOMB I—THE KRIYA

March 21, 1989

There are no breaks between the exercises. Move immediately from one exercise to the next.

1. Bring the edges of the thumbs together; there will be a natural opening between the thumbs at the knuckles. The fingers are relaxed with the fingertips touching. Place the thumbs on the lips and breathe through the hole between the thumbs. Inhale long and deep and exhale long and deep through the mouth. **5 minutes**.

2. Put the hands on the knees and begin moving the shoulders up and down. Move the shoulders together. After **1 minute**, begin whistling as you continue bouncing the shoulders. *Music: Ardas Bhaee, Instrumental Version.* **Total: 3½ minutes**.

Normally we move the shoulders when we say we don't care. That's the body language of the shoulder: "I don't care." Just move them like that. You will relax. You need to be extremely relaxed to get back into the womb. You have always wanted that, you know? So let's do it today.

3. Place the palms against the chest with the right hand on top of the left hand. The fingers are parallel to the ground, the right fingers point to the left and the left fingers point to the right; the thumbs touch, creating a triangle with the hands—the *tattva* triangle. Place the mudra wherever you feel your Heart Center is and just relax. Close the eyes and look at the tip of the nose through closed eyes. Breathe as long and deep as possible. The gong is played for the first few minutes of the meditation and for the final few minutes of the meditation.

Music: I Am Bountiful, Blissful and Beautiful by Nirinjan Kaur and Guru Prem. **26 minutes**.

Don't copy me. Fix your mudra wherever you feel your Heart Center is. See this finger? This is the ego, this is Jupiter, this is Saturn, this is Sun, this is Mercury; if any imbalance is happening, then you are out of shape. Pull it together so that you get into an elementary state of yourself.

4. Maintain the mudra and begin to breathe consciously, deeply, and heavily. Music continues. **2 minutes**.

TO END: Inhale deep, suspend the breath briefly, and exhale. Inhale again, suspend the breath for 20 seconds, and squeeze the entire body tight; exhale. Take two powerful quick breaths and then inhale deeply; suspend the breath for 20 seconds. Squeeze the entire body, from the toenails to the tips of the hair. Exhale. Take three powerful quick breaths; then inhale deeply and suspend the breath for 20 seconds. Consolidate everything—shrink, shrink, shrink; this is *pratyahar*. Exhale and relax.

5. Release and remain seated in Easy Sitting Pose. Sing with the mantra: *I Am Bountiful, Blissful and Beautiful*. **3½ minutes.**

6. Shake the hands and move the body. **15–30 seconds.**

7. Talk to one another. Talk about earthly things; not spacey things. **1 minute**.

◆

" Your life is not based on reconciliation with a situation. Your life is not based on the innocence of life. Your life is not based on being simple, straight, and smiling. No, your life is based on action and reaction. "

– Yogi Bhajan

REMOVING FEARS FROM THE FIFTH MONTH IN THE WOMB II

March 22, 1989

You all want happiness, but to adjust to happiness, you require innocence; just as to digest food, you require saliva.

WHEN YOU GO TO MEET A FRIEND, you don't know what shall happen there; but you expect that it will be fine. Sometimes it is what you expect and sometimes it is not. Your life is not based on reconciliation with a situation. Your life is not based on the innocence of life. Your life is not based on being simple, straight, and smiling. No, your life is based on action and reaction. In the Oriental science of the mind, it's called karma. If things are right, you respond right. If things are not right, you respond not right. Your preference is for life to balance itself out, one way or the other. But where does this preference come from?

It comes from your idea that you have to preserve yourself. It comes from your idea that you have to protect yourself. It comes from your idea that you have to survive. But did you know that if you are attacked very badly and you don't react, it will actually destroy the person who attacks you? No, you didn't know that, because your normal response is, "You attack me; I attack you." That's your normal response. But the law of physics says that if somebody comes at you with all his force, you just move aside, and by his own force, he goes down.

Paapee ke marne ko paap mahabali hai.
Sinner, the sin itself is enough to kill the sinner.

You don't have to do anything; don't get involved, because your involvement is actually a protection for the bad person, for the attacker. If you don't involve yourself and just give a slip, that will work.

There are five billion people on this Earth. You all love God, but none of you trust God. Whenever you are attacked or you have a question or you are confronted, you don't see God in it. You just see threat in it, you see belittlement in it, you see insecurity in it; and then you react to it. But that's a waste of life energy; that's not what we need to do. We have to be extremely relaxed when we are in adversity, and we have to be extremely consciously grateful when we are in prosperity, because both things are very dangerous. In adversity, your automatic self-saving device—the sixth sense—is automatically alert. In prosperity, it is not. So in prosperity you can actually fall apart faster than in adversity. You all want happiness, but to adjust to happiness, you require innocence; just as to digest food, you require saliva.

There are five billion people on this Earth. You all love God, but none of you trust God.

If you don't chew your food, you create all problems, all diseases. Remember, this life needs stability in your relationships between you and within you.

The curiosity is when you want to know what your relationship is with somebody else. Even after twenty years in the United States, everybody still asks, "What will happen to me? What's my future?" So, I give them the address of Anita—she is a fantastic psychic. In my twenty years here, I think I have met almost every psychic. They are all frauds. Believe me; that's my playtime. I go to the psychics, these gurus, with all kinds of gimmicks and I sit with them. I put my hands before them; I am a very good student. And they start reading me and talking to me, and I start reading their auras. And I think, "My, God. How much can a man lie just to have a few bucks?" Now, I will tell you a story. It's a true story; it's one hundred percent true with one comma or semicolon wrong, that's all.

When I went to Phoenix, there was a church, and in that church was that great psychic. Remember him? I went to the church, and he was supposed to read me. So I sat in a chair and waited for this gentleman to come. When he arrived, he sat down opposite me, and he said, "Do you want to be read?"

I said, "Yeah. This is the exchange we have: You read me, and I will speak in your church."

But then he said, "Oh, my God! You are guarded. Ask your guardian angels to permit me to read you. I can't penetrate."

So I said, "Describe my guardian angel."

"Behind you I see a very, very enlightened man with a white beard. He has very penetrating eyes, and there is nothing I can do. I can't cross in front of you, because there is a woman on a tiger, a Bengal tiger, and she has a lot of hands and a lot of weapons. I can't go across that, so we are through."

To be very truthful with you, I thought that somebody must have told him something I had said, or he must have read something. But I said, "Okay, I will meditate, and I will get you the clearance, if that works for you."

I thought he was very sincere and very professionally known, so there was no joke about it. I meditated: "*Ong Namo Guru Dev Namo*. Please help this creature. It is no big deal. I have voluntarily come. My Lord, it is not that I don't trust Thee or that You are not the ultimate. But I have the right to play games, and this is my pastime, so don't mess it up. Let this guy come through."

Then he started reading, and he was so accurate that it blew my mind. It just impressed me. He said certain things that only my mother knew or I knew. There were certain other things that neither my mother knew nor my father knew nor anybody except me knew. He was so accurate. It was a half-hour continuous bombardment of things that you cannot even believe.

In the end, he said, "Reading you is like writing on the water's surface. I am reading it just for now. A minute later, it may all change."

I went to his church, and I saw something that you wouldn't believe. This psychic man stood up in the pulpit, and they tied his hands, and they plastered him—even his nose. I asked, "What are they going to do to him?"

Someone answered: "He is going to read your questions."

"Why do they have to do this to him?"

"Because people don't trust him; they think it's a gimmick."

So they put on blinders and big huge tape, and then they put a turban over it. I thought to myself that even if somebody gave me a hundred million dollars for this act, I would not do it. So, the basket went around, and people wrote questions. (We used to do that gimmick in Guru Ram Das Ashram. I used to lie down and sleep, and people used to write questions. And I would say, "Don't write this; your spelling is wrong; this is the word." We used to impress people and find their dogs and cats.) So anyway, he picked up a paper, read the question and the name and everything, and gave the answer. It was a fabulous, enjoyable situation. I was very impressed because I finally had found somebody who was very professional in his thing.

The next day in his church, I spoke to the people. At the end, he called me to his private study and asked, "What did you do?"

I said, "What? You know what I did."

"I do all that stuff, read these people's questions, I have been with them for so many years, but yesterday's collection was only six hundred dollars."

I said, "That's great; it's a lot of money."

He said, "Today you just spoke, and I don't know what you said, but the collection is over two thousand dollars."

"This is how you measure—by these dollars? I didn't say anything."

"When you speak, you do something to these people."

I said, "I didn't do anything, but I appreciate you. I really love you; whatever you can do with covering your face for all that drama."

"Why don't these people trust me?"

"Well, kick them out. They can go to hell if they don't trust you. Why do you have to deal with that?"

"Sir, I don't understand," he said.

Either you are who you are, or you say who you are, or you are not what you say you are. So I said, "If you sit on a throne, don't use it like a commode."

He said, "That might be what's wrong with me."

Then he gave me a half-hour lecture about the difference between Americans and everyone else. Americans don't trust anybody—not their father, not their mother, not their neighbor.

I said, "Do you know what the difference is between the Western and the Oriental mind? In the Orient, we do not doubt; we start our day with trust, and we trust so much that we trust the doubt also."

It is not something wrong with you; it is something wrong with your basic training. You have been ill-advised from day one. You have been told that you have to find God, you have been told that you are born in sin, you have been told that things are not going to work out for you, you have been told many things. And all those things can be said in this: If God can rotate the Earth, he can take care of your routine.

Jo tudh bhaavey sa-ee balikaar
Tu sadaa salaamat nirankaar.

- Guru Nanak, Siri Guru Granth Sahib, page 3 (from *Japji Sahib*)

Whatever Thy will is, O my Lord, that's my blessing,
You are ever and everlasting my Lord. O, Thou the Creator of the universe.

There is a difference in our teachings, there is a difference in philosophy, there is a difference in understanding. You become aggressive just to draw attention; we become aggressive to kill. To us, aggressiveness is only permitted in one area: when somebody's life can only be saved at the cost of your own life. Otherwise, everything is negotiable—we talk and communicate and resolve things. There is no need for fighting; when we do fight, it's the last resort.

I think that since I came here twenty years ago, I only had to fight once. I used to wear those Dr. Scholl's sandals. I was taking a walk around the ashram, and somebody had pulled a girl into the alley and wanted to rape her, and she was crying, "Please, please, please." When I saw this scene, I looked at the man and said, "I hope you let her go. She is telling you to let her go." I didn't say anything from my side.

He said, "Hey you, what are you doing here?"

"I am just telling you that the girl is telling you to let her go."

He held out this long iron thing and said, "You know, man, this can go in your stomach. Do you want it?"

I said, "No."

"Then go away."

"No, I am just telling you that this girl is telling you to let her go."

I am a trained fighter. I sat down and with a twist of my heel, my Dr. Scholl was on his shin. Next thing, he was lying down, and that big iron was in my hand. I said, "May I have your permission to let this girl go?"

He didn't know what to say.

I said, "Just lie down where you are. If you move, this whole iron will not go in your stomach; it will go through your chest into this metal ground, and you will be nailed permanently. I am a commando-trained person. You just trusted my white beard and thought that I was an old man. But I told you to leave this girl alone."

I told that skinny girl, "You run. Go, get into your car, and move out. Go to the police station and file a report, whatever you do."

She said, "No, no, no. What you are going to do with him?"

I said, "That's between me and him; you go." So she left.

When he got up, I gave him that big iron and said, "Never use it. Go."

"You trust me?"

"No, I don't, but I definitely know I can snatch it again, and I can nail you next time if you are ever around this area again. I am letting you go to send a message. We live here and it's our temple and it is not for these acts. Don't do it again; take this away and go." He walked away.

That was my only fight. Once I had decided, I had to be very aggressive. You must understand that life without honor is not worth living. That's the highest stage of divinity that man reaches through innocence. Right or wrong—once you give somebody your word, live by it. Do your human duty at the cost of your life; don't ask for a reward. The highest thing in this world is to satisfy your own self, your own honor, your own grace.

You all want to love and be loved. But just love yourself; if you love yourself, you will love your honor, you will love your divinity, you will love your dignity, and you will love your grace. That's the highest skill of the human. It is just like a rose: When the bud opens, fragrance goes out, and everybody feels good. When everybody knows your behavior, your grace spreads around, and you will be loved. But you need that basic innocence, about which we are going to meditate today. We are going to get deeper into it so that we can qualify ourselves. Remember, we are going to the fifth month in the womb.

You need that basic innocence, about which we are going to meditate today. We are going to get deeper into it so that we can qualify ourselves. Remember, we are going to the fifth month in the womb.

◆ ◆ ◆

Consciously breathe. First of all, Los Angeles is a bad city with bad air. Secondly, you breathe very shallowly. One is bad food and second is half cooked, so how are you going to eat it? Breathe deep, breathe through your nose and please breathe consciously. It's a very self-healing treatment. If you ever want a nervous wreck to go away do this eleven minutes by yourself, it's the best acupuncture you can do for yourself. (*See Exercise 1.*)

Okay, tongue out and breathe, your dog does it so it is not something you don't know. (*See Exercise 3.*) In and out, quick, cool off your liver. Okay, open the lower jaw fully. Your hypothalamus and your whole tongue will relax. It's not a big deal, you can do it in the bathroom, in an office and you can get rid of all your inverted

Nobody is born defective. Nobody is born to be poor. Nobody is born to be sick or diseased. Nobody is born to be wrong. Almighty God created you in His own image, and He created you the best that He could.

tension, your nervousness, it's highly relaxing. We are directly affecting the metabolism to relax our body so we can get into a state of *pratyahar*, synchronize into that state of the body when you were five months old in your mother's womb. (*See Exercise 6.*)

◆ ◆ ◆

There is a perpetual trauma in the womb that you carry with you. It's not your mother's fault, and it's not your fault. It's the fault of not being trained to become a mother and not being trained to become a father. If you really want to do something, take a pregnant woman, ask her to sit down, and just throw an iron plate on the ground to see how the baby moves in the womb. We have technical training in India for when the baby moves in the wrong direction. If the mother and midwife cannot do it, we don't take her to the hospital. We just play the three-and-a-half sound current of the gong, and the baby automatically adjusts. We don't touch the baby; we just know that it happens because it is very common knowledge for us.

Anyway, the problem is that the man sleeps with the woman because he loves her that day. He tells her that he loves her very much, and she tells him that she loves him very much. Then God knows what happens, but somewhere a spermatozoa gets to the egg. This isn't planned; they aren't prepared; they don't even know for sure if it is his. There is no ritual; there is no blessing asked of the angels, the heavens, God, Jesus Christ, and Moses. Nobody is consulted. It is just two people who started exchanging bacteria, and one thing leads to another, and something happens down there.

But when that thing happens, the man's attitude changes. This is called the reflection of the seed. You do not know anything about this in the West. But with the reflection of the seed, the seed starts reflecting through the mother's womb, and the father's attitude changes automatically. You don't have to consult Freud on this; it just is. That reflection of the seed through the mother gives an attitude change to the father. Even if the father is not living with the mother and happens to be far away, wherever he is on the planet, his attitude will change. That is called the seed law, and it changes in proportion as the seed sprouts. Whatever the father mentally feeds the mother, that will be her strength. It is a telepathy that is provided by Nature. You must understand, the pollen does all the work; it's like magnetic, electromagnetic pollen in conception and the pregnancy. However, the by-product is you, me, and us. Then, somewhere, sometime the electromagnetic fuse goes off, and you carry a perpetual birth blackout in your personality.

It's a simple physics; it has nothing to do with you. That's why after one hundred and twenty days, we want the woman not to work but to meditate. And we want the father to be in a certain way. After a month or so, we want them to walk three to five miles together. When a child is born in 3HO, we want the mother not to leave

the room for forty days, to give the baby basic perpetual security, affection, love, and understanding. But you say you can't invest that money. You can invest money on a dog, but you can't invest money on a child. That's our national problem. You say that when the poor guy grows up, he will be left in a day care center anyway, so no big deal. Or he will be raised by a nanny who has not gone to school. Or maybe there is some girl in the neighborhood who is very nice and sweet, and she makes about two dollars an hour baby-sitting that little guy. All of this is not considered the most important thing in life. But as we grow up, we carry those blackouts with us, and we express them in life in many, many ways.

So when you come here next time, we will start talking about it, start working on it, and see what we can do about it. But just understand, we all have these issues, right? You are perfect, you put powder on your face, and you think I am beautiful. But no, behind this shell there is strength of mind and grit of self—two things that you don't have. You're just a billboard. If a billboard says that Sacramento is in two hundred fifty miles, that means you have to travel two hundred fifty miles. It doesn't mean that the billboard is Sacramento. So you have to travel the journey of your life. Nobody is born defective. Nobody is born to be poor. Nobody is born to be sick or diseased. Nobody is born to be wrong. Almighty God created you in His own image, and He created you the best that He could. There is nothing wrong in you whatsoever. It is the highest insult and religious sacrilege to feel that you are born in sin. I am not contradicting your faith; I am not contradicting anything. But no human being born of a woman wants to do wrong, wants to be wrong, or wants to be poor and miserable. But the fact is, we all are. The question is, Why? The answer is that we carry with us these baby blackouts. As we grow up into adults, our neurons form their own formations from these blackouts and create their own thought forms, and that becomes our basic idea.

There was a guy in our congregation who wanted to marry a woman who was almost twice his age. I was asked to give my blessing. I thought, "Wait a minute. Normally a woman should be five years younger than a man, as that's a normal biological need. But this woman is almost double his age. Is he going to marry his mother? I mean, what is this? I want to see." So I interviewed both of them, and I allowed the marriage, because it was right and they were both happy. So it is not that somebody wants to do something wrong. We are all different, and we each have a different magnitude, a different attitude. We have each been attributed differently; we are all individuals molded by different electromagnetic fields. Some people are very sensitive, some are very corrupt and sensitive, some are absolutely corrupt and insensitive, some are just "holier than thou" and highly corrupt.

The person who is most corrupt is the person who pretends to be holier than other people; he denies God. Do you know what is a slap on the face of God? It is

when you think somebody is wrong, somebody is inferior, somebody is shallow, somebody is a thief; when you put down another creation of God, you insult God. If you don't believe me, go to the artist's gallery and just look at one picture and appreciate it and then put another painting down, he will kick you out of his gallery. God doesn't like negativity. He created the Earth to enjoy the positive. So, where does this anger come from? Why are we so sad and sorry? Why are we such attention seekers? Why are we angry? Why do we have our own formulas and our own agenda? Why do we wear a mask and play our games? We are never straight, simple, and smiling. Why? Because we carry in our personality these blackouts from the womb.

God only created one thing in humans—just remember, one thing. God did not create holy men and unholy men. He didn't create superior men and inferior men. The greatest blindness and insult to God is when we feel that somebody is superior and somebody else is inferior. That's where you are off the road, where you fall in the ditch. Nobody is superior and nobody is inferior. This is very difficult to understand, because if a rich man comes, you lie flat; but if a poor man comes, you take the first club in hand and kick him out. If some beautiful girl comes, you ooh and aah. But if her teeth come out or are not brushed or if she is an old woman, you say, "What are you doing here?" You have an attitude, but it's not your fault. You are just stupid—that's all it is.

God didn't make anybody superior, and He didn't make anybody inferior, not at all. There's a purpose for it all. Why are there more bad people? So the one good person can be recognized. It's like a game of attention, a chess game; it has nothing to do with good and bad. Three hundred bad people make one good person, right? It's some proportion like that; it's nothing that you have to worry about. Bad has to be really bad to do the job as well as a good job, and a good job has to be really good to do the job as well as a bad job.

"There is neither good nor bad, but thinking makes it so."[1] Our thinking is very, very confused. As human beings, we have no brain capacity to think. Do you know who thinks? The animal thinks. The human intellect automatically releases a thousand thoughts per wink of the eye. So you don't have to think; you are already being bombarded. You are reigned over by those thoughts. All you have to do is shut yourself up and just be yourself, and your intellect will release a thousand thoughts. That's why they call the brain the thousand-petaled lotus. If you pick up one thought, it will become your emotion, and out of your millions of emotions, there will be feelings, and out of those feelings, there will be attachment, and out of attachment, you will have desires, and out of desire, there will be objectivity or completion or subjectivity or destruction or construction. And the game will go on. But I'm not discussing that at length; I'm just letting you know that animals have to think. When its tummy says, "I'm hungry," the animal doesn't go to the refrigerator in the middle of the night to get some leftovers. But this guy pretentiously says, "Oh, tonight, I'm not eating. I'm on my diet." Then at midnight, look at him as he sneaks to the refrigerator and empties it out, you know? It's because he's a human and not an animal. An animal gets up in the

[1] Shakespeare, in Hamlet, Act 2, Scene 2

morning, crawls around, looks around, yawns, and sings something to the God. If it's a bird, it will fly away. If it's an animal, it will move and find something to eat. What a simple life. You guys eat junk and pay dollars for it. It goes on.

Our life is just like that. We grow up and say, "Don't judge anybody." But then we judge all the time. "Your nose is no good, but I'm not judging"—that's how we say it. "I love you, but I don't know how to talk to you." What kind of love is this? "I hate to tell you this, but I'm going shopping, and there's not a dollar or a dime in my purse." The husband knows what she's saying, and he knows why she's saying it. But if the husband is wise, he will say, "Darling, go window shopping, and you will never need a purse." But we have certain impulsive necessities to express ourselves. Impulsive necessities are not realities. We waste eighty percent of our energy on impulsive necessities, and only twenty percent on our basic reality. The day we switch—the day we make impulsive necessities twenty percent and reality eighty percent—we'll be the most comfortable people on Earth. You will have a twenty percent goofing arrangement—that's the leverage you will have. But for the rest, you have to be exact.

I'm not teaching a psychology class. I'm just going on record because when psychology is taught a thousand years from now, man will have a very improved personality, and people will relate to the realism of a fulfilling and happy life. Entertainment will just be to enjoy the bliss and to be in ecstasy and to love each other in the real sense of light and brightness. Man shall have a very powerful, developed, beautiful mind. There'll be no aggression, no fear, and no death. That is how the Infinite God's Image in finite man shall be on Earth. It will be contained, content, and continuous truth. However, for now we have to deal with what we have to deal with today. Thank you for tonight, for the beautiful music, the beautiful rainbow aura, and the wonderful way you were. That makes my day.

In the next class, we will deal with the perpetual fear that we pick up in the womb of the mother. It is a heavy workshop, and I suggest that people who are pregnant should not to come to the class. Otherwise you are most welcome.

May the long time sun shine upon you,
all love surround you, and the pure light within you, guide your way on.

Tranquility, harmony, grace—may Thy gift be with us. Love, affection, kindness—may they
be with us as we live and walk in Thy light. May compassion be our attitude, aptitude,
and sustenance for Thy humanity, for that prayer. By that virtue we can be fulfilled.
Give us that power, that understanding, and that knowledge; bestow on us
that perceptivity so we can love each other and see Thee in all forever.

Sat Nam

REMOVING FEARS FROM THE FIFTH MONTH IN THE WOMB II—THE KRIYA

March 22, 1989

There are no breaks between the exercises. Move immediately from one exercise to the next.

1. Bring the hands up to the level of the ears, 8–12 inches to each side, palms facing forward. Fold the Sun (ring) and Mercury (pinkie) fingers into the palms and press the tips of the Jupiter (index) finger, Saturn (middle) finger, and thumb together. With a powerful inhalation through the nose, open the fingers, and with a short, powerful exhalation through the nose press the tips of the three fingers together again. The Sun and Mercury fingers remain folded on the palms throughout. The pace is strong but moderate: Inhale and exhale about once per second. Breathe consciously. **3 minutes**.

When Jupiter and Saturn are mixed together with your ego, it gives you grit. If you breathe consciously, it will change your metabolism.

2. Continue the mudra but begin inhaling and exhaling quickly and powerfully through an O-shaped mouth. Open up the ribcage. **1½ minutes**.

Breathe from the diaphragm; open up your mouth and inhale and exhale with a Cannon Breath.

3. Continue the mudra but extend the tongue and breathe through the mouth—Dog Breath. The pace is the same as a Breath of Fire—two cycles per second. **30 seconds**.

Breathe in and out quickly. Cool off your liver. Hurry up!

4. Continue the mudra but make a clucking sound with the tongue against the upper palate. Fully open the lower jaw with each repetition of the sound. **1 minute.**

It will relax your inverted tension. It's not a big deal. You can do this in the bathroom or in an office to get rid of all the tension and nervousness; it's highly relaxing.

5. Return to the breath and movement in Exercise 1. **30–60 seconds**.

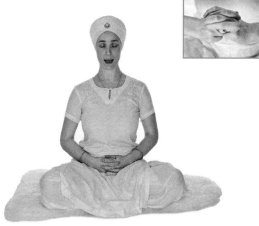

6. a. Interlace the Jupiter (index) and Saturn (middle) fingers of the two hands. The thumbs will naturally cross. The Sun (ring) and Mercury (pinkie) fingers fold down toward the palms. Place the mudra on your Navel Point. Close the eyes and look at the tip of the nose through closed eyes. Concentrate as the gong is played. **9 minutes**.

b. Begin playing the mantra *Bountiful, Blissful Beautiful* by Nirinjan Kaur and Guru Prem Singh; the gong continues. Meditate mentally. **2 minutes**.

c. Begin singing with the mantra; the gong continues. **11 minutes**.

d. Silence the gong and continue chanting. **9 minutes**. **Total: 30 minutes.**

Let yourself go, let it float. Please float in the womb as you were. Self-hypnotize yourself, self-hypnotize yourself, just float in the womb, that's all.

7. Meditate in silence and press your Navel Point with the mudra as hard as you can. Yogi Bhajan played an African sound box, like a xylophone. **6½ minutes**.

TO END: Inhale and suspend the breath. Pump the navel as hard as you can. 30 seconds. Exhale. Inhale and suspend the breath. Pump the Navel. Move! 30 seconds. Exhale. Inhale again, suspend the breath, and pump. Move the navel! 30 seconds. Exhale; Inhale, exhale; inhale, exhale; inhale deep—move the navel quickly! 20 seconds. Exhale. Inhale, exhale; inhale, exhale; inhale, suspend the breath and move. 20 seconds. Exhale. Take 3 quick powerful breaths, and then inhale deeply and exhale completely. Hold the breath out and move the navel. 20 seconds. Inhale and relax.

8. Turn and talk to one another. *Bountiful, Blissful, and Beautiful* begins again. **5–7 minutes**.

If you think that you talk too much, this is the best thing you can do for yourself: Say something that you don't believe. Say something very earthy. You have to just do the opposite of what you think. This is how the polarity works. You just had some experience, but don't talk about the experience. Talk about something very gritty, earthy, something that you can't believe yourself. Tell the other person about it. In other words, you have to diplomatically lie in order to feel miserable about yourself. Can you afford it? Try.

9. Wherever you are and in whatever position you are in, start whistling with the music. **1 minute**.

"The child develops at a certain frequency of the electro-magnetic field, in the processing of the mother's neurons and her circulatory system and her nervous system. All of that allows the child to develop and forms the child's characteristics—it determines whether he will be cool, calm, beautiful, wonderful, crazy, saintly, or horrible."

– Yogi Bhajan

CLEARING THE MAGNETIC BLOCK FROM THE WOMB I

March 28, 1989

Sometimes a circuit breaker sparks and sparks and sparks until finally it is totally useless, and you have to replace it. Circuit breaking of the mother affects the child.

WHAT WE ARE TALKING ABOUT TODAY IS ALL USELESS. But the idea is not to please you or to please myself. The idea is to let you know that there is a faculty of human knowledge where a human as a father, as a mother, as a parent has a responsibility. This is not the playboy sexual story; it only belongs to those who really want to be parents. But according to the known science, we are not prepared to be parents. We don't graduate to become parents; we don't work to become parents. There are so many flaws with who is a parent and who is not and with who act as parents and who do not. We have so much missing knowledge of all this. We have created a human in the body of a human but in an environment that is worse than that of an animal, worse than that of a bird. I will tell you a story.

On the one hundred and twentieth day, the soul enters the body of the child in the mother's womb. It's just like when you break the ground and you make a house; you furnish it, you invite your friends, and then you move in. Just like that, the egg and spermatozoa meet and start making a shape and a base. Finally the shape is good enough and understandable enough that the soul can reside there. That's how it is. But all of that is not enough. From the hundred and twentieth day to the day of delivery, if the mother's electromagnetic field, which has a corresponding relationship with the neurons of the brain, sets a pattern that stops the energy in the child's development, then that handicapped child has to live the rest of his life like that. He is condemned. That is called magnetic block.

You can well understand how cozy, calm, meditative, beautiful, and what smiling mothers we have. I am not blaming anybody. I am telling you how I don't want to say that word, this situation is so you can fix the word. It's not my fault, it's not your fault, it's not anybody's fault. But who is going to suffer for this? Me? Yes. You? Yes. We? Yes. If you say there is a way out, you are wrong. If you don't understand, imagine going into a house and seeing the circuit breaker. Sometimes a circuit breaker works, but sometimes you find a weird, broken circuit; it sparks and sparks and sparks until finally it is totally useless, and you have to replace it. Circuit breaking of the mother affects the child.

In child development, it is not that somebody is sitting there, taking a piece of meat like Earth or clay, putting some herbs in it, and cleaning it out. That's not

how the child develops. The child develops at a certain frequency of the electromagnetic field, in the processing of the mother's neurons and her circulatory system and her nervous system. All of that allows the child to develop and forms the child's characteristics—it determines whether he will be cool, calm, beautiful, wonderful, crazy, saintly, or horrible. The mother's electromagnetic field determines whether somebody will be a criminal, somebody will be a prostitute, somebody will be gay, somebody will be successful, somebody will be a fanatic, somebody will be a religious cheat. Whatever the patterns of the electromagnetic field are shall live in the child. If you build a six-bedroom house, it is not going to be a nine-bedroom house and it is not going to be a three-bedroom house. If you do not put in a bedroom or a bathroom, it is not the engineer's mistake or the designer's mistake. It is the owner's mistake that the house doesn't have a bedroom or a bathroom.

From the child's conception to delivery is the subtlest issue; it is extremely sensitive. That's why, when I was born, my mother had to do a certain definite routine after the hundred and twentieth day—calm, quiet, peaceful, happy, religious, giving alms and doing all that kind of stuff. After I was born, my father couldn't see me for forty days, period. But I was never separated from my mother for those forty days. And that's what we do in the ashram even today, even in the United States. We do it because of the shock of birth. Just imagine being born from a cozy little pouch and being tugged into a room and placed in blankets at night. Do you call that comfortable?

You are creating cold cutthroats by your own actions. Almost one-third of the 3HO people leave me when they hear that after a child is born, he should not be separated from the parents; that he should sleep in between the two parents. I say, "You both did it, and you both should raise it." But they say, "We don't want this kind of life." Then go out the door; there is no toll road here.

On the fortieth day of my life, my father wrapped me around his neck, and he, my mother, and I took a journey to sixty-eight holy places. Can you believe that they dipped me, a little child, in cold icy waters at least sixty-eight times?

Well, that is my story. Poll everybody else about theirs. What do you project psychomagnetically? What do you understand about your thought form? The highest, most beautiful, most bountiful thing is one thought. God is a thought. If you can't touch it, it is a thought. Love is a thought. Romance is a thought. Do you know what thought does? A thousand thoughts per wink of the eye. This *sahasrara*, the thousand-petaled lotus they call it, releases a thousand thoughts without you doing anything. One thought made Hitler put five to six million people to death. One thought told him he wanted a superior Aryan race and that Jews did not fit in. One

thought said that airport belongs to Poland, so we started World War II. Twenty-five, thirty miles of land, fifty million, sixty million people died. One thought says, "I am American." One thought says, "I am not American." "There is nothing good and there is nothing bad but thinking makes it so."[1]

Now think of a mother: "I am pregnant. I can't move. I cannot go. I am big. Who is he moving in with? Which secretary is he choosing? Where is he tonight? He didn't come home. He smells different." This is a totally deadly insecure mother who has a baby in the womb and facing every day and every night.

Do you see birds do that? Have you seen that when the female bird is hatching the egg that the male birds go to the club? When the female birds hatch the egg, do the male birds run away with somebody else? And you can't even learn from these birds? I mean, you are so superior, right? But these electromagnetic blackouts are fuses that exist within us. They do not exist in our arm or in our leg, and they do not live with our degrees on the wall. They exist in the strength of the neuron patterns in our very brain, and that formation gives us the characteristics. It is called our basic strength; that's what I am talking about.

There is no more powerful thing in the world to correct things in a human than the diagonal force. Parallel and perpendicular forces can be experienced, but diagonal forces cannot be experienced. They have to be used. And a human has only two powers known to him so far: One is the lens, and one is the lever. The force used by the lever is called the tantric force, while the force by the lens is called the specific force. In a microscopic or a telescopic sense, you understand things; with diagonal force, you can move that which you cannot move.

I didn't invite you to this class tonight because I had to. I just thought that we have to start somewhere. Why do some of you like to dance and others don't want to dance at all? Why do some of you want to just drink all the time and others don't? Why are some of you escapist and others are not? Have you ever thought about the answer to these questions? Why are some gay and others are not? Why are some tall and others short? There is an answer for all this. But don't ask me. Ask a horticulture expert; he will tell you that if the seed is this, is put this way, and if the temperature is this, then it will grow this way. So, what about you?

You don't even measure the seed first. Somewhere around the middle of the night, you become passionate. And you get into her and she gets into you; you exchange bacteria on the top and something underneath and something gets set, period. And then, after a month or so, when she misses her period, she declares that she didn't know it was that time. But a real woman will know exactly at the time she has conceived, to the second. In one second, she will know that she has conceived.

They exist in the strength of the neuron patterns in our very brain, and that formation gives us the characteristics. It is called our basic strength; that's what I am talking about.

[1] Shakespeare, in Hamlet, Act 2, Scene 2

A human has only two powers known to him so far: One is the lens, and one is the lever. The force used by the lever is called the tantric force, while the force by the lens is called the specific force.

But modern woman—the woman of the modern civilization—after a month, when she misses that four days of period, she will say, "Hi, John, I have a news for you." And he says, "What honey?"

"Well, I just tested that five dollar thing, and it came out positive."

Then these two jackals start howling and laughing. And that doesn't mean anything. It doesn't mean that he comes home at exactly five o'clock, and it doesn't mean that she is waiting for him, and it's not that he gives her a foot message. Nothing. No, it happens in birds; it happens in animals. And somehow a child is born. In my way of life, we send off mother and father and ask them to walk five miles every day, praising the Lord and passing the loot to the child. Every day has to be right. But here, nobody does that. When a child is born, it should not be a crying child; that crying is manufactured in the womb. A calm, quiet, peaceful, self-growing, self-elegant, self-contained child is not contemporarily indifferent to the world and its magnetic field and its vibrations.

Once, I visited somebody's house and was very shocked to see a baby wrapped up and hanging from the door in his crib. His legs were hanging down, and he was stuck to the outside of the door.

I said, "What happened?"

The Mother said, "I can't take it when he cries all the time." So she put the crib on a hook in the door and put him in and hung him there.

I think he must have cried and gone to sleep. When the door opened, he came in, along with the door.

And I said, "What is this?"

"Sir, I am tired of him. I can't sleep at night. I can't sleep during the day. I can't sleep in the house. We have a little apartment, so I hang him out there, and at least he goes silent."

I said, "Do you carry him and move him?"

She said, "You try it."

"Are you frustrated?"

"Ah, I wish I had never been pregnant, I really have given a birth to a devil."

"Don't say it; that's not good."

So we gave him a remedy, and in three, four days, he was fine. There was no problem. It didn't take much. Just two dollars and thirty-five cents with tax, and the child was okay. Those sweet little pills calmed his nervous system.

I sat down with her three days later when she came to thank me for that.

I asked, "When you were pregnant, what happened?"

She said, "It was hell. The father never came home at night, and I was worried in the morning. We went through hell."

See, that's the product—mental coercion, not physical coercion. What I am explaining to you is that you will go through those feelings in the womb tonight. What I am trying to explain to you is that the psychosomatics of the electromagnetic field of the human nucleus work in proportion to the psyche of the personal existence of the impulses of the human characteristic. These are all formed and developed within the mother's womb in those very days. The tragedy occurs—and it's a serious tragedy—when the child goes through the acid bath and loses half of its brain and gets those two little plums and little banana underneath. That's all it takes to call himself a male. He loses half the brain, and in that seventy-two hours, if the current of the electromagnetic field fuses, it affects an organ and causes a permanent effect in the functional aspect of the human body. That's the tragedy if that doesn't happen. Then the seventh month is what they call the most crucial month. The senses and psyche, intuition and projections are set in place and everything is checked off the list, like checking to see what the attack capacity is of an airplane's missiles. This is all in the seventh month. And after that is just a delivery. Right?

◆ ◆ ◆

We will be working with the five antennas of the brain. If you know the kinesiology, cut the ten parts of the body in half. This is how you work: We say *Saa-Taa-Naa-Maa*. Do you remember that? This *Saa-Taa-Naa-Maa* business looks religious and ritualistic and like people being converted and all that. But all it does is one thing: It gives the brain a working strength. To me, religion is a science of reality; it is not a gimmick. When we sit down to do *Saa-Taa-Naa-Maa*, we may look like idiots because we are repeating the same thing again and again. But that is how things are done; that's how we perpetually energize our brain, and it works for us.

You have to explain the reason for these exercises to future generations. Don't be an idiot; don't just do whatever I say. These are your problems, not mine. I didn't have a problem in the womb; my problem started when I was out of the womb, because that's when I started realizing what the problem is with others.

I used to ask my colleagues, "Why are you doing this?"

"Well, we want to."

"What do you mean you want to do this? Does every idiot do this thing that you are doing?"

"This is what we want to experience."

"Why do you want to experience it?"

"You don't understand; go away."

Now balance it, do it, apply yourself consciously, create a science out of it, create an art out of it, and you will realize what it does to you.

Kundalini Yoga doesn't believe in more than three minutes. So every three minutes you are going to change your attitude, aptitude and altitude of your physical electromagnetic field.

The first time I did this exercise I was nine years old, because when you are nine years old you ask the question, "Where is God? I have not yet found it." They got so mad at me that they took me early in the morning and made me do it. By one o'clock I said, "I have found God." They said, "No, keep doing it."

It is true, I am not lying to you. I am sitting here in your presence, and I am not going to leave this room until you start realizing God. It will only take a couple of minutes; it is not something that we are going to wait for or anything. That's what I wanted to tell you: God is within you! It's not some gimmick. Religion is the biggest hypocrisy I have ever experienced, telling you to find God. Stay within you and within your own grace and just find within you the God and the strength to do it. Prepare yourself. Today you are opening up your Third Eye so much that it has to be closed later.

Kundalini Yoga doesn't believe in more than three minutes. So every three minutes you are going to change your attitude, aptitude and altitude of your physical electromagnetic field. When the release happens it should have a cannon impact, do it like a cannon impact. Create a cannon effect; the breath will automatically become deep and needed. The moment your breath becomes deep and needed you have achieved the stage. It will create the sound of the breath of the snake. When he puts his split tongue out it's called hiss. The breath will create a sound like a hiss. That's why the Kundalini is represented by a snake. Consciousness is represented by a snake because the snake is your word; it means *sanake*. In our Oriental language they call it *naga. Naga,* where nothing can go it goes. In simple English, *sanake* means where nothing exists it can exist. Therefore, the snake is not a thing of death, it is perpetual life.

Normally eleven minutes of this exercise will tire out the biggest champion of the boxing ring, that's how powerful it is. *(See Exercise 2.)*

In the scripture, they say, "Say goodbye to the souls." God knows which souls. In the armpits are three magnetic fields, plus all the parasympathetic action of the nervous system. So put your elbows out and just say goodbye to the soul. This stimulates the meridian points in the armpits. *(See Exercise 3.)* So open it up and move the arms back and forth. Say goodbye to the ancestors. Say goodbye with a smile and have a positive attitude.

Sitting straight will be very difficult. *(See Exercise 4.)* You will automatically bend forward, but try to keep it straight. It is a magnetic field; it's not you. This is how the body language is. When you put your hands there and try to be straight, you won't be. But if you consciously try to be straight, you will start feeling in a few minutes a sting, which you don't like to feel. I am not trying to make you yogis and great meditators. I am just going to get rid of the garbage you brought with you

when you were born. I am trying to make you feel unhandicapped. We are handicapped people. The purpose of this exercise is to keep the spine straight so that your impotency can be reduced.

If you keep the tongue reasonably out, it is Lion's Breath. If you put the tongue on the side, it becomes Dog Breath. Between dog and lion there is only a little difference. So, you can breathe either way or alternatively; it doesn't matter. (*See Exercise 8.*)

◆ ◆ ◆

Now this is something we want to do when you come next time. It's very difficult to mentally imagine the subtlety of getting into the seed stage. The real purity and potential and expansion of a person happens when that person can do *pratyahar*. *Pratyahara* is known as constriction—bringing yourself to *shuniya*, or zero. *Sun sumad paaye so jetah.* That's what the Guru says: In the beginning, there was just all but silence. From the light, he created all life. You are the by-product of light; by yourself, you are nothing. You don't have to go and make an opportunity. You don't have to go and make a statement. You don't have to win a friend. If your Radiant Body, at a classical three-and-a-half cycle, connects with the Subtle Body, then you shall win, no matter what.

I remember once a person was on trial. On his way to the judgment, he stopped at my office. I said, "How is it going?"

He said, "It's absolutely fine."

"I understand the prosecution has a very strong case against you, and your defense attorney didn't do right."

"Who cares about the defense attorney and all that. I just want it to be over. Are you going somewhere on tour?"

I said, "No, I will be in my office."

"Well, we will have lunch together, because I will not be guilty."

I didn't say anything, because I knew he was not going to be guilty. A guilty judgment was not possible because he was absolutely radiant like a Sun. How could anybody convict this guy? So he went to court, and the jury was told, blah, blah, blah about the procedure. Then they went out and came back in and read the judgment: Not guilty. When he got out, he came and asked me to lunch.

I said, "Wait a minute. I can understand the case was this and that and you might be innocent. But I personally feel there was some hanky-panky; you were afraid?"

He said, "No way."

You have a Subtle Body, and that Subtle Body is the guardian of your soul. You also have a presence and a projection, and that's the Radiant Body. You have ten bodies; you are not just one physical body. If your personality and the facet of your identity and your projection of your reality can beam at three-and-a-half cycles, then there is nothing in the world you can lose. Three-and-a-half cycles, the rhythmic cycle of life, is called one impulsation. In other words, with one beat of the heart—or one impulsation all over your body—your Radiant Body is three-and-a-half psychosomatic projections. It is simple to work out if you know trigonometry.

With this rhythm, there is nothing that you can lose; victory is granted. That's all it takes. You think you can manipulate intelligently and do this and that, but that doesn't work. You think you can argue and win a debate; well, you can win a debate but not happiness in life. You can have money but not happiness in life. You can have sex but not happiness in life. You can have a twenty-six-bedroom house but not happiness in life. You can be married to the most beautiful wife or husband or whatever you want. You can have the whole universe. The pathway to your house can be studded with twenty-pound emerald brick. And still you won't have happiness. Happiness only comes when, per the psychomagnetic field, the Radiant Body projects three-and-a-half cycles for each impulsation of the body.

◆ ◆ ◆

May the long time sun shine upon you,
all love surround you, and the pure light within you, guide your way on.

Sat Nam

CLEARING THE MAGNETIC BLOCK FROM THE WOMB I—THE KRIYA

March 28, 1989

Note: Pregnant women should not practice this kriya.
There are no breaks between the exercises. Move immediately from one exercise to the next.

1. Sit straight and bring the elbows by the ribs, with the hands facing each other in front of the shoulders. Apply the mudra, alternating between (a) and (b) with each repetition. Lift the arms along a 60-degree angle and release the mudra, as though you are flinging something into the heavens. Release the fingers forcefully; it should have a cannonlike impact. Maintain a regular rhythm. **11–15 minutes**.

Mudras:

a. Jupiter (index) and Saturn (middle) fingers touch the thumb.

b. Sun (ring) and Mercury (pinkie) fingers touch the thumb.

See next page for Guided Comments for this exercise.

Guided Meditation

Touch and let it go, touch and let it go, touch and let it go; you will create a systematic response. Within three minutes, you must begin to breathe consciously or you'll fall behind. This exercise will give you a sense of sensitivity, and if you have any kind of headache, it will start dealing with it. When you do this, you start realizing God in a couple of minutes; it is not like we are going to wait for anything. That's what I wanted to tell you: God is just within you; it's not a gimmick. Religion is the biggest hypocrisy I have ever experienced: Telling you to "find God." Those who go out to find God, their house is always taken away by thieves. Stay within you and within your own grace. Just find within you the God and the strength and do it.

Imagine that you are sitting on the foothill of Mount Shasta and the ancient ones are coming and talking to you; imagine some gimmick to keep you going—that's all. For example, the moons are in line, and California has gone into the ocean, and you are sitting in Tucson. Figure out some extraordinary gimmick, some imagination—spiritual or nonspiritual. Whatever you do, do it with a systematic zeal and create a continuity. Do it as a science, do it now seriously. Do it because you want to.

Force has to be used to release the touch. It is not light; it's a heavy force—a touch-release system. It will give you a subliminal message to correct your pattern and mend the fuses. Now, you will start breathing deep. It will just start spacing you out a little bit more. But what are you going to get right now? Kundalini Yoga doesn't believe in more than three minutes. So every three minutes, you are going to change your attitude, aptitude, and altitude; your physical electromagnetic field shall change.

Create a cannon effect; the breath will automatically become deep and needed. The moment your breath becomes deep and needed, you have achieved the stage. It will create the sound of the snake; it's called hiss sound breath. That's why the kundalini is represented by a snake. Consciousness is represented by a snake, because snake is your word. In simple English, "Sanake" means "where nothing exists, it can exist." The snake is not a thing of death; it is a perpetual life.

2. Bring the hands on the ground behind the hips and lean back until the spine is at a 60-degree angle. Drop the head back and lift the gaze. Open the mouth wide and begin breathing through the mouth. Pace: 22 breaths every 15 seconds—not quite as fast as Breath of Fire; a steady, powerful, rhythmic pace. Move the Navel Point. Yogi Bhajan plays an African sound box, like a xylophone, to keep the rhythm. **3 minutes**.

3. Sit straight. Raise the arms up and forward 60 degrees, in a large V, with the palms facing forward. Keep the arms lifted and straight. Moving from the shoulders, begin crisscrossing the arms. **1½ minutes**.

4. a. Interlace the fingers behind the back at the base of the spine. Cover the fourth vertebra with the mudra, with the palms pressed against the low back. The fourth vertebra is the nervous control center of sexually creative energy. Close the eyes and look at the tip of the nose through closed eyes. Don't get diverted. Consolidate your mind on the fourth vertebra and focus on it. **6 minutes**.

The purpose of this exercise is to keep the spine straight. For the first 6 minutes, Yogi Bhajan tries diverting the students with politics and other small talk. Then gong meditation begins, followed by the mantra.

b. Begin playing the gong. **4 minutes.**
Start thinking that you are entering the womb now. Now!

c. Begin the mantra: *Bountiful, Blissful, and Beautiful* by Niranjan Kaur and Guru Prem Singh; silence the gong. **3 minutes**.

d. Begin singing with the mantra. **3 minutes.**
Total: 16 minutes.

Break: Open your eyes quickly and shake your hands out. Shake your shoulders, move your body, break the trance. After a minute, begin talking to each other and relax. Shake hands with each other; confuse the energy. Touch each other's hands. Move about the room greeting one another.
Total: 2 minutes.

5. Return to the mudra from Exercise 3 and sing with the mantra. Sing loudly from the heart. Let the breath resound from the ribcage. **4 minutes**.

6. Repeat Exercise 2 and breathe powerfully through the mouth. Yogi Bhajan plays an African percussion box, like a xylophone, to keep the rhythm. **1 minute**.

7. Sit up and shake out your hands. **1 minute**.

8. Bring the right hand on top of the left in front of the diaphragm and clap the backs of the hands together; clap them hard. **1½ minutes**. Continue clapping and begin Lion's Breath, by extending the tongue and breathing powerfully through the mouth. **Total: 2 minutes**.

Wake up! It will wake up the Shakti in you. Do you understand that when you clap the palms together, you create a sound to attract the power; but when you clap with the back of the hands, you invoke the power within you? Nobody taught you that? Whenever you are in extreme tension and you do not know what to do, remember this: Go to the restroom, lock it from inside, keep the water running, and get this going.

9. Whistle with *Ardas Bhaee*, Instrumental Version. **2 minutes**.

10. Talk and chat with each other to ground yourself before going home. Listen to *Ardas Bhaee* by Anahata Choir. **3–5 minutes**.

◆

" This is what the yoga sutra says: "Man is born in the image of God; there is nothing good and bad." When a pair of opposites does not work on a human, the work of a person is always neutral, and in neutral, he can do justice to himself as well as to all. Because good for all is the best for him, and the best of him is good for all. That is just a translation of one of the sutras. "

– Yogi Bhajan

CLEARING THE MAGNETIC BLOCK FROM THE WOMB II

March 31, 1989

Your inner demands have to be met by your own energy within you. But there are also outer demands that have to be met by you at an equal level, an equal rate.

IN THE HISTORY OF HUMANKIND, WE HAVE NEVER BEEN PERFECT. I can tell you how imperfect we are and you can learn from this story: There was a woman who had never had a child. She told me that she needs a child, and the father said, "We will be blessed if we have a child."

I said, "Pray to Guru Ram Das, and you will have a child."

"We have prayed a lot, and it doesn't work." You know this American attitude. I said pray again.

Eventually they conceived, and before the child was born, I said to the couple, "Are you ready to be parents?"

"Oh, we are all right; we will take care of it blah, blah, blah."

A girl was born, and she was raised to become so neurotic that the psychoanalysis is freaking her out. Whatever this girl wants, she throws a tantrum; she throws such a heavy tantrum that it is a hell of a job to live in that house; it's a living hell. She cries, she screams, and she freaks out everybody.

Today I called the mother to discuss something. But the girl wanted the attention all to herself; she didn't want her mother to attend to the phone call. I heard her crying and saying, "Don't answer the phone! Talk to me." And the mother said, "I am talking to Siri Singh Sahib." The moment the girl heard that, she yelled and screamed, and the mother said, "Don't cry; don't do that!" But the girl yelled and yelled, to the point that I could not hear the mother and she could not hear me. And I thought to myself, a three-year-old girl cannot do this. That energy must be vibrating the whole house. And I said to the mother, "Do you know what a monster you have created? You were not ready to have it but you told me you were ready, and now see what it is?"

She said, "Yeah, it's painful. At night, we don't sleep because she gets into this. I eventually just send her to her room."

"That's a terrible thing; that gives her an escape to rethink but not to regroup her energy."

"What should I do?"

And I knew that the mother was reaching a breaking point and that it would be the end of it. So I said, "Take cold water and splash it on her face. It is called hydrotherapy."

If you cannot meet those outer demands at an equal rate, then your inner demands cannot be met. If you meet all your inner demands but not your outer demands or if you meet all your outer demands but not your inner demands, it is a mess.

"Will it create a mess on the floor and all that?"

"Yeah, the carpet will be bad. God knows where it is going to fall. But just do it without thinking about it."

She did it and the girl cried, "You can't do this to me! You have to listen to me, baa, baa, baa." But then she started crying a little less, but still steady. And I said, "Tell her not to cry." After the mother told the girl not to cry, I heard a very high scream. So the mother took another big bucket of water and splashed her with that. And after that there was silence and a smile. Can you believe this? Silence and smile. And the mother said, "Now, she is silent and smiling. What should I do now?"

I said, "It's the same thing. All she wants is attention. The cry didn't mean anything and neither does the smile."

She said, "But it works?"

I said, "When somebody creates a little hell, you create a bigger hell than that, because that's what they understand."

It's just hydrotherapy, nothing else. When mothers cannot handle the commotional trauma of their own lives, they reach a breaking point. The electromagnetic field of the mother goes berserk or goes off for a moment. But the child growing in the womb needs constant energy, constant development, and that shock treatment creates an electromagnetic field breakup for the child. That breakup sets the neurons in the brain and creates their patterns, as well as the communicative color situation of the intercommunication between the different parts of the brain. This all results in very unsettled affairs. And later in life, we try to settle those unsettled affairs. Nobody is gay, nobody is a lesbian, nobody is a prostitute, nobody is a thief, nobody is a king, nobody is a president, nobody is an actor, nobody is rich, nobody is poor—it is all a result of the circuitry that we follow. And that is the total sum of the game of life. The game is set from the hundred and twentieth day in the mother's womb to the day of delivery. The rest is a workout.

This thing was recognized by yoga as a science. This is what the yoga sutra says: "Man is born in the image of God; there is nothing good and bad." When a pair of opposites does not work on a human, the work of a person is always neutral, and in neutral, he can do justice to himself as well as to all. Because good for all is the best for him, and the best of him is good for all. That is just a translation of one of the sutras.

I am going to be sixty years old, and in sixty years not only have I been a yogi and a spiritual leader, but I have also been a very successful workman. In all that time, I have come to conclude a very simple theory about why there is trouble on this Earth. It's simple: In the small, we do not see the all; and in the all, we do not see the small. This simple conflict is the cause of all our insecurity and our handicaps. The way we are, the way we act, the way we understand everything all depends on two words—the word small contains all, and the word all has to come from everything that is small, otherwise there is no all.

In our real life, we have no problems. We are born as idiots to this Earth. We do not know how to walk, so we crawl. When we learn to walk, we don't know how to speed up. So we build cars. Then we build airplanes, and then we make supersonic airplanes. We can mechanically build this outside speed. For inside speed, we start taking herbs, we start taking drugs, we start taking other kinds of stuff, because the outside demand and the inside energy must be equal. Do you understand what I am saying?

Your life has inner demands. You can do one of the most stupid things in the world and say it was because of your inner demands. But if you lay the number on somebody else, that is the biggest lie you can live. No, your inner demands are your inner demands. Nobody else has anything to do with it. People can suggest, people can give opinions, people can talk to you, but your inner demands are your inner demands. And those inner demands have to produce enough energy for you to meet those inner demands. Nothing from outside you, nor for anybody.

Then there are outside demands. These are your social responsibilities, your spiritual responsibilities, your moral responsibilities, your economic responsibilities—call it anything. So your inner demands have to be met by your own energy within you, but there are also outer demands that have to be met by you at an equal level, an equal rate. If you cannot meet those outer demands at an equal rate, then your inner demands cannot be met. If you meet all your inner demands but not your outer demands or if you meet all your outer demands but not your inner demands, it is a mess. So you have to assess your mess every time; you can't recess. There is no recess in life; there is no *shastar*, there is no *mañana*. There is nothing; you can't stop.

I have seen some people driving a car. There is a big stop sign, but they don't stop the car. They just hit the brakes and then go. Stop means stop, but they don't like it, because in life they do not know how to stop. It takes a lot of art, consciousness, intelligence, and reality to stop when you have to stop. When you have to start, you don't start; when you have to stop, you don't stop; when you have to go, you don't go; when you do not have to go, you go. Who are you? That's the question. Why does this happen in human life? Why? We are in the image of God, we are intelligent human beings, we have religion. In fact, religion has been goaded down our throat and on every corner there is a church and a temple and a padre and a swami and a yogi. It's all worth a couple million; it's not something very small. Religion has been with us for centuries, and it will continue to be with us for more centuries. So what is it? Why are we not happy? It's a simple thing: Happiness comes when you win, and sadness comes when you lose.

When you lose, you are unhappy. When you gain something, you are happy. But this gain and loss is continuous. It cannot be that somebody's gain is your loss and that somebody's loss is your gain. So, what are we talking about? Well, when you start living above this gain and loss business, that will be when you take a first step in life. When your loss is not your loss and your gain is not your gain, when it is all part of the game, then you have started the game of life. Why can't you do this? It is very simple: You are insecure. Why are you insecure? What is this word insecurity? Insecurity is when your inner energy cannot meet the outer energy; and when your inner energy cannot meet your inner energy, you have to satisfy two demands as one person: inner demands and outer demands, centripetal and centrifugal force.

Let us come to the physics. When the centripetal force and the centrifugal force balance at the equilibrium of both, everything is normal. That's the law of physics. Centrifugal force goes this way, and centripetal force goes that way. It may not make any sense to a lot of people, but the fact is that everything moves inward and outward with that force. Inward and outward have to balance. When inward and outward, outward and inward do not balance, you are out of balance. It's like if you keep on drawing checks, then you are living on credit. But soon you will be surprised to find your credit has a limit. This is how our economy works. We give you credit, and you feel four hundred thousand dollars rich today, because that is your credit line. But do you understand that for the four hundred thousand dollars of which you are so proud and egomaniacal, you have to pay eighteen percent interest on it, and you have to return it? It's such a cruel credit system that nobody on this Earth can stand it.

There is tension in this credit economy; there is tension in the insecurity of the home. There is tension in the sexual misunderstandings of the projected sexually inhibited life. There is tension in the cohabited sexually interrelated life. There is diversion in the social life. There is absolute fear of the international life: When is World War III going to start? When is the atomic energy station going to blow up? When is the plane going to fall and burn thirty houses and two blocks with it? When is somebody in an airplane going to tear it up and nine people are going to fly out without knowing where they are going? When is a plane going to land with its top absolutely gone? Nobody knows. It's too technical.

Some people don't ever watch the news. Thank God that when we view the news, after every fifteen minutes, there is sports. Watch CNN: They will give you fifteen minutes of world news. For those fifteen minutes, you will hear news that will make your stomach turn inside out. Then they will give you sports news. Then they will give dollars and cents—not sense, but dollars and cents. Then in the end they will pick up some little story to cool you off. It's like candy, a lollipop. Otherwise

they know people will switch off and never watch the news. You read the newspaper—six hundred people got shot, three hundred got blown up, a car blasted this, that person is getting thirty million dollars. We do not know what that means. We don't even have thirty dollars, and these guys are getting thirty million dollars? Who is doing what?

We are doling out money everywhere in the world, but here at home we are homeless and sleepless and foodless and hungry. How can we justify that? It's not all as dandy and as sweet as you think it is. These is a lot of pressure from the outside world, there is a lot of pressure from the inside world. Between those two pressures—those two grinding stones—one must live safe and clear.

People do not understand the science of yoga. You people think the science of yoga is just stretching legs and exercising and jumping around—cat and cow. Some people think it gives tranquility, peace, and good sexual potency. Have you seen what they say about yoga on TV? They are all stupid. They do not know what yoga is. For them it's a monkey game, and monkeys are describing it.

Yoga is a simple union in which a person can live loftily in his or her excellence between the two grinding wheels of the universe—the inner and the outer. It's a science, and it's an art. It doesn't belong to hanky-panky.

A funny thing happened today. Somebody said to me, "You said this."

I said, "Yes." And then I was told that I said it another way.

I said, "No."

"Why not?"

I said, "What I said was as a teacher. There are three personalities in me—one is Bhajan, one is Yogi Bhajan, one is Siri Singh Sahib. So, please, understand that what I said was as a teacher. Now, I can say things as a father, too, but I won't lie no matter what." But then I asked, "Suppose that I said you are obnoxiously neurotic and you are going to put yourself into hell." That is the teacher talking; that's not me. I see it, I perceive it, I intuitively compute it, I understand it, and I am just laying it out. But as a father I would say, "Well, ask so-and-so and get something to work it out. Figure it all out. It can all work out. Miracles are not far away. They are always around a corner. Hope is the best thing. Let us do it; let us deal with it. Have courage. Everything is all right. Life isn't what matters; it's the courage we bring that matters." There are six hundred things I would say after saying, "You are a stupid idiot; you are in hell."

Wrong is wrong, and once there is a wrong, you have to sing a song around it and keep going until the wrong is remedied. But I do believe every wrong is remediable, because wrong cannot live long, and right cannot get out of sight. This is a law that is eternal. Everybody has tried to tell me I am a nuisance, I am a charlatan, I am

> *Yoga is a simple union in which a person can live loftily in his or her excellence between the two grinding wheels of the universe—the inner and the outer. It's a science, and it's an art. It doesn't belong to hanky-panky.*

a womanizer, I am a cripple, I am left, I am right. God only knows all the things I have heard in twenty years. But it doesn't matter. Negativity cannot wipe me away; death cannot take it away. Man does not live by negativity and does not finish with death. Man has only two things: perpetual memory and the ability to create perpetual time through memory. You live by that perpetual memory. You were born by that perpetual memory. And nobody dies, even if that perpetual memory is written in the Akashic records. Let us take one example that you in the West can understand.

There was a thirty-seven-year-old carpenter named Yesu. His mother was Fatima; you call her Mary. This carpenter was worth thirty-two gold pieces or something. He was sold for that. Thirty pieces of silver at the rate of six dollars an ounce today; let's say it is twenty dollars. Those pieces were not thick; they were very thin things. So that Yesu the carpenter was worth twenty dollars. Let's give him a little credit and say he was worth ninety dollars. Let's gossip about it and say he was worth nine hundred dollars. Big deal. That's all he was. They hung him on a cross and they were done with it.

According to the Roman journal written by the commander in that place: "This guy is a simple lunatic. He doesn't want to listen to anything. He thinks he is a king. There are about two hundred and seventy people who follow him, and they put palm trees down when he walks, and they put their shawls on when he relates to them. Today I wanted to let him go; I wanted that thief to be crucified. But the majority of people let the thief go and let this man be crucified. Therefore I washed my hands of it." Now, this is his history of that time. But today you cannot make a movie about it and say something wrong without seeing how many protest! Hazrath Mohammed—today nobody knows who he was or how good he was. He is just Hazrath, the messenger of *Allah*. Today somebody predicted the situation. What is the prediction? In the Koran it is written that there has to be a heaven, and in heaven you will get rivers of wine and young boys for sex and young virgins for sex—it is written. But, in America that's already available. So why to go to heaven? Anyway, it's all there in the Koran. But somebody reproduced it in a satanic way, and now look at what is happening. The whole world is in turmoil. "How can you say that against our Prophet? This is how the Prophets are, and this is how the world is!"

Did Guru Nanak ever have a fever? Did no mosquito bite him? You don't remember those things, because he is a perpetual high frequency of energy that lives above the two grinding wheels of time and space.

The deeds you perform have to be so universal that they engulf everybody above time and space. Now, what is the problem in that? Very simple: You have to let your "I" go. People who have their "I" for themselves do not have the Third Eye. They only have two eyes; that's it. I make things very simple because that is the way they are. So long as your I is your eye, you don't have a Third Eye. The moment you let your Third Eye in, your I will go. You cannot sit in a luxury liner and go on a vacation while at the same time swimming through the ocean while at the same time playing with the sharks while at the same time ballroom dancing. It doesn't happen. But that is your situation—you want it both ways.

Man is born or woman is born to create a perpetual memory above time and space. But the problem is with the short-circuiting. You must understand that I am considered the stupidest person on Earth, and now I am a confirmed stupid person, because my staff tell me, "Sir, this is wrong? Sir, you are wrong? Sir, you are doing it again." But they do not even know the spelling of a thing called kindness and compassion. In kindness, you have to be kind and compassionate; you have to be kind again and again and again and again.

In kindness, you have to be kind and compassionate; you have to be kind again and again and again and again.

Once there was a scorpion that fell into the water. A saint was sitting by the corner. So he put in his finger to pull the scorpion out. When the scorpion came out, it stung his finger. The scorpion laughed as it fell in again. But then when the scorpion started drowning, the saint put his finger in again and pulled it out. Again the scorpion stung him and fell back into the water. This continued for about twenty times. The saint's disciple said, "My master, can I ask something?"

"What?"

"Can I do something here?"

"Put your finger into it?"

"No, that is not my idea."

"What is your idea?"

"This is a scorpion, and its habit is to sting you."

"I am a saint, and it is my habit to get the scorpion out. If a scorpion cannot leave his habit of stinging me, I cannot leave my habit of saving him."

"What will happen?"

"Time will tell."

This story is in our perpetual memory. We do not know who that saint was. We do not know who that scorpion was. We do not know where it happened. But it comes to us in a perpetual memory. We always tell it, we always sing it, we always know it, and we always feel that this is what a human is: If you are good, you should be better. If you are better, you are best. If you are best, don't rest; keep going. When you are for yourself, be for others. When you are for others, be for all. When you are for all, be for small. When you are small and all means one to you, you have made your life a perpetual time in history. Otherwise you should keep acting, and time will keep reacting. Today you will have friends; tomorrow they will become your enemies; tomorrow you will have enemies, and then they will become your friends. Back and forth.

People must understand that this world is an association to conquer time and space. This world is not about subjecting yourself to time and space. Those perpetual short-circuits that happened in the mother's womb are not small things. I will tell you how small they are: Take a record and make a dent in it; then play it on the gramophone. You will be shocked to hear what it does. When it comes to that song "I Love You" and between the "love" there is a dent in the vinyl—"I la, I la, I la, I la" until your ear starts hurting. Either you have to stop the gramophone or you have to break it. The record won't go one step further—that one little dent is short-circuiting, that is denting. That's why in your life it is the same thing again and again and again and again. In the morning you promised, but that night you are doing the same thing. At night you promise, but in the morning you do the same thing. After you promise, you do the same thing in the afternoon. You promised God and you break the promises at the same time. Why? Because it is what it is.

My idea is that it doesn't matter how many books you read and it doesn't matter what you do. If somehow we cannot get you to a state where you can break those little blocks, then it's not going to work. It will be again and again, the same and the same. Man is followed by his own shadow; a person is shadowed by his own subconscious. That's what all the subliminal gimmicks say—they say they are sending the message to the subconscious. I am not challenging them, but where do they get the ways to penetrate? They say that vocal cords strike each other like bamboo sticks and create words and then eardrums get the vibration and tell it to the brain. The brain decodes it and compares it with the words and language we know and understand. So they say if eardrums get subliminal messages, they vibrate, and instead of our conscious brain getting the message, it goes to our unconscious or subconscious. What a freaky thing that is. Can you believe it? What a gimmick that is.

If you have the power to reach your subconscious, you should do it consciously; you should consciously participate in it. They leave that part out of that commercial. That part is missing. It is an easy thing to do: *Japa, Japa*—it means repeat. Anything you consciously repeat becomes you or you become it. That's the law; it can never change. Anything you repeat consciously becomes you. You just start saying one word only: "Power, power, power, power." Consciously you will become the power. Ekakshri mantras are there to be repeated. There is a Guru Gaitri in *Jaap Sahib* by Guru Gobind Singh that was given when the Sikhs said, "We are tired of fighting one against a hundred thirty thousand people; it's too much. We can't do it. Don't you see, Guru?"

He said, "What is the problem?"

"One person going against a hundred twenty, a hundred fifty thousand. Sometimes we are forty and they are a hundred fifty thousand. Now what is the match?"

At that time, the Guru in *Chacheri Chand* uttered eight words: *Gobinday, Mukanday, Udhaaray, Apaaray, Hariang, Kariang, Nirnaamay, Akaamay.*

He said, "Just repeat them." And it's a recorded history: There were thirty-two Sikhs attacked by forty thousand elite army. Forty thousand elite army of the emperor attacked thirty-two Sikhs, and among the Sikhs there was one langary, a kitchen man, and one horseman and one who just happened to be there. Out of the thirty-two, only twenty were professional who knew the rites of the sword and self-defense. They say the war started early in the morning. The army encircled them after their prayers, when they were trying to have a morning nap before starting their journey. The fight started, and the rule in those days was to fight from dawn to dusk. After that, you pick up your dead and everything else. Do you believe that those thirty-two people defeated the entire army and sent them on the run? At night they counted and came to thirty-two. And around them there were thousands and thousands of dead bodies. When they came out of all this, they understood what had happened, because in those days there were expectations of superpowers. They said, "Well, super forces came and took care of us."

But the fact is that when a man becomes one-pointed, his total energy becomes unison; he becomes deathless. Such a person never dies, whether he is in physical action or in mental action or in spiritual action. That's the only difference between animal and man. You have the capacity of unisoness, and that's what the *Japa* is about. That's what the Hail Mary is about. The Jews have something like it—Kabbalah and all that. The science of every religion is basically in repeating some affirmation. What is an affirmation? It gives you a strength beyond you. What is beyond you? God? No, it is the God within you. The moment the energy demands within you and the strength within you are balanced, you become one, then God becomes one with you.

There is no way to find God. Everything else is a crock. It is a sellout, it is a lie, it is just to collect money from you. The fact is that when within you the demand and the supply become one, and outside affairs are settled, you at once become useful. But there is a catch-22: If the inside you becomes one, that Big One, it bothers everybody because nobody else knows or trusts how to become one inside.

There is a simple way. Guru Nanak said, "Leave the inside to Him, and He is going to take care of the outside anyway, so forget it." He said the easiest way is: "Inside don't hustle; just give it to Him. Outside He has promised to take care of anyway, so relax."

But if it is so simple, why are we not trusting? Because we don't trust anything, especially our inside things. The difference between id and ego is that ego tells us to hold inside, and id tells us as it is. For thousands and hundreds of thousands of years,

What is an affirmation? It gives you a strength beyond you. What is beyond you? God? No, it is the God within you. The moment the balance of the energy demands within you and the strength within you become one, then God becomes one with you.

man has not solved this problem, the problem of how to intermix id and ego at the same time. In other words, how do I mix I and Thou at the same time? Within you, there is nothing outside; outside affairs will be taken care of—that is a promise. This is because outside is all His creation; but inside is your little world. When your little world is in absolute balance, the outside worlds fall into balance.

◆ ◆ ◆

We are working tonight toward that goal. We will work it out as freely as we can. My only stipulation is that you must understand that you are not wrong. This is my statement. I don't want you to believe it or agree with it, but I have the right to say it: You are not wrong. You have been wronged, and now you are paying for it. God, the Perfect One, never makes imperfections. Those who He trusted (your family) couldn't deliver their part well, because they take the perfect and the imperfect and bring something together. You are never wrong, and neither can you be somebody who has wronged us. Therefore we have to correct the wrong done for our sake, because it's no favor to anybody. Good deeds are not for others; good deeds are for the goodness of our own self. Therefore, please understand that tonight is very special. I am fully prepared for it, and I hope you will cooperate.

All right, let us start the day. I hope this long preface and introduction inspired you a little bit. I did it with the idea that this class is hard, and I want everybody to participate.

When you are in a frenzy and in fear, that's where you get this breath. Other-wise it's not a normal breath. But once done consciously, it works as an antidote. (*See Exercise 4.*)

When you do this consciously, it takes away the nervous system. The nervous-ness is out. (*See Exercise 5.*) The eyelashes must move faster under your conscious command. They meet, connect, disconnect, connect, disconnect. I'm not asking you to roll your eyeballs up in ecstasy. Just meet the eyes and connect and discon-nect.

I have to balance you before I can put you through the trance. My simple idea is that you have to produce it, you have to participate. Come on, do it; we have to reach a point where we have an arcline into total clarity. (*See Exercise 7.*)

Whistle, and keep whistling. (*See Exercise 8.*) Listen to these four love songs; they are the best songs and the credibility of these songs are that whoever sings them, he becomes one with God and God becomes one with him (or her whatever the case is). Everybody's love life is messed up in one way or the other; we just want to just mess up the mess and get out of this mess. Keep whistling; it's a very loving way of singing.

Keep moving, this energy is not a joke. (*See Exercise 9.*) Give your whole body and your muscles a chance to play with it. Oh, come on, bring those instruments, boys. [*Musicians come forward to play in class.*]

Takes time to tune in. Any part of the body that feels weak, please move it more than others, including your head and the brain inside. If you have a foot problem, a toe problem, move it right now. Do self-healing. If you shake up the whole inner being you are going to be all right, it will take care of it.

❖ ❖ ❖

May the long time sun shine upon you,
all love surround you, and the pure light within you, guide your way on.

Sat Nam

CLEARING THE MAGNETIC BLOCK FROM THE WOMB II—THE KRIYA

March 31, 1989

There are no breaks between the exercises. Move immediately from one exercise to the next.

1. a. With the elbows at the sides and hands in front of the shoulders, bring the tips of the Jupiter (index), Saturn (middle), and thumb together.

   b. Release the thumb and bring the Jupiter and Saturn fingers of both hands together in front of the throat. The thumbs don't touch.

Alternate between (a) and (b).

After **2 minutes**, begin to increase the power of the motion. It becomes a jerking motion as the hands return to the original (a) position. The breath becomes strong and automatic. **Total: 5 minutes**.

Make those fingers harder and harder, and tighter and tighter, and give them the quality of steel. Become this whole rhythmic system, make it into steel; you will have a gold effect. It's called metal energy. Metal energy is a creative energy. When you start with steel, you end up with platinum. Hard—those fingers should be tough. Just feel they are steel fingers. They meet, they touch, they create that sound, and the entire body responds to it effectively and actively.

2. Roll the tip of the tongue up toward the center of the upper palate. Open the mouth as wide as possible and drop the jaw. Begin a powerful breath through the mouth. Pace: 22 breaths every 15 seconds. It is not as fast as Breath of Fire, but it is a powerful, rhythmic breath. Yogi Bhajan plays an African sound box, like a xylophone, to keep the rhythm. **4 minutes**.

3. *Amrita Kriya*: Lock your back molars. Invert the tongue against the upper palate and begin swallowing. Try to swallow the tongue. Create a solid flow of saliva. **4½ minutes**.

Guided Meditation

The nectar starts flowing and the yogi drinks it. Lock your back molars; if you don't lock the back molars, you can cut your tongue so be careful and lock them well. Then this tongue gets into place, and you start drinking it. All the glandular system around the tongue starts secreting the saliva, which normally happens when you chew food. In a while your cheeks will start salivating, which they rarely do. Once the cheek's salivary gland starts mixing with the other parts of the mouth, the combination is called nectar. It's the youthful way. It's how yogis keep themselves youthful. It's true; there is no gimmick in it. They will tell you, "Oh, all we do is pray to the Lord and the Lord comes down and He has a ladder and a staircase and we did this" and all that. A big production for a little thing—just lock your teeth.

Now there is fear, and you are going to face dry mouth for one minute because you are not habituated to it. But keep on and your fear will go away. This is a normal action; you put your food in your mouth and start chewing automatically. Think of your tongue as your food. Meditate, meditate, meditate; this is what we are going to do. You are going to become young. Keep sucking it. Try it. Drink as much as you can; your stomach needs it; it is the only alkaline concentrate you have in the body.

4. Lock the teeth together, lift the cheeks into a smile, and breathe around the teeth. Inhale and exhale through the mouth through both sides of the mouth, both cheeks. **3 minutes**.

5. Place the hands on the Heart Center, with left hand under and right hand over. Begin blinking the eyes as fast as possible. **2 minutes**.

6. Move the lips together and apart very quickly, making a light popping sound. **4 minutes**.

Self-degradation has got to go. After this exercise it should be gone! Try this exercise anytime. When you have a problem, in exactly 30 seconds the problem will go away. It's such an effective formula.

7. With the mouth open and the jaw slightly dropped, stick the tongue out and pull it in; fully out and fully in. Move quickly. **5½ minutes**.

It will pull on the central nerve and tune up the entire nervous system. That's why we do it—not just to make a face.

8. Sit straight, with the hands on the Heart Center and the eyes closed; right hand is over the left with the fingers parallel and thumbs pointing up. Become very still. Stable and still.
   a. After **1 minute**, gong meditation begins. Start floating. **Total: 4 minutes**.
   b. Begin playing Nirinjan Kaur's *Mere Man Loche / Love Me* along with the gong. **7 minutes**.
   c. Gong is silenced and the music continues. **2½ minutes**.
   d. Begin singing with the mantra. **9 minutes**.
   e. Begin whistling. **2½ minutes**.

Total: 26 minutes.

Note: Yogi Bhajan intermittently stops the music several times during the meditation to allow silence and then begins the music again.

TO END: Inhale deep. Inhale more. Inhale more. Press the Heart Center for 15 seconds. Exhale. Inhale, inhale a little more, inhale a little more. Press the Heart Center for 15 seconds. Exhale. Inhale and exhale quickly several times. Then repeat once more.

Listen, these are four love songs, the best songs. The credibility of these songs is that whoever sings it becomes one with God and God becomes one with him or her. Everybody's love life is messed up one way or another. We want to just mess up the mess and get out of this mess.

9. Relax. Talk and move. Stretch and socialize. Ground yourself. Shake the hands and move. While still sitting, dance the body. Don't sit still. Sing contemporary songs that everyone knows. Be social. Laugh. Enjoy. **18 minutes**.

10. Clap your hands rhythmically. Yogi Bhajan plays an African sound box, like a xylophone, to keep the rhythm. **1 minute**.

◆

Appendix

Walking Up the Mountain

Lyrics by Guru Dain Singh Khalsa. Music by Gurudass Singh Khalsa.
Vocals by Gurudass Singh & Krishna Kaur

CHORUS

Walking up the mountain, and I got you by my side
I got thunder in the valley, and this bone-dry mountain high
Walking up the mountain, climbing side by side
Walking up the mountain, with you

In the Jemez Ponderosa where the piñons meet the sky
And the hard-as-granite mountains meet the rain clouds
   flying by
As you and I look out and see the world spread out below
With different eyes and hearts and all the different things
  we know
There are cars down on the highway, ten miles to the east
See the glint of distant sunlight in the rat-tat dancing heat
But to you, you see their faces and the failing lives they lead
Then you wink at me and reckon there's a way
   I might succeed

CHORUS

With you I'm never certain just exactly where I stand
You scare me when you do the things I just can't
  understand
If I slow down you tell me that I'm moving up too fast
If I speed up you tell me, slow down kid, you'll never last
When I ask you how to live my life, you laugh and ask
  me why
You tell me I'd be better off to ask you how to die
Come with me we'll climb up through the sandstone
  to the sky
Oh Yogi, son of Guru, come and see with your own eyes

CHORUS

As the rain fell on the mountain I saw every human life
Has the value of a raindrop falling from the sky
It don't matter to the heavens just who lives or just who dies
It don't matter to the rain clouds where the rain falls
   from the sky.
As the clouds blew off I saw the stars shining in the night
In the trillion points of light I saw that each one had a life
And if nothing seems to matter, tell me what's a life to do
He said the only thing that matters is the memory of you

CHORUS

I don't know where we're going, won't you help me
   find the way
You say it doesn't matter 'cause we don't know anyway
We'll walk back down the mountain, there beneath
   the setting sun
See the time of evolution has only just begun.
We've got thunder on the mountain and sunlight
   on the plains
We're always moving forward, never pass this way again
With a smile and a wink you turn and walk away
Oh Yogi, son of Guru, there's still a chance, you say.

CHORUS

Flowers in the Rain

Lyrics & Music by Gurudass Singh Khalsa.

He walked into the room so silently
And looked at him straight into the eyes.
He said, "I don't fear your hate or anger,
And neither do I fear your earthly might!"
And we heard the sound of steel clashing,
And the blood of a saint dripping from the sword.

Those who wait to be re-born,
in the glory of the Name,
They're like flowers in the rain,
Waiting for the sun,
'Til their souls shall be re-born,
In the body of a saint,
Who shall live forever
In the hearts of those who know love.

He stood up on Baisakhi Day, with steel in his hand,
Asking for the head of a brave young one.
Many did they run away, and many did they hide,
But for those who gave their lives to him,
    their souls were glorified.
And we heard the sound of steel clashing,
And blood dripping from the Master's sword.

Those who wait to be re-born,
in the glory of the Name,
They're like flowers in the rain,
Waiting for the sun,
'Til their souls shall be re-born,
In the body of a saint,
Who shall live forever
In the hearts of those who know love.

He raised us from the dirt and mud,
And made each one a man.
He taught us how to live as saints, and to always be as one.
He told us of the days ahead, and to learn to sacrifice,
For it's not to die that matters, it's the courage in your life.
For to die for truth is to live forever,
Though for some, the cycle of fear may never end.

Those who wait to be re-born, in the glory of the Name,
They're like flowers in the rain, waiting for the sun,
'Til their souls shall be re-born, in the body of a saint,
Who shall live forever, in the hearts of those who Love God.

'She'

She is she contains the he.

Is she is she, if she cannot contain he.

She can talk, she can think, she can walk,

She in me, trust and jewels, Diamond and XXX,

Or she can move into a sexual fonder.

She can be a punk, junk and crazy

With lotus eyes beamingly gazing.

She can be educated high and great.

Everything coming to her on a silver plate,

Is she is she to contain the he,

Has she done it be a she without that Infinite one the
    he man,

With that duty she can act to reflect the man she wants.

Way is one if she can walk with the strength unto Thee,

He is in her that is she.

Solve this mystery you will be a page of history,

Without this you have incarnation without solving
    psycho reincarnation.

Woman has a man, female has a male,

She has the he to reflect with her.

Walk tall, walk high and tall contain the he everything
    is solved.

Silk Flowers

Silk flowers no fragrance, no reverence beautiful,
    beautiful

They look real in color, in makeup absolute clear.

They are the flowers what we know make it silk
    we never sow,

No seed, no plant, no leaves, no branch.

They are made to makeup beauty of the eye,

They don't have fragrance which lifts us high

Like empty mind and like shallow talk like silk flowers,
    we all walk.

We go in search of God something wonderful,

Powerful we saw in the past and now and for the future.

Without infinite teacher we pretend to be teacher,

As fragrance to flower as height to a tower

As citrus is sour and candy is sweet.

Human fragrance is a God's treat without Divine
    fragrance

Without light of God human is empty like a silk
    flower facade.

Those who commit they conquer all,

Those who are compassionate they walk tall,

Those who are kind they answer God's call,

Those who serve and problem solved

Their fragrance spread to high, higher than all,
    higher than sky.

They live in a memory of man; they live in the memory
    of man of Infinity,

Because what they left they left behind Divinity.

They shall be a flower with fragrance through Infinity.

Everyday

Everyday the day comes, the day comes everyday.

Everyday, everytime, they say something, something they say everyday.

They are walking; they are walking in a different way,

They are drifting and creating a guff.

But they think it is a bluff,

They fight little, they quarrel little.

Sometimes they have nothing to say,

Yes, nothing to say.

They are dropping, they are divorcing, they call it "parting of the way,"

They are drifting away.

Innocent children. Tender loving hearts in the parent's war,

They are caught.

Their smiles are stolen, their faces are scared.

Heavy Karma to pay.

They are drifting away.

They are not true to God

They are not true to the child.

They all want their emotional ride.

They are drunk, they are junk,

Their life is sunk in their own way.

Everyday they say something,

They say something to say in their own way.

They are sobbing, they are dropping, they are drifting away.

They are mental meat eaters, they eat a life of an innocent child they call a baby.

They call themselves husband and wife.

They make the baby a pawn.

They play the game as a con.

To drift, to shift, they have to say something each day.

To feel good in their mind, to look very kind,

But they kill, brought through the mill

An innocent life which was sunshine's ray.

They loved it, they kissed it but they killed it!

They could not stay together,

To gather life, they could not stay.

The courage, the surge of life has gone away.

They live, they lie, they laugh, they die.

Karma they didn't pay.

Their memory in anger has a deep rage.

It creates in a child a deadly rage.

The free little innocent caught in the cage of insecurity, abnormality.

No parent's together, no good weather,

For a child to grow to enjoy God's show.

They have gone their way.

Drifting, drafting, living,

Dying, laughing, crying.

Silent, silent, they whisper to say:

"I am sorry, I am sorry I never meant it,

I just tried to bend it, the truth of life.

I couldn't live with my wife.

Our chemistry was different,

Our history was different."

Child doesn't know who seeded, who sowed,

Who is that creep, who doesn't want to reap the harvest of life?

What a big strife.

They go their way everyday.

They have nothing to say.

This innocent love,

This peaceful dove,

This new child born,

To scold and scorn, doesn't know what to say,

They have drifted away.

Lovers love, they kiss and hug,

They tease and bug, they fight as a right.

They join in the part heart to heart.

They fall apart. This all goes on. Nothing is wrong.

But what about the child which cannot even crawl,

Which cannot even speak?

So little, so beautiful, so humble, so meek.

What should I say to such an Angel?

What should I say to this human lit candle?

Why this happened.

Why they departed?

Why the thing couldn't get sorted?

Why couldn't they find their way?

Why couldn't they live to stay?

These lovers, these parents undercover.

We brought our child, we raise our child,

We live our child as a part of us.

We are not going to mess.

We will never create any fuss.

But tomorrow the pain of the child and the prayer will follow.

When he will grow up as man who is hurt.

When she will grow up as a lady who is burnt.

What shall I say each day?

That they should pray or I should pray?

Or their parents like hawks on innocent doves

They preyed, they created a mill.

Because of life they draw in their own strife.

Of course they divorced, they will marry again,

Some loss, some gain they will do it again with a smile or with a pain,

Because they have not found their soul.

The child is their soul, God is their soul.

History will come to judge the fact on judgment day.

Results will come through the poll.

They have lost with all the cost.

They betrayed, they drifted away.

Someone has to say: "This is all wrong.

It doesn't fit in with the song."

Let us save our tomorrow, let us reduce our sorrow,

Let us speak God's Word.

Let us be loving, compassionate birds.

To make life a nest of happiness.

Do not allow any snappiness.

So one day we can all say we raised our little ones,

In a conscious game, we stuck together, we lived together,

And we met the end when the end came

And from light to light, and life to life,

We lit the flame.

◆

ASHTANG MANTRA FOR PROSPERITY

January 14, 1989

POSTURE: Sit in Easy Pose.

EYE FOCUS: The eyes are closed. Focus at the tip of the nose.

MUDRA: Using your intuition, choose a mudra for the left hand and place it at the knee. Place the right hand over the heart on the upper left chest.

MANTRA: Chant the mantra. Chant with the tongue, not the mouth.

Har Har Har Har Gobinday
Har Har Har Har Mukanday
Har Har Har Har Udaaray
Har Har Har Har Apaaray
Har Har Har Har Hareeang
Har Har Har Har Kareeang
Har Har Har Har Nirnaamay
Har Har Har Har Akaamay

TIME: **5 to 11 minutes**.

Guidelines for Practice

Practice the meditation for 5 to 11 minutes before going to bed. Then sleep with the mantra playing through the night. The following morning, before you get out of bed, chant this mantra. Sleep with this mantra and wake up with this mantra.

Comments

In the tongue, the pair of **nadis** called the *ida* and *pingala* meet with the central *nadi*, the *shushmana*. That is the only place where the three powers meet—*ida*, *pingala* and *shushmana*; nowhere else is that union possible. Everywhere else they crisscross each other; the tongue is the only place where all three are straight. When you chant this mantra it will create an experience of unison—an intercourse, a merger—and you will be happy. So chant with your tongue not with your mouth. It takes about 30 seconds to chant this. So, in one minute you can chant this whole *Ashtang Mantra* twice.

There are eight powers described in these words—the eight facets of God that you have to deal with, whether you like it or not:

> *Gobinday*, one who sustains us;
> *Mukanday*, one who liberates us;
> *Udaaray*, one who takes us across, uplift us;
> *Apaaray*, one who is Infinite;
> *Hareeang*, one who does everything;
> *Kareeang*, one who by grace everything is done;
> *Nirnamay*, one who is not bound down, he is without the identity of the name;
> *Akaamay*, one who is by itself. These are the eight facets.
> *Har* is a Shakti Yog mantra. *HAR* is the original God, and sometimes, if you chant just that one word,
> *Har*, with me, you will realize God in just a couple of seconds.

When your subconscious hears this mantra at night, it will not allow for garbage. The subconscious will become pure. Acknowledge and practice this for 10-15 minutes in the evening and in the morning; it will do the work. Learn one thing: become the hub and everything will come to you, become the rim and you will go everywhere. When you want two hundred thousand things, where are you going to go? You go crazy running this way and that way, and who cares? That's not living; that is hustling.

Glossary

Age of Awareness: Another appellative for the Aquarian Age (see Aquarian Age).

Aquarian Age: The next in a succession of astrological ages each lasting roughly 2,000 years. Fully inaugurated in ad 2012, the Aquarian Age will witness a radical change in consciousness, human sensitivity, and technology. The central change of this new age emphasizes an increased sensitivity and evolution of our power of awareness and a new relationship to our mind.

Ahangkar: The transcendental ego, the fundamental principle active in nature and mind that creates boundaries, identity, and attachment to things. It creates the sense of "Me and Mine" which is considered a fundamental tendency in the evolution of complexity and differentiation of objects and thoughts in the universe.

Amrit Vela: Literally "ambrosial time." It is the 2-1/2 hours before the rise of the sun. During this special time you are most receptive to the soul; you can clear the subconscious of wrong habits and impulses; and you can connect with the teachers and saints from all traditions. It is the best time to perform sadhana (spiritual discipline).

Antar, Bantar, Jantar, Mantar, Tantar, Patantar, and Sotantar: These describe the sequence of creative expression from inner essence to full manifestation. Antar is the inner essence and being. It is before form. Each essence has an associated structure in time and space, a dimension to it, bantar. This structure is fulfilled by an appropriate matching set of qualities, jantar, which has a unique sound resonance, mantar, and a distinct visual form, yantar. This form and energy interrelate to the universe, tantar, creating a projection and track as it threads through time and space, patantar, until finally achieving its liberated form, beyond time and space, sotantar. This form creates a neutral point that ties together many of the polarities inherent in Prakirti to embed and express the essence of the antar in creation.

Applied Mind: A cultivated capacity of the mind which allows you to focus and respond effectively with intuition, intelligence, and comprehensive comparative consciousness to any demand in the environment or toward your goal. It is creative, stress-free, and can act or not act as needed.

Arcline: One of 10 bodies or containing vehicles of a human being. It is a shiny thin arc that goes from ear to ear over the forehead near the normal hairline. It reflects the interaction of the soul of the person with its vital energy resources, and in it are written the potential, destiny, and health of the person. Females have a second Arcline from breast to breast.

Aspects: The nine mental patterns formed by the interaction of the three Functional Minds (Negative, Positive, and Neutral) with the three Impersonal Minds (buddhi, ahangkar, and manas). In the personality they act like fundamental persona or patterns that you use to engage the world.

Atma: The soul or finite form of the Infinite in consciousness. It is transcendental in nature, not a product of the mind but a part of pure awareness. It is a witness of everything and can only be revealed through itself.

Aura: The radiant field of energy and consciousness that surrounds the physical body and which holds and organizes the seven centers of energy called chakras. Its strength, measured by brightness and radius, determines the vitality, mental concerns, and psychophysical integrity of a person.

Awareness: The pure nature of existence; the power to be consciously conscious without an object or need. A fundamental property of the soul and true self; it is Kundalini as it folds and unfolds itself in existence.

Bana: A specified clothing that projects a consciousness.

Bantar: See Antar.

Bhagat: A devotee of God.

Breath of Fire: Also called agni praan. It is a rapid, rhythmical breath pattern, generated from the navel point and diaphragm with an equal inhale and exhale and usually done through the nose. It is both stimulating and relaxing. It heals, strengthens the nerves, and clears out old patterns and toxins.

Buddhi: This is the first, most etheric manifestation of the Universal Mind from which all other areas of mind are derived. Its quality or function is to give the clarity, discernment, and wisdom that recognize the real from the imaginary. It forms the deepest core of the human psyche but is impersonal, existing independent of the individual sense of self.

Chakra: The word connotes a wheel in action. It usually refers to the seven primary energy centers in the aura that align along the spine from its base to the top of the skull. Each chakra is a center of consciousness with a set of values, concerns, and powers of action associated with it.

Chitta: The mind that permeates all that exists in nature, Universal Mind. It is part of Prakirti, transcendental nature. It is not a single state of consciousness but rather the conditions and material that allow consciousness and experience through the senses. (See also: Universal Mind.)

Consciousness: The nature of the self and being. In the realm of nature, awareness becomes consciousness. It is from the being itself. Being is expressed in consciousness through contrasts and sensations, in awareness through merger, clarity, and reality.

Core Alignment Meditation: A specific meditation technique used to balance and adjust a particular Aspect of the mind. It facilitates an alignment of the Aspect with the central purpose and flow of the self.

Dharma: A path of righteous living. It is both an ideal of virtue and a path of action that is infused with clear awareness and comprised of actions that are the soul in total synchrony with the universe. It is action without reaction or karma.

Dhyan: See Meditation.

Facet: An automatic subconscious predisposition of the mind to act or to prepare to act in a particular way. There are 81 Facets that result from the 27 Projections of the mind interacting with the three Functional Minds. These habits of action can either support your intention and awareness or cloak your consciousness.

Functional Minds: The three minds (Negative, Positive, and Neutral) that act as guides for the personal sense of self.

Gian Mudra: A common hand position used in exercise and meditation, is formed by touching the tip of the index finger to the tip of the thumb. Its effect is receptivity, balance, and gentle expansion.

Golden Chain of Teachers or Golden Link: Historically it is the long line of spiritual masters who have preceded us. Practically it is the subtle link between the consciousness of a student and the master, which has the power to guide and protect the energy of a teaching and its techniques. This link requires the student to put aside the ego and limitations and act in complete synchrony or devotion to the highest consciousness of the master and teachings.

Greater Mind: This is the interconnected network of all minds. The Greater Mind has the ability to sense individual prayer and respond. This is the basis of the power of mental projection to create actions and impact beyond the limits of your own thoughts and concepts.

Gunas: The three qualities or threads that make up the fundamental forces in nature and the mind. Their interactions give motion to the world, stir the larger Greater Mind, and make up the realm of our experience. They are considered inseparable and occur in unlimited combinations. They are abstract; you can only see their effects. They are the sattva guna for clarity and purity; the rajasic guna for action and transformation, and the tamasic guna for heaviness, solidity, and ignorance.

Guru: That which takes us from ignorance to knowledge; from darkness, gu, to light, ru. It can be a person, a teaching, or in its most subtle form—the Word.

Humanology: A complete system of psychology to promote human excellence and spirit. It incorporates the technology of Kundalini Yoga and meditation, the use of the Shabd Guru, and the principles of spiritual counseling.

Ida: One of the three major channels (nadis) for subtle energy in the body. It is associated with the flow of breath through the left nostril and represents the qualities of the moon—calmness, receptivity, coolness, and imagination. It is associated with the functions of the parasympathetic nervous system but is not identical to it nor derived from it.

Impersonal Minds: The three major functions of the Universal Mind that create qualities of experience, cognition, and judgment. They are buddhi, ahangkar, and manas. They are impersonal since they exist independent of or before the individual sense of self.

Intellect: The function of the Universal Mind that releases thoughts, like the churning of the waves on the ocean. It is not the analytical acts of reason. Instead it is the source of the constant stream of thought formation from all levels of the Universal Mind. In this sense, someone who is intellectual is immersed in and often attached to thoughts and the act of making categories.

Intelligence: The use of the mind to create actions that manifest your purpose and the projection of your soul.

Jantar: See antar.

Japji Sahib: An inspired religious scripture, as a mantra, composed by Guru Nanak. Japji Sahib gives a view of the cosmos, the soul, the mind, the challenge of life, and the impact of our actions. Its 40 stanzas are a source of many mantras and can be used as a whole or in part to guide both your mind and your heart.

Jappa: Literally "to repeat." It is the conscious, alert, and precise repetition of a mantra.

Kaam: Desire. It connotes the feeling of pleasure and enjoyment of objects and/or feelings. It often implies a sensual or sexual quality. It is one of the five primary blocks to spiritual development.

Kaamanaa: The desire for higher values such as desirelessness, fearlessness, humility, or kindness. One way to deal with the ill-impact of kaam is to transform it into kaamanaa. Instead of fighting a desire, turn it into the desire for something higher. If you feel greed, be greedy for excellence and humility.

Karma: The law of cause and effect applied to mental, moral, and physical actions. Ego attaches us to and identifies us with objects, feelings, and thoughts. These attachments create a bias toward certain lines of action. Instead of acting you begin reacting. Karmas are the conditions required in order to balance or complete these tendencies. Though necessary, karma is not dictatorial or fatalistic. It is the mechanism that allows the finite experience of existence to maintain and stabilize itself. We all have free will and can take actions to re-direct the momentum of a karma. We can transform it or neutralize it using meditation, jappa, good deeds, or intuition that remove your sense of ego and the identification with that past line of action.

Karta Purkh: See maya and Purkha.

Kriya: Literal meaning is "completed action." A Kundalini Yoga Kriya is a sequence of postures and yoga techniques used to produce a particular impact on the psyche, body, or self. The structure of each kriya has been designed to generate, organize, and deliver a particular state or change of state, thereby completing a cycle of effect. These effects have been codified and elaborated by Yogi Bhajan and form the basic tools used in yoga and its therapeutic applications.

Krodh: Anger. It connotes the negative parts of the experience of anger. Unreleased internal anger leads to confusion and impulsive action. This results in a loss of the inner clarity, wisdom, and sense of guidance derived from buddhi.

Kundalini Yoga: It is a Raaj Yoga that creates vitality in the body, balance in the mind, and openness to the spirit. It is used by the householder, busy in the world, to create immediate clarity. The fourth Guru in the Sikh tradition, Guru Ram Das, was acknowledged as the greatest Raaj Yogi. (See Raaj Yogi.) He opened this long secret tradition to all.

Lobh: Greed. The quality of always grasping and feeling your self through what you have or what you consume. It is a principal block to clear consciousness and the spirit. It is diminished through the practice of non-attachment, contentment, and self-sacrifice.

Mahan Tantric: A Master of White Tantric Yoga. This title and function was bestowed upon Yogi Bhajan in 1971. There is only one Mahan Tantric alive on the earth at any one time.

Manas: The lower or sensory mind. It is one of the three impersonal functions of the Universal Mind. It deals with sensory impressions, sequences, and the desires and impulses generated from their combinations. It is the closest to what traditional western psychology deals with as the mind.

Mantar: See mantra and antar.

Mantra: Sounds or words that tune or control the mind. Man means mind. Tra-ng is the wave or movement of the mind. Mantra is a wave, a repetition of sound and rhythm that directs or controls the mind. When you recite a mantra you have impact: through the meridian points in the mouth, through its meaning, through its pattern of energy, through its rhythm, and through its naad—energetic shape in time. Recited correctly a mantra will activate areas of the nervous system and brain and allow you to shift your state and the perceptual vision or energetic ability associated with it.

Maya: The creative power of the Creator that restricts and limits. It creates the sense of limitation that leads us to identify with experience, the ego, and things. Because of this it is often thought of as the illusion that blocks us from the spirit. But, as Guru Nanak (see Sikh Gurus) reminds us, you need not be attached to the productions of maya. Instead they can be used to serve and express the higher consciousness and spirit. Maya is simply Karta Purkh, the doing of the Great Being. Maya takes the ineffable into the realm of the measurable.

Meditation: Dhyan. It is a process of deep concentration or merger into an object or a state of consciousness. Meditation releases reactions and unconscious habits and build the spontaneous and intuitive link to awareness itself.

Moh: Delusion and attachment.

Mudra: Mudra means "seal." It usually refers to hand positions used in meditation and exercise practices. These hand positions are used to seal the body's energy flow in a particular pattern. More generally it can refer to other locks, bandhas (see Mul Bandh), and meditation practices that seal the flow of energy by concentration.

Mul Bandh: This literally means "root lock." It is a body lock used to balance prana and apana (see prana) at the navel point. This releases reserve energy which is used to arouse the Kundalini. It is a contraction of the lower pelvis—the navel point, the sex organs, and the rectum.

Naad: The inner sound that is subtle and all-present. It is the direct expression of the Absolute. Meditated upon, it leads into a sound current that pulls the consciousness into expansion.

Naam: The manifested identity of the essence. The word derives from Naa-ay-ma , which means "that which is not, now is born." A Naam gives identity, form, and expression to that which was only essence or subtle before. It is also referred to as the Word.

Naam Simran: This refers to the state and act of deep meditation by dwelling and merging into the names of the Infinite, of God.

Nadi: Channels or pathways of subtle energy. It is said that there are over 72,000 primary ones throughout the body.

Navel Point: The sensitive area of the body near the umbilicus that accumulates and stores life force. It is the reserve energy from this area that initiates the flow of the Kundalini energy from the base of the spine. If the navel area is strong, your vital force and health are also strong.

Negative Mind: One of the three Functional Minds. It is the fastest and acts to defend you. It asks, "How can this harm me? How can this limit or stop me?" It is also the power to just say no, stop something, or reject a direction of action.

Neutral Mind: The most refined and often the least developed of the three Functional Minds. It judges and assesses. It witnesses and gives you clarity. It holds the power of intuition and the ability to see your purpose and destiny. It is the gateway for awareness.

Patantar: See Antar.

Pavan Guru: Literally, the "breath of the guru." It is the transformative wisdom that is embedded in the patterns of breath, especially those patterns generated in the expression of naad in sound or mantra.

Pingala: One of the three major channels (nadis) for subtle energy in the body. It is associated with the flow of breath through the right nostril and represented the qualities of the sun—energy, heat, action, and projective power. It is associated with the functions of the sympathetic nervous system but is not identical to it or derived from it.

Positive Mind: One of the three Functional Minds. It elaborates, magnifies, extends, and assists. It asks, "How can this help me? How can I use this? What is the positive side of this?"

Prakirti: Transcendental Nature. It is creation as we can experience it. It includes mind and matter. It is formed from the motion and interaction of the gunas. It is multi-leveled and evolved from the original consciousness of the Absolute.

Prana: The universal life force that gives motion. It is the breath in air. It is the subtle breath of the purusha as it vibrates with a psychophysical energy or presence. Prana regulates the modes and moods of the mind.

Pranayam: Regulated breathing patterns or exercises.

Pratyahaar: One of the eight limbs of yoga, it is the synchronization of the thoughts with the Infinite. To quote Yogi Bhajan; "Pratyahaar is the control of the mind through withdrawal of the senses. The joy in your life, which you really want to enjoy, is within you. There is nothing more precise than you within you. The day you find the you within you, your mind will be yours. In pratyahaar we bring everything to zero (shuniaa), as pranayam brings everything to Infinity."

Projection: A stance of the psyche projecting into action. It is an attitude of your mind that is a tendency to approach action in a certain way. There are 27 Projections that arise from the nine Aspects of the mind interacting with the three Functional Minds.

Purkha: The great Being of existence.

Purusha: The transcendental self, soul, atma, or spirit. It is the first contained embodiment of the unlimited consciousness and is formed with the subtle body. It is the consciousness and witness of the spirit that indwells the body.

Raaj Yogi: A yogi who follows the royal or highest path. One who excels and exalts the self in the midst of life without monastic withdrawal. One who places the self on the throne and presides with consciousness over all domains of manifestation, internal and external. (See Kundalini Yoga, Yogi.)

Sadhana: A daily spiritual discipline; the early morning practice of yoga, meditation, and other spiritual exercises.

Saa-Taa-Naa-Maa: This is referred to as the Punj Shabd Mantra (panj means five). It is the "atomic" or naad form of the mantra Sat Naam. It is used to increase intuition, balance the hemispheres of the brain, and to create a destiny for someone when there was none.

Sat: Existence; what is; the subtle essence of Infinity itself.

Sat Naam: The essence or seed embodied in form; the identity of truth. When used as a greeting it means "I greet and salute that reality and truth which is your soul." It is called the Bij Mantra— the seed for all that comes.

Sattvic: One of the three basic qualities of nature (gunas). It represents purity, clarity, and light.

Shabad: Sound, especially subtle sound or sound imbued with consciousness. It is a property or emanation of consciousness itself. If you meditate on shabd it awakens your awareness.

Shabad Guru: These are sounds spoken by the Gurus; the vibration of the Infinite Being which transforms your consciousness; the sounds and words captured by the Gurus in the writings which comprise the Siri Guru Granth Sahib.

Shakti: The creative power and principle of existence itself. Without it nothing can manifest or bloom. It is feminine in nature.

Shuniyaa: A state of the mind and consciousness where the ego is brought to zero or complete stillness. There a power exists. It is the fundamental power of a Kundalini Yoga teacher. When you become shuniaa then the One will carry you. You do not grasp or act. With folded hands you "are not." It is then that Nature acts for you.

Shushmanaa: One of the three major channels (nadis) for subtle energy in the body. It is associated with the central channel of the spine and is the place of neutrality through which the Kundalini travels when awakened. When mantra is vibrated from this place it has the power of soul and consciousness.

Sikh Gurus: In the Sikh tradition there were 10 living Gurus and one Guru, the Shabd Guru—the Word that guided and flowed through each of them. This succession of 10 Gurus revealed the Sikh path over a 200-year period. They were:

1st Sikh Guru: Guru Nanak	6th Sikh Guru: Guru Hargobind
2nd Sikh Guru: Guru Angad	7th Sikh Guru: Guru Har Rai
3rd Sikh Guru: Guru Amar Das	8th Sikh Guru: Guru Har Krishan
4th Sikh Guru: Guru Ram Das	9th Sikh Guru: Guru Teg Bahadur
5th Sikh Guru: Guru Arjan	10th Sikh Guru: Guru Gobind Singh

The 10th Sikh Guru, Guru Gobind Singh, passed the Guruship to the Siri Guru Granth Sahib, which embodies the writings, teachings, and sound current of the Gurus.

Simran: A deep meditative process in which the naam of the Infinite is remembered and dwelled in without conscious effort.

Siri Guru Granth Sahib: Sacred compilation of the words of the Sikh Gurus as well as of Hindu, Muslim, Sufi, and other saints. It captures the expression of consciousness and truth derived when in a state of divine union with God. It is written in naad and embodies the transformative power and structure of consciousness in its most spiritual and powerful clarity. It is a source of many mantras.

Sotantar: See antar.

Subtle Body: See Ten Bodies.

Synchronization Meditation: A meditation used to balance or develop one of the 27 Projections of the mind. It synchronizes the Projection to support the associated Aspect in action.

Tamas: One of the three basic qualities of nature (gunas). It represents heaviness, slowness, and dullness. It is inertia and confusion.

Tantar: See Antar.

Tattvas: A category of cosmic existence; a stage of reality or being; a "thatness" of differentiated qualities. In total there are 36 tattvas. Each wave of differentiation has its own rules and structure. The final five tattvas are called the gross elements and have the phasic qualities and relationships of ether, air, fire, water, and earth.

Ten Bodies: We are all spiritual beings having a human experience. In order to have this experience the spirit takes on 10 bodies or vehicles. They are the Soul Body, the three Mental Bodies (Negative, Positive, and Neutral Minds), the Physical Body, Pranic Body, Arcline Body, Auric Body, Subtle Body, and Radiant Body. Each body has its own quality, function, and realm of action.

Third Eye Point: The sixth chakra or center of consciousness. It is located at a point on the forehead between the eyebrows. Associated with the functioning of the pituitary gland, it is the command center and integrates the parts of the personality. It gives you insight, intuition, and the understanding of meanings and impacts beyond the surface of things. For this reason it is the focal point in many meditations.

Universal Mind: This refers to the entire spectrum of mental existence and sentient potential in the universe in whatever form. Mind and matter are considered gradations of transcendental nature, Prakirti, and can exist without or before a particular entity to experience it. (See also chitta.)

Wahe Guru: A mantra of ecstasy and dwelling in God. It is the Infinite teacher of the soul. Also called the gur mantra.

Yogi: One who has attained a state of yoga (union) where polarities are mastered and transcended.

Resources

Rebirthing: Breath, Vitality & Strength is accompanied by the Rebirthing DVD Series: 24 DVDs are available from the original 31 Rebirthing Courses, which Yogi Bhajan taught from the Fall of 1988 through the Winter of 1989. Within this series are smaller series, with similar themes. They include:

Rebirthing, Volumes 1-4
House Cleaning I-IV
The first four Rebirthing classes Yogi Bhajan taught; they address the nature of duality and divinity and our innate capacity to heal ourselves.

Rebirthing, Volumes 5 & 6
Unloading Your Pain and Fear I & II
A 2-class series that helps you unload the pain of the subconscious, the "storehouse of misery," so that you can be You!

Rebirthing, Volumes 7 & 8
Unloading the Pain of Perpetual Memories I & II
A 2-class series that guides you through a process of self-forgiveness, allowing the memories of the past to drop and the future to be defined by you!

Rebirthing, Volumes 9-12
Release Your Garbage, Ardh Kechari Kriya, and Getting Rid of Transit Memories I & II
A 4-class series that addresses the transit memories in the subconscious, which keep you from committing to the fullness of your life, now; these kriyas take away your pain and your doubt; they remove your "maybe."

Rebirthing, Volumes 13-16
Removing Fears from the Fifth Month in the Womb I & II, and Clearing the Magnetic Block from the Womb I & II
A 4-class series addressing the fears from the 5th month in the womb and the magnetic blocks we carry from the mother.

Rebirthing, Volume 17-21
Cleaning the Clutter of the Mind I & II, Cleaning the Mind I & II, and Cleaning the Mind for Deep Meditation
A 5-class series that directly addresses the nature of the mind and the clutter we carry in our conscious and subconscious thoughts. These kriyas prepare you for deep meditation and a profound experience of the Neutral Mind.

Rebirthing, Volume 22
Letting Go of the Pain of the Seventh Year
A profound guided meditation with the Master, Yogi Bhajan, leading you through your Seventh Year of life and dropping the pain to move forward in your cycle of consciousness.

Rebirthing, Volume 23
Clearing Subconscious Stories
We all carry stories from our past. This powerful guided meditation with the Master, Yogi Bhajan, helps you remove the anger of the past and awaken within you the flower of love and trust.

Rebirthing, Volume 24
Dropping Your Personal Pain
Another powerful lecture and kriya to remove the pain of the past and the imprints they leave upon the psyche. Bonus Prosperity meditation included!

Additional Rebirthing Lectures are currently available within the Lifestyles & Lifecycles DVD Series. They include:
A Renewed Self-Concept, Ghost Kriya: Clearing the Ghosts and Opening Intuition, and *Unloading the Subconscious*

Index